THE SERIES

FLUIDIZATION

Max Leva

Consulting Chemical Engineer
Pittsburgh, Pennsylvania

McGRAW-HILL BOOK COMPANY

New York   *San Francisco*   *Toronto*   *London*   *Sydney*

This book is written in memory of my parents
Joseph and Flora Leva

PREFACE

Fluidization as we know it today is a development of the past fifteen years. Despite this recency, the contributions have been very numerous and the data and their interpretations have been varied in many directions. It is the purpose of this book to coordinate these developments and to attempt to construct a framework which will not only accommodate the present-day knowledge in the field but also be of sufficient flexibility to encourage intensive research efforts and permit the inclusion of future results.

The book is designed to serve both as a reference volume for practicing engineers and as a supplementary text for students of the unit operations in chemical engineering. As for adjustment to the needs of practicing engineers, the question of just how deeply applications should be treated arose. Fluidization is still quite novel, and it is not at all confined to a special field, such as contact catalysis, but instead extends into many and apparently quite unrelated regions. In view of these facts, it was felt that writing from a pure application point of view would be very limited and specific and consequently would be soon outdated. Since an intelligent application can result only from a sound understanding of the principles that are involved, it was believed of more lasting value and service to deliver a fundamental approach in the simplest language. Therefore, the book has been so laid out that the reader can grow into the subject as he progresses with the chapters. In this way the book provides the tools for applying fluidization to problems of greatly diversified character. Wherever justified, finalized working correlations have been given. These are indicated in the text by a star following the corresponding equation number. The basic data underlying these correlations are discussed in sufficient detail that they may serve as a guide when extension to actual problems is considered. Moreover, the limits of application of many correlations are plainly stated. In line with the partial reference character of the book, just enough data are given to permit solution of problems that pertain to flow through empty circular conduits. The subject of flow through fixed beds is of course covered in great detail, since this is intimately related to fluidization. Along with elutriation, or solids carry-over, just sufficient consideration is given to terminal velocity that the need for other texts for the solution of simple problems is avoided. In the chapter dealing with mass transfer, fixed beds have been included in sufficient detail to permit solution of problems. However, in this instance the inclusion of the fixed bed was also necessary in order that the essentials of the fluidized bed would be better understood. The book includes a few nomographs and an appendix of useful information.

For the benefit of students, it was decided to include almost all major fundamental developments. Detailed discussions of data trends are used to stimulate the thinking of students along research lines. In this respect a number of ideas have been proposed; so far, they have not been presented elsewhere. For example, mechanisms are proposed for elutriation and for heat transfer in dilute phase and in pneumatic transport, as well as interpretation of mass-transfer data. A brief chapter on the new contacting technique known as spouting has been included. The technique has been discussed in some detail, and attempts have been made to relate it to fluidization phenomena. Finally, the problems dispersed through the text should not only give the student an opportunity to apply some of the correlations presented but also indicate the real scope of the correlations.

The units of measure chosen for the text are based on the English system. In most instances the correlations are dimensionless; however, where dimensional correlations are involved, an effort has been made to adhere to the English system. In some cases where special illustrations from foreign journals had to be given, the original units in the cgs system were retained for practical reasons. The foreign literature and developments from abroad have been covered to the fullest possible extent. The author was aided greatly in this effort by the cooperation of friends and colleagues from overseas; they have provided source information, in the form of reprints, as well as personal discussion. He wishes to thank J. Givaudon and P. Reboux for making available material from the Association Française de Fluidisation, as well as for the latter's assistance with the translation of specific nomenclature terms. The writer is also obliged to G. Hulot of La Société d'Études Chimiques pour l'Industrie et l'Agriculture for then-unpublished works. Gratitude is also extended to H. Trawinski, E. Wicke, and W. Brötz for having provided source material. Interesting data and correlations were made available through T. Shirai; these are appreciatively acknowledged. The assistance of C. Y. Wen as translator from the Japanese was most essential, and discussions with him were most fruitful. Similarly the writer wishes to thank L. Massimilla for providing unpublished data and J. O. Maloney for his translations of this material from the Italian. Unpublished data were also received with appreciation from H. Vreedenberg just in time to be included in the text. The entire source material pertaining to spouting was generously provided by G. L. Osberg. Acknowledgment is due the paper by Osberg and Jacob which led to the thesis by E. Graf, which was appreciatively accepted. Many other reprints were received but cannot be separately mentioned. The author wishes to thank J. M. Dallavalle, Wm. Licht, E. Ohsol, L. J. Jolley, and W. T. Brazelton for favors extended and the many technical journals and their editors for permission to reproduce data and figures. Finally he wishes to thank Daniel R. Pfoutz of the Carnegie Library and his staff for their efforts.

The idea to write this text was not spontaneous; rather, it grew over the years and probably originated when the author was still at the U.S. Bureau of Mines. For a short five years he had the good fortune to work under H. H. Storch, who has been a profound inspiration not only in his capacity as research director but also through his human qualities. It is felt that that association and the truly liberal research atmosphere that prevailed were indeed the beginning. The author wishes therefore to thank all his former associates who have given of their time and efforts. They share in this work.

MAX LEVA

CONTENTS

FLUIDIZATION

CHAPTER 1

INTRODUCTION

The term "fluidization" was invented to describe a certain mode of contacting granular solids with fluids. For the purpose of illustration, let the solids be a well-rounded silica sand contained in a cylindrical vessel with a porous bottom. The fluid is air. As the air is passed upward through the porous bottom into and through the bed, there is a certain rate of flow at which the sand column is just suspended. In this condition the individual sand granules are disengaged somewhat from each other and may be readily moved around with the expenditure of much less energy than would be required if the column were not suspended by the air stream. In its mobility the aerated sand column resembles a liquid of high viscosity. If the outside wall of the aerated vessel is tapped, ripples and waves in the surface of the sand are formed; they are very much like those observed on liquid surfaces. A small wooden boat placed on top of the column will pitch and roll as if the sand column were a liquid. Finally, the column of solids has a characteristic hydrostatic head. These properties, reminiscent as they are of the properties of liquids, make it appear that the solids bed has been "rendered fluid." Hence the operation of achieving this is termed "fluidization."

DEFINITION AND NOMENCLATURE

The transformation of the sand column into the fluidized state involves certain terminal conditions and characteristic states. In the following, the standard accepted pertinent nomenclature is briefly reviewed.[11]*

Originally the sand formed a so-called "fixed bed," the characteristics of which are that the particles contained in the bed are motionless and are supported by contact with each other. In contrast to the fixed bed, a "moving bed," to be discussed later, is a body in which the particles remain in mutual contact but in which the entire bed moves in pistonlike fashion with respect to the wall of the vessel.

As already mentioned, there exists a certain rate of fluid flow at which the solids bed will be expanded to such point that the granules may move within the bed. This condition is known as the "onset of fluidization,"

* Superscript numbers indicate works listed in References at the end of the chapter.

or the "fluidizing point." A bed which has passed the fluidizing point is known as "a dense-phase fluidized bed," or simply as a "fluidized bed." There is a fine distinction between a fluidized bed and a "fluidized mass of particles." The former has a definite upper boundary zone, whereas the latter may be thought of as a portion of a fluidized bed. If this portion is located in the interior of the bed, the upper boundary zone is excluded.

When the air velocity is only slightly above that required for the onset of fluidization, there results what is known as a "quiescent fluidized bed." In this state, which is also known as the "minimum-fluidization state," the particles in the bed display little or no mixing.

As the air velocity is somewhat increased, the bed expands and the solids tend to mix readily. This state is known as a "turbulent fluidized bed." If the air velocity is considerably increased, the bed expands greatly and a condition of great solids dilution is created. The solids are then entrained in the fluid and are carried upward. This state is known as the "dispersed suspension," "disperse phase," or "dilute fluidized phase." As compared with the dense-phase fluidized bed, the solids, when in the dilute fluidized phase, have no upper boundary; the solids move with respect to the wall of the confining vessel; and finally,

TABLE 1-1. NOMENCLATURE

English	French	German[18]
Fixed bed	Lit fixe (also couche fixe)	Ruheschüttung
Moving bed	Lit mobile (also couche mobile)	Wanderschicht
Fluidizing point	Fluidisation commençante	Wirbelpunkt
Fluidized bed	Lit fluidisé	Wirbelschicht
Batch fluidized bed	Fluidisation discontinue	Periodisch arbeitende Wirbelschicht
Continuous fluidized bed	Fluidisation continue	Stetig arbeitende Wirbelschicht
Particulate fluidized bed	Fluidisation particulaire	Homogene Wirbelschicht
Aggregative fluidized bed	Fluidisation aggrégative	Inhomogene Wirbelschicht
Channeling fluidized bed	Renardage	Durchbrochene Wirbelschicht
Bubbling fluidized bed	Bullage	Brodelnde Wirbelschicht
Slugging fluidized bed	Pistonnage	Stossende Wirbelschicht
Dispersed suspension	Suspension diluée	Flugstaubwolke
Turbulent fluidized bed	Lit agité	Turbulente Wirbelschicht
Packing	Garnissage	Schüttgut
Packed height	Hauteur du garnissage	Schüttguthöhe
Packing support	Grille, or plaque	Schüttgutunterlage

the concentration of solids in the gas is of a much smaller order of magnitude than in the dense-phase fluidized bed.

The considerations so far presented have perhaps created the impression that the transformation of the fixed sand bed into the dilute fluidized state occurs quite smoothly and without any disturbances and irregularities. Experience has shown that this is manifestly untrue; in actual practice, deviations from ideal behavior are the rule, and the truly ideal case has so far never been observed. The concepts which describe the disturbances, together with some other definitions, will be defined in their proper place.

Most fluidization research is of very recent date; a new specific nomenclature has appeared, and it is briefly presented below. Also included here are the concepts which will be discussed later in the book. Because much valuable research has been done abroad, it is desirable to give the French and German translations of the nomenclature; it is hardly to be expected that the new terms can, in the near future, be included in technical dictionaries. A few of the more important expressions, in three languages, are given in Table 1-1.

HISTORY

What is probably the earliest recorded application of fluidization has been unearthed by Brötz.[4] It pertains to the purification of ores, as described by Agricola[2] (Fig. 1-1).

The art of purifying municipal water supplies by passage through rapid sand filters dates back to the turn of the century or earlier. The water, carrying coagulated solids, runs by gravity through a graded sand bed. As the deposits accumulate, the bed loses permeability and its capacity for handling flow must be restored. This is easily accomplished by backwashing: the sand bed is expanded by a certain amount and the deposits are washed out. The expansion of the sand bed is an example of fluidization with a liquid medium. In order to prevent sand losses, the wash-water gutters that lead the dirty wash water to the sewer must be located well above the upper boundary of the expanded sand bed. Practical working correlations, developed and extensively used for this type of equipment, are primarily modifications of the Kozeny-Carman flow equation. This will be discussed in a later chapter.

Apparently the first patent that bears on some form of fluidization was issued in 1910 to Phillips and Bulteel.[13] In essence the inventors describe contacting between a gas and a finely divided catalyst. The catalyst is swept by the gas into a reaction chamber. The reaction occurs in the dilute fluidized phase, and the products carry the catalyst into a recovery vessel from which it returns to the catalyst feed point by way of a high-density-solids leg, generally known as a standpipe.

Perfolvi lavandi rationes plurium metallorum venis communes, venio
nunc ad alteram venarum tundendarum rationem : nam de hac prius, quam

Fig. 1-1. That fluidization was practiced in ore processing as early as the sixteenth century is indicated by this woodcut.

Probably the first fluidized unit to operate on a commercial scale was the Winkler gas generator for manufacture of water and producer gas. It was developed by the BASF in Germany in 1921. Briefly stated, the generator shown in Fig. 1-2 is a vertical cylindrical shell into which finely divided brown coal is continuously fed. Depending on the type of gas to be made, either a mixture of steam and air or air alone is admitted into the conical bottom where the reaction occurs. The ashes descend to the outlet.

The first large-scale fluidization application in the United States dates to about 1940 and pertains to catalytic cracking of oil vapors. The process was first described in 1943 by Murphree and coworkers.[10] Initial basic flow studies pertaining to the process were started at Massachusetts Institute of Technology somewhat earlier, and on the basis of these studies a large-scale pilot plant was built to test the principle of catalyst feed by standpipe.[12]

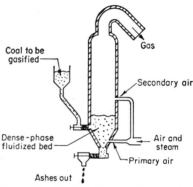

FIG. 1-2. The Winkler gasifier, probably the earliest large-scale commercial application of fluidization.

The catalytic cracking unit of those days consisted essentially of two vessels, the reactor and the catalyst regenerator, communicating with each other by way of catalyst-transfer piping. The carbon-coated catalyst left the reactor and was transported by air to the regenerator where the carbon was burnt off. Reactivated catalyst left the regenerator through the standpipe and was carried by oil vapors into the reactor. Complete continuity was achieved by skillful combination of the dense-phase fluidized beds in a portion of the reactor and regenerator with the dilute fluidized phase that prevailed in the space above the beds and in the catalyst-transfer lines. By this method of operation very large quantities of catalyst could be conveniently handled.

The description and successful operation of the fluid catalytic cracking units precipitated an avalanche of fundamental and applied studies in the field of fluidization. Contributions came virtually from all sources: inventors, laboratories of private industries, government agencies, research institutes, and, last though not least, graduate students and faculty members of academic institutions. Moreover, these contributions were by no means limited to the United States; highly significant advances, both fundamental and applied, were made by workers in about a dozen foreign countries.

The fact of the comprehensive effort made by so many in so short a time is emphasized by the considerable number of fluidization symposia which have been held. Two of the most important of these meetings took place at Massachusetts Institute of Technology in 1948[5] and in London in 1951. The papers of the latter meeting, covering a wide range of subjects, are collected in a special binding.[6] The symposium on process kinetics held at New Haven in 1953[17] had many papers on fluidization and related topics. The meeting held in 1955 at the Brooklyn Polytechnic Institute presented process data and led to a first text on the subject.[12] In the summer of 1956 the French Association for the Study of Fluidization (Association Française de Fluidisation) held a meeting at which fundamental and process papers were presented.[7] In December, 1957, a symposium on fluidization took place in Chicago at the annual meeting of the American Institute of Chemical Engineers. In addition to these symposia, important reviews on the fluidization literature were compiled. In this regard mention is made only of the papers by Brötz,[4] Reboux,[14] and Shirai.[15]

FLUIDIZED-BED–FIXED-BED COMPARISON

Despite the many interesting aspects of fluidization, experience so far gained indicates that a wholesale substitution of fixed beds by fluidized beds is by no means in sight. As with most processes and operations there are advantages and disadvantages on both sides. The most important are as follows:

Advantages

1. Owing to the intense agitation in a well-fluidizing dense-phase bed, local temperatures and solids distribution are much more uniform than in the fixed bed. This may be important in many chemical and catalytic processes.

2. Since in a fluidized bed particle size is of a smaller order of magnitude than in the fixed bed, the resistance to diffusion through the particle is smaller in the fluidized bed. This too may benefit many chemical and catalytic reactions.

3. Fluidization will permit the ready additions of solids to or the withdrawals of solids from the bed. This is an important advantage over the fixed bed, especially where rapid-activity losses are involved. This property of the fluidized system is responsible for the ease with which continuous operation is achieved.

4. Owing to the motion of the particles past internal or external heat-transfer surfaces, heat-transfer coefficients in fluidized beds are higher than in fixed beds operating under comparable flow conditions. Thus the fluidized bed offers a great advantage where highly exothermic or endothermic reactions are involved.

5. Although heat-transfer coefficients between solid particles and fluid appear to be of the same order of magnitude in both fluidized and fixed beds when both are operating under comparable flow rates, the state of subdivision and heat-transfer surfaces are so much greater in the fluidized bed that the rate of solids-fluid heat transfer is actually much higher in the fluidized bed.

6. Owing to the high particle-fluid heat-transfer rates, fluidized solids lend themselves more readily to recovery of heat from waste solids than do the generally larger solids particles of fixed beds.

7. In many instances fluidization will cause a smaller pressure drop than will fixed-bed operation.

8. Fluidization will eliminate catalyst pelleting, an important cost item in many catalytic processes.

Disadvantages

1. The average flow of the solids and fluids in the single-bed fluidized reactor is concurrent. This has an unfavorable effect on the driving force. In order to approach countercurrent flow, a multicompartment reactor is required. This is much more expensive than a fixed bed.

2. From low height-diameter ratios there may result appreciable longitudinal mixing of fluid and solids in the fluidized reactor. This may lead to low conversion rates and a reduction in selectivity.

3. During a fluidized operation, a catalyst may undergo attrition, or size reduction. Thus the fluidization properties of the material may become different and require adjustment of fluid rates.

4. In the fluidized reactor the fluid velocity must be closely coordinated with the properties of the solids so that adequate fluidization results. Thus the fluidized reactor is in this respect restricted, and the fixed bed offers a great degree of freedom and adjustment of space velocity.

5. Fluidization with gaseous components is possible only if no liquids or waxes will form during the reaction. This is a severe restriction and a great disadvantage as compared with the fixed bed, as experience with the hydrocarbon synthesis has disclosed.

6. In fluidized-operation equipment, erosion may be serious. Special and generally expensive designs may be required to eliminate or minimize wear in reactors and transfer lines.

7. Owing to solids carry-over, known as elutriation, installation for fines recovery may be required.

8. Attrition and formation of fines leads to catalyst losses. These must be replaced in the fluidized unit. The cost involved may be appreciable.

APPLICATIONS

It is impossible in the limited space allotted here to cover, with any degree of completeness, all the applications of fluidization that have so far been proposed. The number of journal articles and patents is in the high hundreds. However, it will be of great benefit to the reader if he becomes acquainted with the various types of reactor systems and over-all modes of operation; a process-by-process coverage would of necessity turn out to be an incoherent and voluminous presentation of data.

Any application of fluidization falls into one of these two classes: (1) chemical reactions and catalysis or (2) physical and mechanical processes.

Chemical Reactions and Catalysis. By far the greatest number of fluidized applications involve chemical changes and catalysis. It is therefore not surprising that the greater number of contacting units and systems so far proposed serves these purposes.

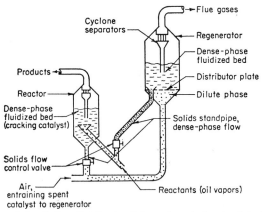

FIG. 1-3. Two-vessel circulating fluidized-solids system dating back to the early days of fluid catalytic cracking. This type of unit constituted the first commercial application of fluidization in the United States.

The catalytic cracking system has already been referred to in the section dealing with the history of fluidization. The proposed apparatus shown in Fig. 1-3 is probably the classical example of the continuous solids-fluid system. With this arrangement immense catalyst quantities of as much as a ton per second or more may be circulated, hence the system is ideally suited for the largest-scale operations with which one may be confronted. To review the situation briefly, the catalyst may be composed of particles ranging from 30 to perhaps 100 microns. The catalyst concentrations in the reactor and regenerator are of the order of magnitude found in a highly expanded, though still dense-phase, fluidized bed. The solids are in a highly turbulent state and substantial entrainment results. It is retained by the cyclones.

The solids are conveyed by pneumatic transport into the reactor and regenerator. The solids density in the transfer lines is of the order of magnitude of 2 to perhaps 10 lb per cu ft, and the vapor and air velocities must be high enough to carry these solids loads. This problem would normally involve velocities of more than 25 fps. The solids concentration in the standpipes is much higher. Frequently provision for extra aeration along the standpipe is necessary to keep the solids moving through the solids-delivery valve.

The flow system shown in Fig. 1-3 may of course be used for a variety of processes and operations that involve solids regeneration or heat recovery. As far as catalytic cracking is concerned, the original system has undergone great changes and improvements. These have been described in a diagrammatic way by Sittig.[16]

The fluidized dense-phase batch reactor is shown in Fig. 1-4. It is merely a cylindrical shell with a support for the catalyst bed. The gas enters from the bottom through a cone and leaves through the cyclone. Any solids that are entrained are returned through the cyclone dip leg. This type of reactor is suitable for a considerable number of chemical and catalytic reactions. As shown, no provision is made for heat removal or addition other than by the entering gas. This may be satisfactory for some reactions, but there are applications for which internal heat-transfer elements must be supplied. One example is the hydrocarbon synthesis by the Fischer-Tropsch method. An iron oxide catalyst of high specific gravity is used, and the reaction is highly exothermic. Moreover, the reaction must be controlled through temperature and space velocity so that no liquids or waxes will condense around and inside the catalyst. Considerable skill and experience are involved in so arranging the cooling surfaces inside the reactor that the fluidization pattern is not impeded and hot-spot formation is avoided.

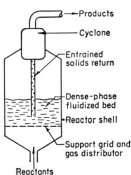

FIG. 1-4. Elements of fluidized dense-phase batch reactor.

For pilot-plant studies, reactors that were cooled from the outside have frequently been used, but they were of sufficiently small diameter that heat removal through the wall was possible. Although this may be a valuable way to get process data, it tells nothing about the required arrangement of cooling tubes inside the reactor. Only fragmentary data on the effect of built-in components on the fluidization performance and resulting heat-transfer properties are available, and difficulties should be expected when it comes to scale-up of the results.

Another dense-phase reactor is shown in Fig. 1-5. It differs from the reactor shown in Fig. 1-4 in that it permits addition and removal of solids. Since the solids from the unit move downward, the reactor has also been designated a "downflow reactor." In this respect it differs from the so-called "upflow reactor" (Fig. 1-6), in which solids are entrained upward through the reactor space. The gas and solids are separated from each other in a cyclone, from which the solids return to a solids feed line. They are then swept back into the reacting space. The downflow reactor is preferred because it requires less headroom, involves less catalyst transport, and permits much higher space velocities owing to the substantial bed densities that prevail.

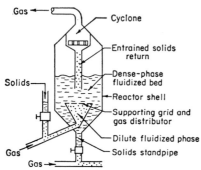

Fig. 1-5. Elements of fluidized dense-phase downflow reactor.

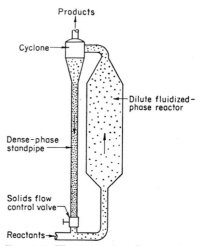

Fig. 1-6. Elements of upflow reactor, operating with the dilute fluidized phase.

The Winkler gas generator, shown in Fig. 1-2, is in a sense a downflow reactor. However, instead of discharging solids from the reactor, to be returned there after treatment, the Winkler generator discards ashes that are disposed of. The greater portion of the solids, namely, the carbonaceous matter in the fuel, is gasified.

In the reactors so far mentioned the solids move through the reactor shell along a turbulent path, and there may be disadvantages due to this flow pattern. Occasionally approach to countercurrent operation is needed, and the multicompartment reactor shown in Fig. 1-7 is then desirable.

In the calcination of limestone, heat economy must be practiced. The reactor has been found very useful because it permits combination of the calcination step with the heat-recovery step. In operation, finely crushed limestone enters the top compartment. There and in the following two compartments it is preheated by the hot CO_2-N_2-air mixture that leaves the calcination compartment below the preheating section. Heat is supplied by injected fuel oil, which is immediately vaporized and burned. Finally, the hot calcined solids enter the bottom compartment, where the entering air is preheated.

The fluidized beds are supported by perforated masonry arches. The fluidizing gases pass through the openings into the solids. The solids overflow from compartment to compartment is by way of solids down-pipes. This mode of transport is similar to the flow of the liquid in a fractionating column, with the downcomers serving as liquid seals. In the multicompartment reactor the flow of solids and gas is much better coordinated than in a single bed. Moreover the contact time between the solids and gas is greatly increased. The gas pressure drops may, however, be somewhat higher than in a single-bed reactor carrying the

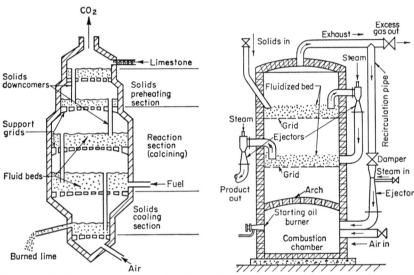

FIG. 1-7. Multicompartment reactor, the type of unit used in the calcination of limestone. It increases gas-solids contact time and tends to render the operation countercurrent

FIG. 1-8. Two-stage fluidized reactor suggested for the activation of carbonaceous material.

same height of solids as the combined beds of the multicompartment unit. This higher pressure drop is due to the additional solids supports. As for elutriation losses from such a unit, they are probably smaller than from an equivalent single-compartment bed.

Another interesting application of a two-stage reactor, for the production of activated carbon, is described by Godel.[8] The unit is shown in Fig. 1-8. Carbonaceous material to be activated is admitted to the upper zone, where it is contacted with a mixture of combustion gases and steam. Next it is conveyed by a steam injector to the zone below, where the activation is completed.

Physical and Mechanical Processes. Probably the most important fluidized-bed physical operation involves heat transfer between gas or vapor streams. Indirectly this involves solids-gas heat transfer, as already discussed in connection with the upper and lower zones of the multicompartment lime-calcination reactor. A simple system for the arrangement of the components and flows involved in heat transfer between two gas streams by way of fluidized solids has been proposed by Reboux.[14] The apparatus is shown diagrammatically in Fig. 1-9. It is similar to the original catalytic cracking unit (Fig. 1-3).

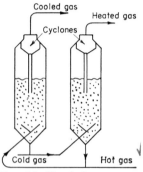

Cooled gas
Heated gas
Cyclones
Cold gas
Hot gas

FIG. 1-9. Simple heat-recovery system, using fluidized solids.[14]

Profiting by the excellent heat-transfer characteristics and high temperature uniformity in fluidized beds, fluidized-solids constant-temperature baths have been proposed.[1] Also, in heat-recovery units fluidization may be useful for the drying of gases by adsorption or the drying of solids by hot flue gases or other dry gases. In all these instances no essentially new units have been proposed, though some specific features might be different, depending on the case.

As far as mechanical applications of fluidization are concerned, only the Airslide solids conveyor[3] and the use of stirred beds as solids blending devices are briefly mentioned.[9] The former, shown diagrammatically in Fig. 1-10, is essentially a porous inclined slab that carries a

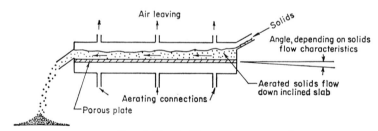

Air leaving
Solids
Angle, depending on solids flow characteristics
Aerated solids flow down inclined slab
Aerating connections
Porous plate

FIG. 1-10. Airslide solids conveyor.[3]

layer of the powder to be conveyed. Air is admitted from below, and the solids next to the slab are put into the minimum-fluidization state. This is in most cases just sufficient to enable the overlying solids to slide down the slab. The velocity of the solids may be controlled to some extent by adjusting air flow.

The combination of a fluidized bed and a proper stirrer may be an effective solids blender. Since in a bed at incipient fluidization the frictional resistance between particles is greatly decreased, such a solids bed may be stirred very much as a liquid is. This property has been used for the development of the air-activated blender. Since fluidized beds display definite internal solids flow patterns, it was found that certain stirrers will accomplish better internal mixing than others. The air-activated blender merely introduces a small air stream into the base of a conically shaped bed. A blade stirrer, with blades arranged in a certain fashion and coordinated with the sense of rotation, agitates the

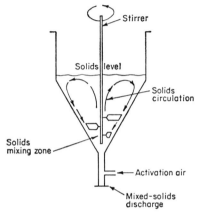

FIG. 1-11. Air-activated solids blender.

low portion of the bed, which acts essentially as the blending zone through which the solids from the upper strata are eventually circulated and mixed. This is schematically shown in Fig. 1-11.

ORGANIZATION OF SUBJECT MATTER

After the introduction given in the present chapter, the discussion will extend in Chap. 2 to the properties of the dense-phase fluidized bed. Owing to the state of the art this discussion will have to be more qualitative than quantitative. However, efforts will be made wherever possible to relate the various properties and phenomena.

Chapter 3 develops and presents working correlations for flow through fixed beds up to the point of incipient fluidization. In the fourth chapter the discussion will be carried through the entire expansion range of gas-fluidized and liquid-fluidized systems. This will then lead into stratification and size separation, which are prerequisites for carry-over of solids components in the fluid stream, a phenomenon known as elutriation. The status of elutriation will be quantitatively examined in Chap. 5.

In Chap. 6 the dilute fluidized phase is reintroduced, but emphasis will remain with it and the entire fluidized-phase diagram will be taken up. This leads then to quantitative considerations of pneumatic transport, high-ratio solids-fluid flow, gravity flow of solids, and moving beds.

Chapter 7, the shortest of all, is entirely devoted to a consideration of the new solids-fluid contacting method known as spouting. A spouting bed comprises a dense-phase and a simultaneous dilute-phase component.

In the following three chapters, heat transfer, mass transfer, and correlations pertaining to solids and fluid mixing in fluidized beds will be examined. The heat-transfer chapter first discusses heat flow through fluidized reactor walls; next, heat flow in pneumatic systems as far as is possible; and finally, heat flow between particles and the ambient fluid. This leads then to the question of mass transfer between the particles and the ambient fluid. The effect of mixing of the solids and fluid on the driving force in both heat and mass transfer is stressed. In the last chapter the individual correlations pertaining to internal mixing are reviewed in an effort to coordinate the findings with each other as far as is possible.

REFERENCES

1. Adams, C. E., M. O. Gernand, and C. N. Kimberlin, Jr.: *Ind. Eng. Chem.*, **46**: 2458–2460 (1954).
2. Agricola, G.: "De re metallica," Phillippum Bechium, Basel, 1556.
3. Avery, W. M.: *Pit and Quarry*, **41**(2): 62–67 (1949).
4. Brötz, W.: *Chem. Ingr. Tech.*, **24**(2): 60–81 (1952).
5. Fluidization Symposium, MIT, 1948: *Ind. Eng. Chem.*, **41**: 6 (1949).
6. Fluidization Symposium, London, 1951: *J. Appl. Chem. (London)*, **2**, Suppl. Issue 1 (1952).
7. Fluidization Symposium: *Journée de fluidisation*, June 11, 1956, Association Française de Fluidisation, Paris.
8. Godel, A.: *Chem. Eng.*, **55**(7): 110 (1948).
9. Leva, Max: paper presented at AIChE meeting, Chicago, Ill., December, 1957.
10. Murphree, E. V., C. L. Brown, H. G. M. Fischer, E. J. Gohr, and W. J. Sweeney: *Ind. Eng. Chem.*, **35**: 768 (1943).
11. Murphy, W. J.: *Ind. Eng. Chem.*, **41**: 1249–1250 (1949).
12. Othmer, D. F.: "Fluidization," Reinhold Publishing Corporation, New York, 1956.
13. Phillips, W. A., and J. G. Bulteel: English patent 23045, Oct. 5, 1910.
14. Reboux, P.: "Phénomènes de fluidisation," Association Française de Fluidisation, Paris, 1954.
15. Shirai, T.: "Review of Fluidization Literature," Tokyo Institute of Technology, Tokyo, 1954.
16. Sittig, Marshall: *Chem. Eng.*, **60**(5): 219–230 (1953).
17. Symposium on Process Kinetics, New Haven, Conn., January, 1953: *Ind. Eng. Chem.*, **46**: 6 (1953).
18. Wicke, E., and W. Brötz: *Chem. Ingr. Tech.*, **24**(2): 58–59 (1952).

CHAPTER 2

THE FLUIDIZED STATE

Abstract

The discussion begins with a qualitative consideration of the entire fluidized-state spectrum to show the relationship between the dilute and dense phases. Thereafter the dense phase and its characteristics are considered in detail.

The expansion behavior of the dense phase is taken up first, followed by definition of particulate and aggregative fluidization and the concept of the minimum fluid voidage.

Pressure-drop–flow diagrams are then introduced and coordinated with a detailed discussion of channeling and slugging. The remainder of the chapter deals with considerations of fluidization performance and the so-called viscosity of the dense-phase fluidized bed.

THE FLUIDIZED-STATE SPECTRUM

An experimental study by Wilhelm and Valentine[26]* has disclosed the sequence of and relationships between the various phenomena that comprise the entire fluidized-state spectrum. The Wilhelm and Valentine apparatus, the elements of which are shown in Fig. 2-1, was essentially a vertical glass tube of 4 in. diameter which was fitted on its side with ports for addition of solids and admission of air. The tube was unobstructed over its entire length. For its operation clay spheres of 0.02 to 0.03 in. diameter were introduced at port s, while air entered simultaneously at port a. Solids and air rates could be varied over wide ranges, and the behavior of the particles was directly observable.

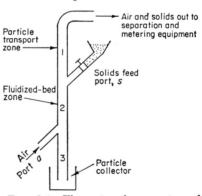

FIG. 2-1. Elements of apparatus of Wilhelm and Valentine.[26]

The results of the Wilhelm-Valentine experiments indicated that, with the proper adjustment of solids and air flows, virtually all phenomena of the fluidized state—extending from the dense-phase bed all the way

* Superscript numbers indicate works listed in References at the end of the chapter.

through the dispersed phase into pneumatic transport—could be produced. The diagrams of Fig. 2-2, suggested by Wilhelm and Valentine, will be helpful in establishing the relationships between solids feed rate, air rate, and resulting bed density.

The sketches of Fig. 2-2 represent the upper two sections of the apparatus of Fig. 2-1. A solids feed rate has been agreed upon and will be kept constant, while the air rate is gradually reduced from its original very high value in (A). Owing to this high air velocity, the particles

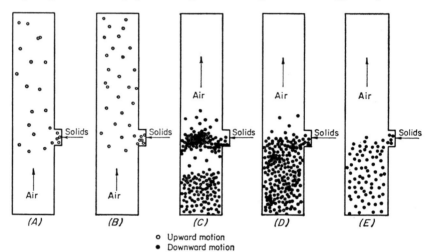

o   Upward motion
•   Downward motion

Gas velocity decreases left to right

FIG. 2-2. Pictorial presentation of parts of apparatus of Wilhelm and Valentine,[26] showing phases in the fluidized-state spectrum. (A) Pure upward transport. Very low particle population in upper section only. (B) Still pure upward transport. Increased particle population in upper column section only. (C) Slugging region. High particle concentration in lower section. Few particles in upper section. (D) Fluidized bed. Maximum particle concentration in lower section only. (E) Fluidized bed. Decreased particle concentration in lower section. (*Courtesy of Industrial and Engineering Chemistry.*)

will be entrained through section (1) out of the apparatus. The void fraction is very high and the pressure drop per unit length of tube is virtually that of the empty tube. This is shown in Fig. 2-3. As the fluid rate is reduced as shown in Fig. 2-2(A) and (B), the particle population increases, the void space decreases slightly, and the pressure drop rises. At this point the solids will still move concurrently upward with the gas. For another small reduction in air rate as represented by Fig. 2-2(C) solids will tend to crowd together and violent slugging will occur, with the solids now moving downward. The void space decreases sharply. A condition of minimum voidage is observed near (D) and the solids now have a well-defined upper boundary. The condition represented in (D) is in effect that experienced in the dense-phase fluidized bed. With a further reduction, the solids inventory in the bed now decreases to reach a limiting value dictated by the rate of addition at port "s." The sequence of events is of course reversible.

The interesting point in these experiments is that they demonstrate the relationship between the various phenomena, although the transition from (B) to (C) in Fig. 2-2 apparently occurs so rapidly that measurements are not readily made for this range. The relationship between the various phenomena has also been investigated by Zenz.[27] His data, though somewhat differently presented, lead to the same coherent picture. The work of Zenz is discussed in detail in Chap. 6.

In industrial processes virtually all the states in the fluidized spectrum find application. As far as extent of study of the individual states is concerned, the bulk of the work pertains to the dense-phase fluidized bed. This will therefore be discussed through the next few chapters.

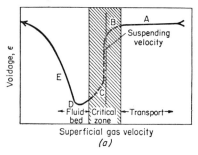

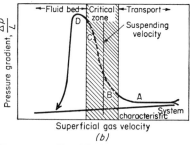

Fig. 2-3. Graphical presentation of transformation in the fluidized-state spectrum. (*Courtesy of Industrial and Engineering Chemistry.*)

THE DENSE-PHASE FLUIDIZED BED

As an introduction to the dense-phase fluidized bed let us assume that a granular material that is well suited for fluidization is available. This will be poured slowly and at a uniform rate from its container into a cylindrical vessel with a porous-plate bottom. The resulting column height will depend to some extent on the mode and rate of pouring, but it will primarily be determined by the size and shape of the particles. If the receiver is gently tapped during the transfer, a voidage ϵ_d will result; it will be somewhat smaller than the ordinary voidage.

Figure 2-4a represents such a column as it is traversed counter-gravity-wise by a gas at a superficial velocity u_d. A pressure drop equal to Δp_d will result; the magnitude of the drop will be determined by the gas rate and the characteristics of the bed. As the gas velocity is increased, the pressure drop will rise. Eventually there will be a condition for which[13,19,25]

$$\Delta p_e = L_e(1 - \epsilon_e)(\rho_S - \rho_F) \qquad (2\text{-}1)^{\star\star}$$

* Finalized working correlations are indicated by a star following the corresponding equation number.

where L_e = bed height

ρ_S, ρ_F = solids and fluid densities, respectively

At the particular gas rate u_e, expansion of the bed will set in.   Figure 2-4b represents such an expanded column, and the voidage has increased from ϵ_d to ϵ_e.   For the condition of Fig. 2-4c the gas rate is u_{mf} and the voidage has reached a value of ϵ_{mf}.   This is the condition required for the onset of fluidization, in fact the bed is now in a pseudofluid state, as may be demonstrated by application of vibrations, which will cause the aerated solids to move like a viscous fluid.

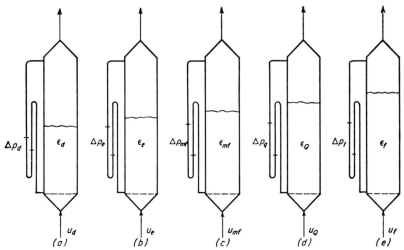

FIG. 2-4. Operating stages of the dense-phase fluidized bed.

As the gas rate is increased slightly to u_Q, the voidage will become ϵ_Q and the particles inside the column will begin to move, i.e., the column will begin to fluidize.   This early state of fluidization, shown by Fig. 2-4d, is known as quiescent fluidization.   If the gas rate is reduced to u_{mf}, a slight drop of bed level will result and particle motion will cease.   Upon further reduction of gas rate to u_e, and allowing sufficient time, the bed level will tend to readjust to the condition of (b).   The conditions of reversibility between stages (b) and (d), demonstrating how the fluidized state follows from the fixed-bed state and vice versa, emphasize that, at least for the early stages of fluidization, the laws of fluid flow through fixed beds apply.   Hence an analysis of initial dense-phase fluidization by way of the laws of fixed beds may be logical and should be expected to produce tangible working correlations.

Increasing gas rate further to u_f will continue to expand the column and render the particles into a more intense state of motion.   Voidage has now increased to ϵ_f, and the pressure drop is still equal to that given by Eq. (2-1).   This condition constitutes dense-phase turbulent fluidization. With further increases in gas rate a condition in which substantial portions of the solid are entrained by the fluid stream will be approached. This will then lead to the dilute phase. The order of magnitude of the fluid-velocity spans which are involved in transforming the bed from incipient fluidization to the dilute phase may be observed from Fig. 2-5. The data have been calculated for silica sands of 160 lb per cu ft density. It will be noted that, for $D_p = 0.002$ in., for instance, the velocity range is nearly hundredfold. As the particle diameter increases, the range narrows considerably. However, even for $D_p = 0.012$ in. it is still about fortyfold. On the average the

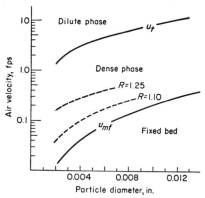

FIG. 2-5. Typical fluid velocities and velocity ranges encountered in the fluidization spectrum.

ratio of the terminal velocity u_t to the minimum-fluidization velocity u_{mf} is about 70. This is in good agreement with a value of 66 proposed by Brötz.[4]

PARTICULATE AND AGGREGATIVE FLUIDIZATION

In the expansion considerations presented so far no distinction has been made between fluidization with a gas and fluidization with a liquid. In fact the general pattern of solids expansion presented in Fig. 2-4 will apply equally well to either system. There are, however, differences performancewise which appear closely related to the choice of fluidizing medium. These were first described by Wilhelm and Kwauk.[25] "Particulate fluidization" was observed with their water-solid systems, whereas the type of fluidization that resulted with air was termed "aggregative."

Particulate fluidization was characterized as a state in which the particles were discretely separated from each other. A mean free path for the particles seemed to exist, and the path length appeared to increase with the fluid rate. "Aggregative fluidization" designated a state of fluidization wherein the particles were present in the bed not as individual units, but rather as aggregates. No mean free particle path was of course discernible.

In aggregative fluidization the gas rises through the bed primarily in the form of bubbles. Within these bubbles there may be entrained solids. Hence an aggregatively fluidizing bed is a heterogeneous body, composed of two separate coexisting phases.

On the basis of empirical data Wilhelm and Kwauk suggested that the value of the Froude number $u_f{}^2/D_p g$, in which u_f is the superficial velocity, D_p the particle diameter, and g the gravitational constant, may be indicative of the type of fluidization. Thus for $u_f{}^2/D_p g < 1.0$ the operation was said to be particulate, whereas for $u_f{}^2/D_p g > 1.0$ aggregative fluidization was said to prevail. The choice of the limiting value was arbitrary, and there may be overlapping areas of considerable extent. The question of what causes aggregative or particulate fluidization is still largely unanswered. As later discussions will show, the proper use of baffles in originally aggregative systems is one method by which a trend toward particulate behavior may be obtained. Doubtlessly other methods will be developed. Generally speaking, the tendency will be toward aggregative fluidization in systems of large solids-fluid density differences. For small differences the trend will be toward particulate operation.

MINIMUM FLUID VOIDAGE

One of the essential features of a fluidized bed is that the particles in the bed must be in motion. It appears that there is a characteristic voidage to which the bed must be expanded before particle motion, as induced by fluid flow, can set in. This voidage, required for the onset of fluidization or minimum fluidization, has been termed "minimum fluid voidage." It is denoted by ϵ_{mf}. A knowledge of ϵ_{mf} is obviously essential for predicting the onset of fluidization.

The minimum fluid voidage of a granular solid is readily determined by subjecting the bed to a rising gas stream and recording the bed height L_{mf} that coincides with incipient particle motion. Then from a knowledge of the buoyant weight of the bed w, vessel cross section A, and solids and fluid densities there results

$$\epsilon_{mf} = 1 - \frac{w}{L_{mf} A (\rho_S - \rho_F)} \qquad (2\text{-}2)\star$$

Minimum-fluid-voidage observations are best carried out in solids-gas systems. Although the nature of the fluid should not influence ϵ_{mf} values, it is conceivable that liquids might give somewhat higher values than gas-borne results, because in liquid-fluidized beds particle motion is not as pronounced at the onset of fluidization as it is in gas-fluidized beds.[10]

Determination of solids density poses no problem when the material has no appreciable internal porosity: it will then be satisfactory to resort to a simple water-displacement method. If, on the other hand, the material has an appreciable internal porosity, water displacement may not be satisfactory and immersion in a more viscous liquid such as mercury is desirable to prevent liquid penetration into the inside pores, which are ordinarily not available to fluid flow through the bed. Of course the ultimate accuracy of the method will depend on the nature of the solids and their degree of vesicularity. For this reason it is perhaps better to determine ϵ_{mf} values from flow studies and surface-area measurements in porous beds. Usually estimation of a shape factor is involved in this procedure, but recent research by Ergun[6] has provided a method for simultaneous determinations of solids density and shape factor. The method will be discussed in detail in a later chapter.

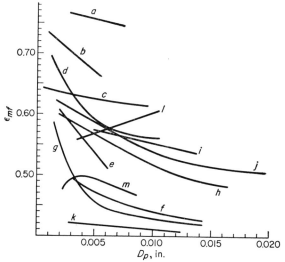

FIG. 2-6. Values of ϵ_{mf} in relation to D_p. Agarwal and Storrow:[1] (a) Soft brick; (b) absorption carbon; (c) broken Raschig rings; (d) coal and glass powder; (e) carborundum; (f) sand. U.S. Bureau of Mines:[13] (g) Round sand, $\phi_S = 0.86$; (h) sharp sand, $\phi_S = 0.67$; (i) Fischer-Tropsch catalyst, $\phi_S = 0.58$; (j) anthracite coal, $\phi_S = 0.63$; (k) mixed round sand, $\phi_S = 0.86$. Van Heerden et al.:[9] (l) Coke; (m) carborundum.

For most ϵ_{mf} determinations water or mercury displacements will be satisfactory. Moreover for most solids a close approximation may be obtained by substituting into Eq. (2-2) a value for bed height that was obtained by pouring the solids carefully from one container into another.

Values of ϵ_{mf} for a wide variety of materials are given in Fig. 2-6. The data of Agarwal and Storrow[1] are generally higher than the Bureau of Mines values.[13] All data, except the coke values of van Heerden and coworkers,[9] show that ϵ_{mf} varies inversely with D_p. Values of ϵ_{mf} increase as sphericity decreases. It is obvious that the less spherical the particles are, the more interstitial space will be required to permit motion.

PRESSURE-DROP–FLOW DIAGRAMS

A good indication of fluidization behavior of a granular material may be obtained from the pressure-drop–flow relationships of the expanded bed. Figure 2-7 represents such data for a material that displays what may be called ideal fluidization characteristics. Branch ϵ'_e-ϵ_e on the log-log plot pertains to fixed-bed pressure drop of the bed, at a voidage ϵ_e. At ϵ_e expansion occurs and continues along the horizontal line. Particle motion sets in when the voidage has slightly surpassed a value of ϵ_{mf}. The bed is then in the quiescently fluidizing state. For the ideal material under consideration here, fixed-bed conditions are reestablished as the flow rate is lowered again. This perfect reversibility occurs at a pressure drop that is exactly equal to the value that may be calculated from the buoyant weight of the bed, to be designated by Δp_w.

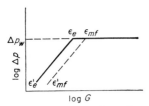

FIG. 2-7. Pressure-drop–flow diagram for ideally fluidizing solids.

Channeling. Very few materials and systems, gas-solid or liquid-solid, have such properties that they approach the perfect behavior just described. Instead most materials show irregularities in the pressure-drop–flow diagram which are indicative of definite abnormalities. The pressure-drop–flow relationship shown in Fig. 2-8 pertains to a system that exhibits channeling. This is an abnormality characterized by the establishment of flow paths in a bed of solids through which disproportionately large amounts of the fluid will pass up the column. Channeling is of course possible in liquid-solid as well as gas-solid systems. In a bed of solids with channeling tendencies the reversibility between the quiescent fluidized state and the fixed bed, approached with solids of near-ideal fluidization behavior, does not exist. Branch ϵ'_e-ϵ_e of Fig. 2-8 again represents the pressure-drop–flow relationship for the fixed bed. The point of initial bed expansion will usually occur at a somewhat higher pressure drop than that calculated from the weight gradient of the bed. The mode of expansion is generally quite sudden, and it appears that a certain, and so far unknown, energy quantity is needed to "unlock" the solid particles from each other. Once this has

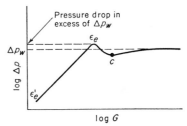

FIG. 2-8. Typical pressure-drop–flow diagram for moderately channeling solids.

occurred, the pressure drop will decrease rather suddenly. As flow rates continue to increase, the pressure drop may continue to decrease or it may increase, depending on whether the minimum pressure drop at point c has been passed. After point c there is always a pressure-drop recovery, but in channeling beds the theoretical value is never quite reached. The amount by which the pressure drop is lower should be indicative of the channeling tendencies of the solid. The difference between the actual and theoretical pressure drop is easily interpreted. Figure 2-9a and b shows two typical cases of channeling. There is "through channeling," as indicated in (a), when the flow paths extend through the entire bed, and "inter-mediate channeling," as in (b), when only a portion of the bed is subject to the irregularity. The intermediate-channeling bed will of course yield the higher fluidizing pressure drop. With increasing fluid rates the channeling tendencies will generally lessen.

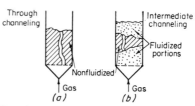

FIG. 2-9. Two common modes of channeling in solids bed.

The effects of channeling on a fluidization application may vary from almost unimportant to very severe. As an example let us consider, purely qualitatively, the case of a simple contact catalysis. Since with channeling the resulting bed density is not homogeneous, there will be local space velocities inside the bed which are greatly different from the over-all planned space velocity. This in turn will lead to erratic tempera-ture profiles, with heat effects and catalyst lifetimes entirely out of line with expectations. In noncatalytic operations—say, for example, the drying of a solid where merely mass is transferred—lack of homogeneous contacting will lead to inefficiency and generally larger equipment designs than would be required for a homo-geneously operating system.

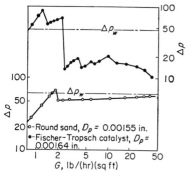

FIG. 2-10. Typical pressure-drop–flow relationship for severely channeling solids.

Qualitatively it is known that size and size distribution of the solid will influence channeling tendencies. Thus Matheson and coworkers[16] re-port channeling, or cohesive flow, as they chose to call it, for beds of syn-thetic cracking catalyst of less than 10 microns size when aerated at velocities up to 1 fps. For the same material, but of 25 microns particle size, cohesive flow still seems to pre-vail, but formation of small aggregate balls is no longer observed. As particle size is increased to 40 microns, good fluidization without channeling results for as low a gas velocity as 0.01 fps.

Shape and density of the solids also are factors that affect channeling. This may be concluded from Fig. 2-10, in which pressure-drop–flow relationships are shown for silica sand and Fischer-Tropsch iron-catalyst particles of virtually equal size.[13] Sphericity factors are 0.86 and 0.58, respectively, for the sand and the catalyst, and particle specific gravities are 2.65 and 5.00. Both materials were air-fluidized in a vessel of 4 in. diameter. The striking difference in behavior is apparent. Another factor known to affect channeling is moisture content of the solid.

Channeling appears to be greatly influenced by the fluidization-chamber diameter. The data of Jolley and Stantan,[11] given in Table 2-1,

TABLE 2-1. COAL-FLUIDIZATION DATA OF JOLLEY AND STANTAN

Size, in.	Gas	Tube diam, in.	$\dfrac{\Delta p_{obs}}{\Delta p_w}$
0.0625–0.0312	Air	3	0.98
0.0165–0.0083	Air	3	1.01
0.0083–0.0041	Air	3	0.97
0.0625–0.0312	Hydrogen	2	1.00
0.0312–0.0166	Hydrogen	2	0.80
0.0166–0.0083	Hydrogen	2	0.85
0.0083–0.0041	Hydrogen	2	0.76

substantiate this. The channeling tendency is reflected by the ratio of the observed to the theoretical pressure drop. A substantial decrease in the ratio results when the vessel diameter is decreased from 3 to 2 in. The fluidizing gas has probably little or no effect, but the increase in channeling tendency with decreasing particle size is quite apparent.

The design of the gas-inlet device has a profound effect on channeling. Thus with porous plates, by means of which the gas distribution into a bed tends initially toward uniformity, channeling tendencies are always smaller than with multi-orifice distributors, by means of which the gas is introduced through a relatively small number of geometrically spaced holes. This will be discussed in more detail in connection with fluidization performance. Conically shaped fluid inlets will tend to induce channeling. In fact there appear to be limiting angles for which fluidization will no longer occur, but at which a phenomenon known as spouting will occur instead. This will be discussed in Chap. 7.

A few attempts have been made to describe channeling in a quantitative sense. Thus Andrieu[2] examined the expansion behavior of beds with channeling tendencies and attempted to define a channeling factor in terms of voidages. Another approach to the problem of finding a quantitative channeling index makes use of the pressure-drop depression at the point of maximum channeling.[13] In order to give meaning to any of these expressions, they should be coordinated with the physical properties of the solids under consideration. This has so far not been attempted.

Slugging. Channeling is an abnormality that is primarily related to the characteristics of the solid phase, but the other frequently encountered abnormality in fluidization, slugging, is considerably more affected by the choice and design of the equipment. Characteristics of solids and fluids are also involved, though to a lesser extent than in channeling. Slugging is most commonly encountered with gas-solid systems, though liquid-solid systems can approach conditions that are reminiscent of slugging.

Slugging is described as the condition in which bubbles of the gas coalesce to a size approaching the order of magnitude of the diameter of the confining vessel. The particle layers, or slugs of granular solids, between such large gas pockets will move upward in a pistonlike manner, reach a certain height, and then disintegrate. The granular matter will then rain through the ascending gas pocket either in the form of smaller aggregates or as individual particles. From this description it can be concluded that a slugging bed is highly heterogeneous as far as gas-solid distribution is concerned. As in the case of channeling, local space velocities may differ widely from the over-all, conceived on the basis of total solids volume and specified gas rate. This will then have erratic effects on yields, temperatures, and catalyst life, as already mentioned. In addition, slugging may accelerate the rate of mechanical attrition of the solid and may thus lead to added expenditures for catalyst-recovery units. Maintenance costs of reactors will also be higher because of a greater rate of wear.

Slugging has been frequently mentioned in the fluidization literature.[1,13,16,19] Almost all of the various attempts to describe its intensity are based on oscillations of the pressure drop. None has been entirely satisfactory, because the oscillations are also dependent on the fluid rate. Thus, setting up a scale for slugging intensity has been largely a matter of individual judgment. Fortunately, more reliable measurements of homogeneity of fluidized beds, to be discussed later, have been made.

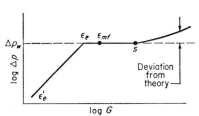

FIG. 2-11. Pressure-drop–flow diagram for slugging solids.

Although they were primarily intended to establish standards of fluidization in a general way, the results correlate quite well with visual slugging observations.

The pressure-drop–flow diagram of a solid will reflect possible slugging behavior. Thus, referring to Fig. 2-11, the solids may approach ideal behavior up to and considerably beyond the point of the onset of fluidization. Beyond a certain flow range, though, the pressure drop will increase above the value calculated from the weight of the bed. This condition, indicated by point s, may be defined as the onset of slugging. As flow rate increases further, the pressure-drop rise continues and the bed will slug even more severely. The evidence is that the pressure-drop excess over the theoretical value is due to friction between the solids slugs and the wall of the vessel. This would suggest that the height-to-diameter ratio of the bed is involved; Fig. 2-12, obtained by cross-plotting data of Lewis, Gilliland, and Bauer,[14] substantiates the hypothesis. Further data indicating a pronounced effect of bed height, as well as bed diameter, on slugging of coals and sands were obtained by Agarwal and Storrow.[1] Their data, pertaining to beds of only 4 cm depth, are given in Table 2-2. For this system, as L/D_t becomes smaller than 1.1, slugging velocities are no longer dependent on tube diameter.

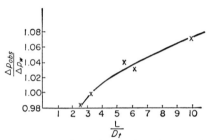

FIG. 2-12. Ratio of observed to theoretical pressure drops in relation to the height-diameter ratio of the beds. The data, observed by Lewis et al.,[14] pertain to glass beads fluidized in air; the relation was established by cross-plotting the data at a Reynolds number of D_pG/μ = 1.5.

TABLE 2-2. SLUGGING VELOCITIES IN TUBES OF VARIOUS DIAMETERS

Material	Slugging Velocities, fps, for tubes of following diam, in.				
	0.38	0.98	1.4	1.5	2.5
Coal, 36–72 mesh.......	0.43	0.55	0.62	0.61	0.63
Sand, 36–72 mesh.......	0.58	0 67	0.73	0.75	0.75

TABLE 2-3. SLUGGING VELOCITIES IN RELATION TO DEPTH IN A TUBE OF 1.64 IN. DIAMETER

Bed depth, in.	Slugging velocities, fps, for following materials	
	Coal, 36–72 mesh	Sand, 36–72 mesh
2.37	0.63	0.60
3.17	0.50	0.57
3.45	0.42	0.50
4.70	0.35	0.40
5.50	0.31	0.34

Bed-height effects were investigated by the same authors for the same materials; they are indicated in Table 2-3. Again as bed depths and thus L/D_t increases, the charges begin to slug at progressively smaller fluid rates. Although the two solids have widely differing densities, slugging velocities appear to be approximately equal. Since one would expect the heavier solids to slug more readily, it may well be that such factors as particle shape and size distribution may also be involved.

Some systematic particle-size effects upon slugging have been reported by Agarwal and Storrow for coals of wide size ranges. The data are shown in Fig. 2-13, in which particle size is plotted vs. a reduced slugging velocity. Smooth operation increases very markedly as particle size decreases. The 72- to 100-mesh coal size offers a slug-free operating range that is almost three times as large as that of 14- to 32-mesh coal particles. Based on the data discussed, Agarwal and Storrow propose

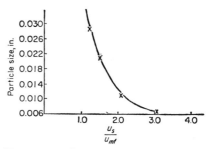

FIG. 2-13. Relation between particle size and reduced slugging velocities for coal particles observed by Agarwal and Storrow.[1] $D_t = 1.64$ in.; settled bed depth, 10 in.

$$u_s = 6.8 \frac{u_{mf}^{0.6}}{L^{0.8}} \qquad (2\text{-}3)$$

where u_s = gas velocity for incipient slugging
u_{mf} = gas velocity for minimum fluidization
L = bed height

The dimensions are to be in feet per second and feet. For the data underlying the formula, bed depth ranged to about six inches.

PHENOMENA SEQUENCE IN DENSE-PHASE FLUIDIZATION

With most of the important fixed-bed elements now discussed it is well to review everything briefly. The diagram of Fig. 2-14, originally proposed by Reboux,[20] is particularly helpful for such a purpose.

Starting from below, the fixed bed is first encountered. Barring any channeling tendencies this will then transform to an incipiently fluidizing bed, and thereafter it will expand. Depending on whether the fluid is a gas or a liquid, aggregative or particulate fluidization will result. Finally both systems will reach the dispersed phase. The transformation in the liquid-fluidized bed will be gradual and most likely without slugging. However in the gas-fluidized system the transformation from the dense-phase fluidized state to the dispersed phase will in any case pass through a slugging zone. Details pertaining to this transformation will be discussed in Chap. 6.

If the solids have channeling tendencies and if the system is gas-solid, the path to follow is indicated by the dotted line. Depending on the severity of the channeling tendency, the solids may transform into a state which is between incipient fluidization and the aggregative dense

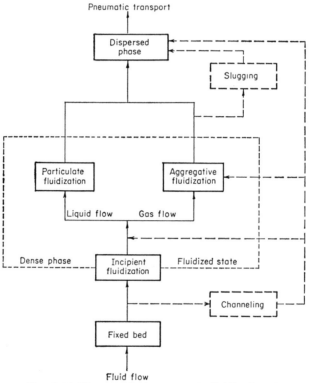

Fig. 2-14. Phases and phenomena in fluidization.[20]

bed, they may return directly to the aggregative bed, or they may transform directly to the dispersed phase. Obviously, in the last instance there will not be a dense-phase fluidized bed at all.

Liquid-solid systems as well as gas-solid systems may show channeling tendencies. The patterns will then be similar. However, in liquid-fluidized systems channeling will never be so severe that the fixed bed will pass directly into the dispersed phase. Hence there will always be a particulately fluidizing dense phase.

FLUIDIZATION PERFORMANCE

Description of a fluidization operation in terms of approach to ideal behavior can, at best, be only qualitative and therefore not entirely objective. This has long been recognized, and it is without doubt for that reason that efforts have been made to arrive at more exact definitions of the quality of fluidization. An interesting approach to this problem has been given by Morse and Ballou.[17] Using their so-called capacitometer, they succeeded in expressing fluidized-bed densities in terms of a capacitometer voltage, by means of the dielectric properties of the elements of a fluidized system. The condenser plates were small enough to be inserted into fluidized vessels; they permitted local explorations without seriously affecting the fluidization itself. Thus variations of bulk density were recorded over a definite time interval, as indicated in Fig. 2-15, and a uniformity index was defined as being equal to the ratio of the per cent of average deviation to the frequency.

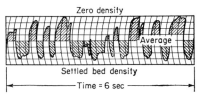

FIG. 2-15. Uniformity index of Morse and Ballou.[17] (*Courtesy of Industrial and Engineering Chemistry.*)

From experience, uniformity indices have been associated with quality of fluidization as follows:

Uniformity index	Degree of uniformity
1.0	High
1.0–5.0	Fair
5.0–60	Poor, with increasingly large slugs

Obviously, for perfect uniformity the index has a value of zero. With this method Morse and Ballou systematically investigated the effect of major system variables on uniformity. The observations are believed to be sufficiently important to justify detailed discussion.

Particle-size Distribution. Two samples of a metal oxide catalyst, one possessing a wide and the other a narrow size distribution, were fluidized under identical conditions of bed height, vessel diameter, and gas rate.

TABLE 2-4. SIZE DISTRIBUTIONS OF METAL OXIDE, DATA OF MORSE AND BALLOU

Screen analysis, mesh	Wide cut, % on	Narrow cut, % on
48	26.8	36.1
65	17.8	25.1
100	16.6	23.5
150	10.1	12.2
200	6.7	3.1
270	3.7	
Pan	18.3	

Size distributions are indicated in Table 2-4. The narrow cut was prepared from the wide cut by removal of the finer components; a consequence of the screening process was a slight increase in geometric mean size, from 0.185 to 0.245 mm. This, however, was not sufficient to account for the very severe increase in uniformity index, from 3.8 to 32, observed by the authors.

Gas-velocity Effect. The wide-cut material of Table 2-4, when fluidized under various gas rates, gave the following results:

Gas velocity, fps	Uniformity index
0.25	2.5
0.50	7.6
0.875	8.9

The low gas velocity of 0.25 fps was only slightly above the minimum-fluidization rate. A doubling of gas velocity in the low-velocity range caused a much faster rate of fluidization deterioration than a virtual doubling at the higher gas-rate level. From this one may conclude that, for the relatively coarse solid employed, the excess gas over that required to initially fluidize the charge passed through the bed not as a homogeneous phase, but rather as large bubbles. This will not apply, however, to beds of small particles, which are known to expand more nearly uniformly and over a greater range of gas velocities.

Effect of Bed Height. In scale-up problems the uncertainties associated with effect of bed height are felt most directly. It is important to be able to predict behavior in the additional height of column, as compared with that used in a pilot reactor, and a reliable appraisal should also account for possible effects which the greater bed height will have on the lower bed strata originally present. Capacitometer explorations may here be of great value. In Table 2-5, uniformity indices are given for the two cuts of metal oxide catalyst which are described in Table 2-4. Capacitometer explorations were made at the 6-in. bed level, and the data indicate, therefore, the effect of superimposing bed height on an already existing layer.

TABLE 2-5. EFFECT OF BED HEIGHT ON FLUIDIZATION QUALITY AT 6 IN.

Material	Uniformity indices for following settled bed heights			
	8 in.	16 in.	28 in.	40 in.
Wide cut.........	2.3	2.2	1.7	1.2
Narrow cut.......	3.7	3.7	2.5	3.2

It is interesting to note that, at the 6-in. level, performance in the narrow cut was virtually unaffected by additional bed height. In the case of the wide cut, however, a definite improvement resulted. As column height was increased to 40 in., over-all performance was also observed for both cuts. Average data for the entire charges were as shown in Table 2-6. It should be noted that both charges showed deterioration in performance. However, the wide cut, which originally fluidized better, exhibited a much smaller rate of deterioration than did the narrow cut.

TABLE 2-6. EFFECT OF BED HEIGHT ON OVER-ALL PERFORMANCE

Material	Over-all performance at following bed heights			
	6 in.	16 in.	28 in.	40 in.
Wide cut.............	0.95	2.7	8.8	7.9
Narrow cut..........	3.2	10.0	33	63

The technique of Morse and Ballou has also been used by Martin and Andrieu[15] for evaluating uniformity indices in beds of glass beads and clays. The fluidization chamber was of 100 mm inside diameter and the air was admitted through a porous bronze disk. The sounding element was a condenser of the same construction as that described above as used by Morse and Ballou. From their experimental data, Martin and Andrieu concluded that:

1. The uniformity index is directly proportional to height above the gas inlet.

2. The local uniformity index at any specific position in the bed is little or not at all influenced by bed height that may be beyond the point of interest.

3. The uniformity index is proportional to the logarithm of the superficial gas velocity.

Typical data observed by Martin and Andrieu are given in Fig. 2-16. They pertain to glass beads in beds ranging from about 3 to 15 in. in height. The data support the last-mentioned observation, namely, that the uniformity index i is proportional to log u_f. The slopes increase as bed height decreases, and the three lines tend to intersect near $u_f \approx 2.8$, for which value the uniformity coefficient $i \to 0$. It is of interest to observe that this limiting value of superficial air velocity is in good agreement with $u_{mf} = 2.45$ cm per sec, calculated for this particular solid. The coinciding of the individual lines at or near u_{mf} and the resulting $i \to 0$ are to be expected because, at incipient fluidization, the gas-fluidized bed should tend to be largely homogeneous. As a preliminary step toward correlation, the suggestion to let $i \propto \log\,(u_f/u_{mf})$ has therefore been made.

Fluidization performance has also been investigated by Reboux.[21] The principle of his study involves the recording of pressure pulsations in the fluidized column. For this purpose a brass tube, properly fitted into a fluidized column, transmits the pressure vibrations to a very thin metal diaphragm which is opposite to another stationary metal diaphragm. The two diaphragms together form an electric condenser, and owing to the rapid deformations of one diaphragm, the capacity of the condenser will change in accord with the pulsations caused by the pressure variations. By proper electric amplification the vibrations are readily projected on a screen for recording purposes.

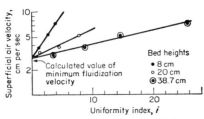

FIG. 2-16. Data of Martin and Andrieu[15] showing effect of air velocity on the uniformity index. The bed was composed of 65- to 150-mesh glass beads.

Tests were made with a variety of solids and were reported for alumina in a bed of about 15.5 in. height. As the fluidizing air rate increased from 0.11 to 0.28 fps, the amplitudes of the vibrations were first observed to increase. Thereafter the period itself seemed to increase appreciably as higher air rates prevailed. The fluctuations were recognized as being due to:

1. The migration of small particle components through the bed interstices

2. The passing of gas bubbles past the pressure-transmitting element

As far as local observation was concerned, the pressure fluctuations were more severe in the upper-bed region than in lower positions. They were less pronounced near the wall of the vessel than in the center.

Data on over-all bed performance were also given by Shuster and Kisliak.[22] They investigated performance of fluidized beds in a way somewhat similar to that used by Morse and Ballou; however, since they recorded essentially pressure-drop fluctuations over the entire bed, they were not in a position to report local-performance data. Their index was defined as the average pressure-drop deviation observed divided by the fluctuation frequency. For perfect fluidization the value of the index is also equal to zero and increases as performance deteriorates.

The measurements of Shuster and Kisliak[22] support the observations of Morse and Ballou on variation of over-all performance of beds with change in bed height. This is readily apparent from Fig. 2-17. At low expansion ratios, the effect of bed height on performance is felt more strongly than in more expanded columns. This is understandable because, at the high expansions of 200 per cent, dilute-phase conditions are approached by all beds.

Effect of Height-to-diameter Ratio. Fluidization performance is influenced not only by the height of the bed but also by the vessel diameter and the resulting ratio of height to diameter. Although the relationship is well known from practice and direct visual observations, there are only a few data to substantiate it quantitatively. The measurements which Shuster and Kisliak give are significant and agree qualitatively with the slugging data of Agarwal and Storrow. Thus, Fig. 2-18 reports the variation of their fluidization index with L/D_t for glass beads

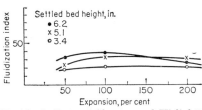

Fig. 2-17. Data of Shuster and Kisliak[22] showing the over-all bed-height effect on the fluidization index. Data pertain to air fluidization of 0.028-in.-diameter glass beads in a 3.75-in.-diameter tube.

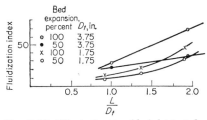

Fig. 2-18. Effect of ratio of height to tube diameter on fluidization index. (*Compiled from the data of Shuster and Kisliak.*[22])

of 0.011 in. average diameter fluidized in 3.75- and 1.75-in.-diameter columns. The important observations are as follows:

1. Fluidization performance deteriorates as L/D_t increases. This follows also from qualitative observations of slugging.

2. The rate of deterioration with increasing L/D_t is greater the higher the expansion rates.

3. For $L/D_t < 1.0$, performances of 50 and 100 per cent bed expansion tend to approach each other. This is also in accord with experiences gained from slugging.

4. For the same expansion ratios and values of L/D_t, the large-diameter beds exhibit a poorer performance than the small-diameter beds.

The last observation is especially interesting, since it emphasizes that the ratio L/D_t by itself is not sufficient to define the performance of a fluidized system. Obviously then, since performance seems to deteriorate as the vessel diameter increases, one is led to assume that initial gas-distribution problems in the base of the column are also involved. This has been stressed by Morse and Ballou and seems to be specifically involved here.

Effect of Fluid-distributor Design. In a series of simple tests Takeda[23] showed quantitatively how the design of the fluid-inlet device of a fluidized bed can affect fluidization performance. Resorting to the working method of Shuster and Kisliak, Takeda fluidized silica sands in cylindrical as well as conically shaped vessels. The cylindrical vessels could be operated with perforated-hole distributors having various hole sizes and layouts; inlets of various cone angles, as shown in Fig. 2-19, were tested with the conically shaped vessels.

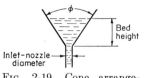

FIG. 2-19. Cone arrangement of Takeda.[23]

For a silica sand of $D_p = 0.0017$ in. and other conditions as indicated, performance in the cylindrical and conical vessels is compared in Fig. 2-20. For very low bed heights, fluidization performance is the same in both vessels; however, a rapid deterioration with increasing bed heights is observed in the cylindrical vessel. In Fig. 2-21 the effect of the cone angle is shown; it is interesting to observe that there is an optimum cone angle. For the material investigated under the conditions specified it is nearly 50°. The effects of conical fluid-inlet devices on fluidization—in fact, on fluidizability—have been further studied in connection with the new contacting phenomenon known as spouting, described in detail in Chap. 7.

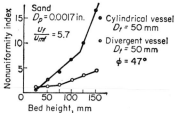

FIG. 2-20. Data of Takeda[23] showing effect of geometry of fluidization vessel on uniformity of fluidization. The nonuniformity index of Takeda is the equivalent of the fluidization index of Shuster and Kisliak.[22]

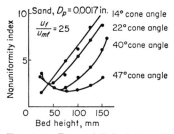

FIG. 2-21. Data of Takeda[23] indicating how fluidization performance is affected by the cone angle in divergent vessels.

The effect of fluid distributor as it pertains to gas-fluidized systems has also been investigated by Grohse.[7] The method of analysis was by way of X-ray absorption. No foreign objects required immersion in the bed; hence there was no interference with the normal flow pattern. The method should also be preferable to a pressure-drop-oscillation method. Results from the latter require interpretation of the data, whereas X-ray absorption directly yields densities, which, after all, are the required data.

The three different distributors considered were a multi-orifice plate, a screen, and a sintered porous plate. Details of the devices, used with a

3.33-in.-ID column, are shown in Fig. 2-22. The solid fluidized was an irregularly shaped silicon powder, ranging from subsieve size to 74 microns.

Pressure-drop–flow diagrams are given in Fig. 2-23. For the multi-orifice plate the point of incipient fluidization is not well defined. The gradual pressure-drop increase up to that theoretically demanded suggests that the bottom portion of the bed is not fluidized to the same extent as the upper region. With the screen distributor, a certain amount of channeling probably occurred. There is the possibility that the holes in the screen were locally blocked; this could create a condition favorable

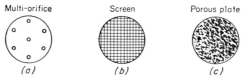

FIG. 2-22. Gas distributors used by Grohse.[7] (a) Sheet metal, $\frac{1}{16}$-in., carrying a 0.052-in. hole per square inch of area. (b) A 300-mesh screen on 0.017-in. thick plate, carrying twenty-four 0.021-in. holes on triangular diamond pitch. (c) A $\frac{1}{8}$-in. sintered-metal plate of 0.0008-in. mean pore opening.

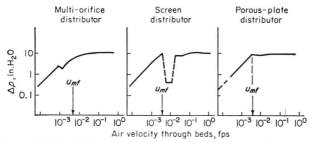

FIG. 2-23. Data of Grohse[7] showing effect of gas distributor on the onset of fluidization. (*Courtesy of AIChE Journal.*)

for channeling. With the porous plate the point of incipient fluidization is well defined and there is no tendency for channeling. In view of these strong effects exerted by the distributor, it is reasonable to expect an effect on the expansion behavior. Observations have confirmed this.

Local bed densities were obtained for the range of flow rates shown in Fig. 2-24. Considering first the operation with the porous plate, bed densities are remarkably constant through the entire column. Except for the highest flow rates, oscillations between maximum and minimum values are not excessive. For the other distributors the bed-density data are quite irregular. Considering first the multi-orifice distributor, operation at the low velocity shows that the bottom portion of the bed was not expanded, hence it was not fluidized. Apparently the air leaving the holes could not flare out sufficiently fast to contact the low-bed region effectively. This condition should improve at higher air rates mainly because of the effect of turbulence. Regarding oscillations, the operation is much less steady than with the porous plate. The screen distributor is similar in its functioning to the multi-orifice plate. There is considerable channeling in the low-bed region. The bed-density data are of

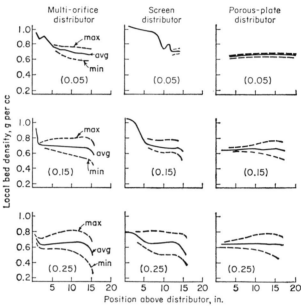

Fig. 2-24. Data of Grohse[7] showing effect of gas distributor on local bed densities. Data in parentheses are the prevailing air velocities in fps; max, avg, and min refer to maximum, average, and minimum values of observed bed densities. (*Courtesy of AIChE Journal.*)

course compatible with the specific pressure-drop–flow diagram data shown in Fig. 2-23.

DENSE-BED VISCOSITY

Since early observations of dense-phase fluidized solids appeared to reveal certain analogies with Newtonian liquids, it is not surprising that efforts were made quite early to measure the "viscosity of fluidized solids." The first measurements were reported by Matheson and coworkers.[16] The apparatus was a modified Stormer viscometer using a paddle ¾ in. wide and 1½ in. high. It was immersed in an aerated bed of solids 3 in. deep. Matheson pointed out that the measurements in the solids bed do not really yield a true viscosity because, in addition to whatever fluid shearing forces are involved, substantial velocity components are required for imparting particle acceleration and for overcoming purely frictional forces between the solids. It is to be borne in mind that the numerical values thus obtained not only are dependent on the material tested but also will be related to the dimensions and design of the testing unit. Nevertheless, significant data will result if aerated solids are subjected to tests with standardized equipment. The viscosity data actually reported by the Stormer viscometer are the weights required to spin the immersed paddle at 200 rpm.

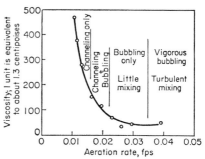

FIG. 2-25. Data of Diekman and Forsythe[5] on viscosity of catalyst in relation to aeration. (*Courtesy of Industrial and Engineering Chemistry.*)

Bed viscosity decreases as aeration rate increases. The rate of decrease of viscosity is greatest near incipient fluidization; thereafter the rate of decrease lessens. This property has been used by Diekman and Forsythe[5] to describe flow properties of fluidized solids. Typical data pertaining to a well-flowing cracking catalyst are shown in Fig. 2-25.

Matheson found that bed viscosity increases with particle size and solids density. Particle shape affects the internal resistance also. Thus spherical cracking catalyst required a greater weight for moving the Stormer viscometer paddle than did irregularly shaped particles. The reasons for this are not known.

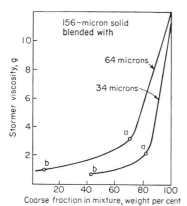

FIG. 2-26. Data of Matheson, Herbst, and Holt[16] showing effect of fines on the "viscosity" of mixtures.

Size distribution and fines content have a marked effect on the viscosity. This is indicated in Fig. 2-26. The viscosity is at first little affected by the change in composition. However, a critical-concentration range seems to exist beyond the region *ab*, where for a relatively small decrease in fines concentration an unusually large viscosity increase results. This phenomenon has been the subject of an interesting speculation by Trawinski,[24] who envisions the role of the fines not unlike that of ball bearings between moving surfaces. The model conceived by Trawinski is shown in Fig. 2-27. It is believed that, at point *a* in Fig. 2-26, just enough fines are contained in the mixed bed to act as rollers between the larger component particles. Thus a further small depletion of fines will tend to reduce the interstitial fines concentration critically.   The roller action will be lost and the internal bed friction will increase.   For the purpose of estimating the critical fines concentration, Trawinski proposes that

$$c = \frac{0.565(3n + 3n^2 - r)}{1 + 0.565(3n + 3n^2 - r)} \tag{2-4}$$

where n = diameter ratio of fines and large component
      r = expansion of bed relative to unexpanded bed height
    Fluidized-bed viscosity was also studied by Kramers.[12]   The fluidiza-tion tube was of 3.4 in. ID, and the air entered by way of a nylon filter cloth.   The rotating element consisted of a pair of horizontally arranged 1-in.-diameter dumbbells.   It could be adjusted along the vertical axis

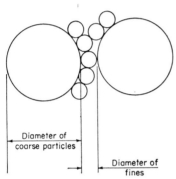

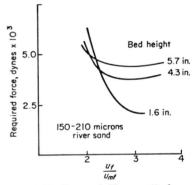

FIG. 2-27. Model of Trawinski[24] describing the relative position of coarse and fine particles at point a in Fig. 2-26. (*Courtesy of Chemie-Ingenieur-Technik.*)

FIG. 2-28. Data of Kramers[12] show-ing typical relation between fluidized-bed viscosity and fluidized-bed height.

of the bed, hence it permitted sectional explorations.   Some typical data shown in Fig. 2-28 relate the required force for moving the dumbbells at a speed of 5 cm per sec to the reduced fluidization velocity.   The data pertain to three immersion heights of the stirring element.   As already discussed, the resistance at first decreases as the gas rate increases.   How-ever, there follows a tendency for an increase.   The initial decrease is of course readily explained by the resulting disengagement between the particles.   However the tendency for an increase would indicate that at the higher fluid rate the bed becomes more turbulent.   This tendency becomes more accentuated at increasing bed heights.   For very much greater bed heights, not shown, the internal resistance decreases again, and Kramers inferred that large gas bubbles must now have formed. They would, of course, offer much less resistance to the stirrer than a homogeneous bed would.   The nonhomogeneous character of the bed at these heights was further apparent from an erratic velocity pattern of the stirrer when rotating in the upper bed strata.   Kramers points out that the entire gas-solids distribution pattern is very sensitive to structural details of the unit.   These effects must obviously be accounted for in any scale-up problem.   Since almost no data are so far available on these effects, the value of small-scale data for the purpose of extension to large-scale units is seriously questioned.   Kramers also points out that the gas-fluidized bed, with its nonhomogeneous character, is in reality not at all like a liquid, as erroneously assumed.

A number of expressions have been proposed for correlating aerated-bed viscosity with bed voidage.   These have been reviewed by Johnson,[10] who himself proposes that the fluidized-bed viscosity is related to bed voidage by

$$\mu_a = \mu \; \frac{1 + 0.5(1 - \epsilon)}{\epsilon^4} \left(\frac{1 - \epsilon}{\epsilon} \right)^9 \tag{2-5}$$

where μ = fluid viscosity
ϵ = bed voidage

It is to be noted that, as $\epsilon \rightarrow 1.0$, $\mu_a \rightarrow 0$.   Equation (2-5) has been used with good results by Reboux[20] for correlating extensive data for sands and coke particles.

OTHER CONSIDERATIONS

From process-development studies it is well known that small-scale fixed-bed reactors frequently do not perform as well as large-scale units. This is of course also true of fluidized reactors.   Thus a problem that occasionally arises is that of modifying either the design or the operation of the fluidized reactor so that large-scale performance is simulated.

The methods most frequently resorted to involve internal stirring and internal baffling.   Recently, application of sonic energy has been mentioned.[18]   It is, however, still largely exploratory and may perhaps in the future be applied to large-scale units.   Both stirring and baffling have been described in the literature.[3,8]   Stirring is usually more objectionable than baffling because of the mechanical problems involved.   One may experience catalyst breakup due to mechanical attrition in bearings. Introduction of impurities and fluid leakages may be other serious objections.   Considerations of power requirements in a pilot plant are not important because large-scale beds are usually not intended to be stirred.

Baffling is by far the more attractive method of providing smooth operation of a unit.   Some typical conventional baffles are shown in Fig. 2-29.   Usually they are installed in tubes ranging in diameter from one-half to several inches.   The value of baffled fluidized reactors in catalyst testing and assaying is best understood by considering a problem. Thus Hall and Crumley[8] proposed to fluidize a charge of 500 cc of Fischer-

Tropsch iron catalyst with 30 cu ft per hr of synthetic gas. The temperature of the bed was 300°C, and the pressure was 300 psig. The fresh-gas space velocity desired was to be equal to 1,000 volumes of gas under standard conditions per hour per expanded volume of catalyst. Recycle ratio was 2:1, and a linear gas velocity under reaction conditions of 0.6 fps was desired. Under these conditions a bed of 80 in. depth and of only 1 in. diameter was required. The magnetic iron oxide catalyst considered has a true density of about 5 g per cc and will slug formidably in such a tall reactor. Thus local space velocities would be entirely different from the anticipated over-all value. After a few tests in glass

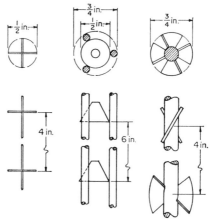

FIG. 2-29. Typical small-scale-reactor baffles.[3] (*Courtesy of Industrial and Engineering Chemistry.*)

models it was concluded that, by inserting into the vessel a central rod to which small disks of 10-mesh steel gauze, dished slightly convex to the direction of gas flow, were attached at regular 2-in. intervals, smooth fluidization was achieved for the 72- to 170-mesh catalyst through a velocity range of 0.3 to 1.0 fps. In similar fashion smooth fluidization was substantially achieved by the introduction of a mechanical stirrer rotating at low speeds.

REFERENCES

1. Agarwal, O. P., and J. Anderson Storrow: *Chem. & Ind. (London)*, 278–286 (1951).
2. Andrieu, R.: "Etudes des systèmes fluidisés liquides-solides," Ph.D. thesis, University of Nancy, France, 1956.
3. Beck, R. A.: *Ind. Eng. Chem.*, **41**: 1242–1243 (1949).
4. Brötz, W.: *Chem. Ingr. Tech.*, **24**(2): 60–81 (1952).
5. Diekman, R., and W. L. Forsythe, Jr.: *Ind. Eng. Chem.*, **45**: 1174–1177 (1953).
6. Ergun, S.: *Anal. Chem.*, **24**: 388 (1952).
7. Grohse, E. W.: *AIChE Journal*, **1**(3): 358–365 (1955).

8. Hall, C. C., and P. Crumley: *J. Appl. Chem. (London)*, **2,** Suppl. Issue 1, S47–S55 (1952).

9. Heerden, C. van, A. P. P. Nobel, and D. W. van Krevelen: *Chem. Eng. Sci.*, **1**(1): 37–49 (1951).

10. Johnson, E.: *Inst. Gas Engrs. (London)*, *Rept.* 1949–1950, *Publ. No.* 378/179.

11. Jolley, L. J., and J. E. Stantan: *J. Appl. Chem. (London)*, **2,** Suppl. Issue 1, S62–S68 (1952).

12. Kramers, H.: *Chem. Eng. Sci.*, **1**: 35–37 (1951).

13. Leva, Max, M. Weintraub, M. Grummer, M. Pollchik, and H. H. Storch: *U.S. Bur. Mines Bull.* 504, 1951.

14. Lewis, W. K., E. R. Gilliland, and W. C. Bauer: *Ind. Eng. Chem.*, **41**: 1104–1117 (1949).

15. Martin, J., and R. Andrieu: *Journée de fluidisation*, June 11, 1956, pp. 59–67, Association Française de Fluidisation, Paris.

16. Matheson, G. L., W. A. Herbst, and P. H. Holt 2d: *Ind. Eng. Chem.*, **41**: 1099–1104 (1949).

17. Morse, R. D., and C. O. Ballou: *Chem. Eng. Progr.*, **47**: 199–204 (1951).

18. Morse, R. D.: *Ind. Eng. Chem.*, **47**: 1170–1175 (1955).

19. Parent, J. D., N. Yagol, and C. S. Steiner: *Chem. Eng. Progr.*, **43**: 429–436 (1947).

20. Reboux, P.: "Phénomènes de fluidisation," Association Française de Fluidisation, Paris, 1954.

21. Reboux, P.: *Journée de fluidisation*, June 11, 1956, pp. 53–58, Association Française de Fluidisation, Paris.

22. Shuster, W. W., and P. Kisliak: *Chem. Eng. Progr.*, **48**: 455–458 (1952).

23. Takeda, K.: *Chem. Eng. (Tokyo)*, **21**(3): 124–129 (1957).

24. Trawinski, H.: *Chem. Ingr. Tech.*, **25**(4): 201–203 (1953).

25. Wilhelm, R. H., and M. Kwauk: *Chem. Eng. Progr.*, **44**: 201 (1948).

26. Wilhelm, R. H., and S. Valentine: *Ind. Eng. Chem.*, **43**: 1199–1203 (1951).

27. Zenz, F.: *Ind. Eng. Chem.*, **41**: 2801–2806 (1949).

CHAPTER 3

FIXED BED AND ONSET OF FLUIDIZATION

Nomenclature

a = component pertaining to Ergun equations (3-15) and (3-15b)

A = surface area of arbitrarily shaped particle, sq ft

A_p = surface area of spherical particle, sq ft

b = component pertaining to Ergun equations (3-15) and (3-15b)

B = generalized shape factor of van Heerden et al., dimensionless

c = experimental constant, dimensionless

C = function of D_pG/μ in Eq. (3-24), dimensionless

C_1C_2 = function of specific surface area, Ergun equation (3-16)

C_D = drag coefficient $D_pg_c\rho_F(\rho_S - \rho_F)/2G^2$, dimensionless

d_p = component diameter in a mixture of particles, ft, $d_p = \sqrt{d_1d_2}$, where d_1 and d_2 are rated openings of adjacent sieves

D_h = hydraulic diameter, ft

D_p = particle diameter, ft

D_t = circular-conduit diameter, ft

f = empty-pipe friction factor, dimensionless

f_{CC} = Chilton and Colburn friction factor, dimensionless

f_k = kinetic friction factor of Ergun, dimensionless

f_m = modified friction factor, dimensionless

g_c = gravitational conversion factor, 32.2 (lb mass)(ft)/(lb force)(sec)(sec)

G = fluid mass velocity, lb/(hr)(sq ft) (lb/sec-ft²) for eq. 3-15

G_{mf} = fluid mass velocity for minimum fluidization, lb/(hr)(sq ft)

k, k' = constants, dimensionless

$K_{\Delta p}, K_{\Delta\rho}$ = correlation parameters of Wilhelm and Kwauk, dimensionless

L = bed height, ft

L_{mf} = bed height at point of minimum fluidization, ft

L_ϵ = actual average path length of a fluid particle in a bed, ft

m = number of particles per cubic foot

M = molecular weight of fluid flowing

n = state-of-flow factor, dimensionless

p = fluid pressure, lb per sq ft; p_1 = upstream pressure, p_2 = downstream pressure

P = entire wetted perimeter, ft

r_h = hydraulic radius, ft

R = gas constant

Re = Reynolds number, D_pG/μ; $\text{Re}_h = 4r_hG/\mu$

S_v = surface area of solids per unit volume of solids (Ergun)

S = cross-sectional area of unpacked tube, sq ft

S' = entire available flow cross section of a packed conduit, sq ft

T = absolute temperature, °R or °K, depending on dimension of R

u = local fluid-particle velocity component in direction of over-all fluid flow, fps

u_0 = velocity of approach of a fluid to a packed section; also superficial velocity through bed, fps

u_{mf} = average superficial fluid velocity required for minimum fluidization, fps

u_Q = average superficial fluid velocity required for producing the quiescent fluidized state, $u_Q \approx u_{mf}$

u_ϵ = actual average fluid-particle velocity in a bed, fps

v_1, v_2 = specific volume of fluid, cu ft per lb

V = volume of a spherical particle, cu ft

w = fluid flow rate, lb per hr

X = weight fraction of a size component in a mixture, dimensionless

Z = gas compressibility factor

Δp = pressure drop, lb per sq ft; $\Delta p = p_1 - p_2$

ϵ = over-all bed voidage fraction, dimensionless

ϵ_{mf} = bed-voidage fraction at point of minimum fluidization, dimensionless

θ = angle

μ = fluid viscosity, lb/(hr)(ft) *(lb/sec-ft) for eq 3-18*

ρ_b = bulk density (Ergun and Baerg et al.), lb per cu ft

ρ_B = bulk density of solids at point of minimum fluidization (van Heerden et al.), lb per cu ft

ρ_S = solids density, lb per cu ft

ρ_F = fluid density, lb per cu ft

ϕ_s = particle-shape factor, $\phi_s = V^{2/3}/0.205A$

ψ = function of

Abstract

This chapter consists of three sections. In the first section the basic equation for flow through empty conduits is presented, with adaptations to laminar and turbulent flow. The second section deals with flow through fixed packed beds. On the basis of certain assumptions regarding fluid velocity, length of fluid path, and hydraulic radius in the packed bed, the open-conduit flow equation is modified to Kozeny-Carman-type equations that apply to laminar turbulent flow through fixed beds. Next follows a discussion of the parameters which are required for pressure-drop estimates. Specifically this pertains to bed voidage and voidage distribution, wall effect, velocity distribution, shape factor, roughness effects, and vesicularity.

In the third section the basic equation for estimating the onset of fluidization is developed by equating the pressure gradient across a fluidizing bed to the analytical expression for pressure drop. The correlation is then developed further into a generalized equation which obviates shape-factor and voidage data. The chapter closes with a presentation of the most important correlations for minimum fluidization proposed in the literature.

FLOW THROUGH EMPTY CONDUITS

For empty-conduit flow, knowledge of the involved variables and dimensional analysis yields

$$\frac{\Delta p}{L} \propto \frac{\rho_F u_0^2}{2 g_c r_h} \left(\frac{4 r_h u_0 \rho_F}{\mu} \right)^{n-2} = \frac{k}{g_c} \frac{\mu^{2-n}}{\rho_F^{1-n}} u_0^n D_t^{n-3} \qquad (3\text{-}1)$$

In Eq. (3-1) n is termed the state-of-flow factor. It was found empirically that the state-of-flow factor ranges from 1 to 2. Thus for completely laminar flow $n = 1$, whereas $n \to 2.0$ as the flow tends to become wholly turbulent.

Laminar Flow. Substitution of $n = 1$ into Eq. (3-1) and evaluation of the experimental constant results in

$$\Delta p = 32 \frac{\mu u_0 L}{g_c D_t^2} \qquad (3\text{-}2)\star$$

This is the well-known Hagen-Poiseuille law for isothermal laminar flow of noncompressible fluids in round conduits. The law is also readily derived from purely theoretical considerations of fluid viscosity and the characteristic velocity distribution in streamline motion.

Another way of writing Eq. (3-2) is by

$$\frac{\Delta p \, g_c D_t}{2L \rho_F u_0^2} = k \left(\frac{D_t u_0 \rho_F}{\mu} \right)^{-1} = f \qquad (3\text{-}3)\star$$

The dimensionless left-hand part of Eq. (3-3) is known as the friction factor in the well-known Fanning equation. By comparison with Eq. (3-2),

$$f = \frac{16\mu}{D_t u_0 \rho_F} \qquad (3\text{-}4)\star$$

Turbulent Flow. For streamline flow $n = 1$, and hence friction factors are inversely proportional to the Reynolds number. Since for turbulent flow n is not constant but depends on the state of turbulence, the friction-factor–Reynolds-number data relationship for turbulent flow is best represented in graphical form. This is given in Fig. 3-1.

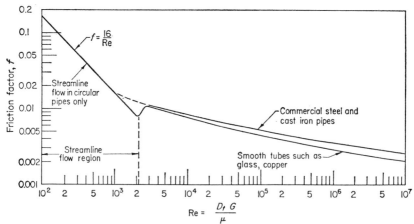

Fig. 3-1. Friction-factor–Reynolds-number relation for isothermal flow of fluids in circular conduits.

Besides being a function of Reynolds number, friction factors in turbulent flow are also affected by the roughness of the surface which is in contact with the flowing fluid. This has been investigated extensively. Probably the most exhaustive, though not most recent, study was made by Moody.[17]* Figure 3-1 gives friction factors for smooth tubes as well as commercial steel pipe.

FLOW THROUGH FIXED BEDS

Equation (3-1) was conceived from considerations of flow through empty tubes. With the proper modifications it may be altered[18] to apply to flow through packings, operating through wide flow ranges.

Average Fluid Velocity. Let Fig. 3-2 represent the lower portion of a packed bed. The fluid approaches the bed at the velocity u_0. Passing through the packing support plate and entering the packing it undergoes a velocity readjustment. This is in accord with the extent and character of the voidage of the bed.

If the bed is of over-all voidage ϵ,

$$u_0 S = u_\epsilon S \quad \text{and} \quad u_\epsilon = \frac{u_0}{\epsilon \cos \theta}$$

Dye-injection experiments by Carman[4] into beds of ¼-in. glass spheres in a 1-in.-diameter tube indicated that $\cos \theta$ varied between its extreme limits, 1 and 0. The extremes were, however, relatively infrequent and were evenly distributed about the mean 45° angle. Hence for spherical particles

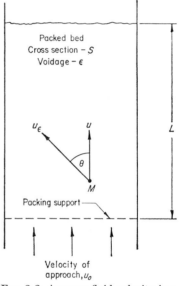

Fig. 3-2. Average fluid velocity in a packed bed.

$$u_\epsilon = \frac{u_0}{0.707 \; \epsilon}$$

Mean values of $\cos \theta$ should be expected to depend to a certain extent on the shape of packing and the arrangement in the bed. In a sense $\cos \theta$ should therefore give an indication of the effectiveness of the void space in the bed so far as fluid flow is concerned. Unfortunately, however, this has not been pursued further.

---

* Superscript numbers indicate works listed in References at the end of the chapter.

Flow Path. Considering a differential packed section of height dL and following the path of a unit mass of fluid through the bed, the differential path length actually traveled becomes

$$dL_\epsilon = \frac{dL}{\cos\theta}$$

Assuming that the proportion of effective voids in the bed, as possibly indicated by $\cos\theta$, is independent of bed height, the differential equation may be integrated to yield

$$L_\epsilon = \frac{L}{\cos\theta}$$

Again letting the average value of $\theta = 45°$,

$$L_\epsilon = \frac{L}{0.707}$$

Hydraulic Diameter. By definition the hydraulic diameter of any arbitrary conduit

$$D_h = \frac{4S'}{P}$$

where S' is the entire available flow cross section of the conduit and P is the entire wetted perimeter. Again for the bed of spheres of average voidage ϵ referred to in Fig. 3-2,

$$S' = \epsilon S$$

The wetted perimeter becomes:

$$P = D_p{}^2\pi mS$$

Also,

$$m = \frac{6(1-\epsilon)}{D_p{}^3\pi}$$

Eliminating m,

$$D_h = \frac{2\epsilon D_p}{3(1-\epsilon)}$$

Working Equations. The preceding analysis of flow through packings has led to the following modifications:

Average fluid velocity between particle

$$u_\epsilon = \frac{u_0}{\epsilon\cos\theta}$$

Average length of flow path

$$L_\epsilon = \frac{L}{\cos\theta}$$

Hydraulic diameter of section

$$D_h = \frac{2\epsilon D_p}{3(1-\epsilon)}$$

When these modifications are applied to the basic equations for laminar and turbulent flow through empty conduits, working equations for single-phase packed-bed flow will result.

Laminar Flow. For any packed section,

$$\Delta p = \frac{32\mu u_\epsilon L_\epsilon}{g_c D_h{}^2} \tag{3-2a}$$

Replacing u_ϵ, L_ϵ, and D_h by their respective values as obtained above,

$$\Delta p = c \frac{u_0 L \mu (1 - \epsilon)^2}{D_p{}^2 g_c \epsilon^3} \tag{3-5}$$

On the basis of $\theta = 45°$, as reported by Carman,[4] $c = 144$. However Carman found $c = 180$, whereas Lewis et al.[14] found $c = 154$. The packed-bed studies reported by the U.S. Bureau of Mines[12] disclosed $c = 200$. There seems to be a serious discrepancy so far as c values are concerned. The deviation appears less important, though, when judged on the basis of angle θ. Thus assuming that $c = 144$ corresponds to $\theta = 45°$, an angle of $\theta = 37°$ would satisfy the condition, so that $c = 200$ is the correct experimental constant. The observed variations in c values actually reflect the extent of the experimental error that is involved in measurements of this sort. Since $c = 200$ yields the most conservative values of pressure drop, the constant has been retained. Thus for laminar flow through packed beds of spherical particles

$$\Delta p = 200 \frac{u_0 L \mu (1 - \epsilon)^2}{D_p{}^2 g_c \epsilon^3} \tag{3-5a}$$

The particle diameter in Eq. (3-5a) is the diameter of the "equivalent-volume sphere." Hence for spheres the diameter is given by

$$D_p = \frac{6V}{A_p}$$

For particles of any arbitrary shape the diameter in Eq. (3-5a) will still be the diameter of the equivalent-volume sphere. However since the nonspherical particle of volume V has a larger surface area than the sphere of volume V, the diameter of the particle of arbitrary shape

$$D_p = \frac{6V}{A \phi_s} = \frac{6V}{A_p}$$

The quantity ϕ_s is a dimensionless number and is known as the shape factor of the particle. In essence it denotes the ratio of the surface area of the equivalent-volume sphere to the surface area of the arbitrarily shaped particle.

Replacing D_p in Eq. (3-5) by $D_p\phi_s$ will then extend the correlation to cover flow through beds of particles of arbitrary shape. Thus

$$\Delta p = 200 \frac{u_0 L \mu (1 - \epsilon)^2}{D_p^2 \phi_s^2 g_c \epsilon^3} \qquad (3\text{-}6)\star$$

Expressed as a function of Reynolds number as suggested by Eq. (3-3)

$$\frac{\Delta p \, D_p \phi_s g_c \epsilon^3}{2u_0^2 L \rho_F (1 - \epsilon)^2} = 100 \left(\frac{D_p \phi_s u_0 \rho_F}{\mu}\right)^{-1.0} \qquad (3\text{-}7)\star$$

or $\qquad f_m = \dfrac{\Delta p \, D_p \phi_s^2 g_c \epsilon^3}{2u_0^2 L \rho_F (1 - \epsilon)^2} = 100 \left(\dfrac{D_p u_0 \rho_F}{\mu}\right)^{-1.0} \qquad (3\text{-}8)\star$

where f_m is termed the modified friction factor.

Turbulent Flow. For flow through packed beds in general one may write

$$f_m = \frac{\Delta p \, D_h g_c}{2 L_\epsilon \rho_F u_\epsilon^2} = \psi \, \mathrm{Re}_h \qquad (3\text{-}9)$$

If their modified values as derived earlier are now substituted for u_ϵ, L_ϵ, and D_h, there results

$$f_m = \frac{\Delta p \, D_p g_c \epsilon^3}{2u_0^2 L \rho_F (1 - \epsilon)} = \psi \, \mathrm{Re}_h \qquad (3\text{-}10)$$

But $\qquad \mathrm{Re}_h = \dfrac{D_h u_\epsilon \rho_F}{\mu} = k' \dfrac{D_p u_0 \rho_F}{(1 - \epsilon)\mu}$

Equating the last term with f_m and replacing D_p by $D_p\phi_s$ results in

$$f_m = \frac{\Delta p \, D_p \phi_s g_c \epsilon^3}{2u_0^2 L \rho_F (1 - \epsilon)} = k \left[\frac{D_p \phi_s u_0 \rho_F}{(1 - \epsilon)\mu}\right]^{n-2} \qquad (3\text{-}11)$$

The state-of-flow factor n, already referred to, will vary between 1 for laminar flow and 2, at most, for completely turbulent flow. When $n = 1$ is substituted into Eq. (3-11), Eq. (3-7) for laminar flow is obtained. For most turbulent-flow conditions, n assumes an average value of 1.9. For this value and smooth-surfaced particles such as glass the equation becomes

$$\frac{\Delta p}{L} = \frac{3.50 G^{1.9} \mu^{0.1} (1 - \epsilon)^{1.1}}{D_p^{1.1} \phi_s^{1.1} \rho_F g_c \epsilon^3} \qquad (3\text{-}12)\star$$

For a generalized presentation of pressure-drop data, use of the modified friction factor together with modified Reynolds number is suggested. Thus

$$f_m = \frac{\Delta p \, D_p \phi_s^{3-n} g_c \epsilon^3 \rho_F}{2 L G^2 (1 - \epsilon)^{3-n}} = \psi \frac{D_p G}{\mu} \qquad (3\text{-}13)\star$$

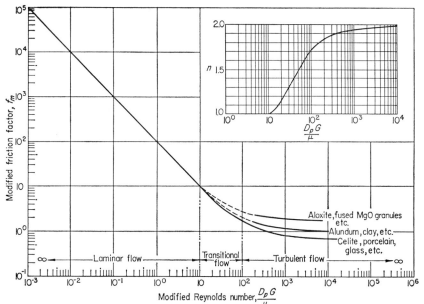

Fig. 3-3. Modified friction factors vs. Reynolds number.

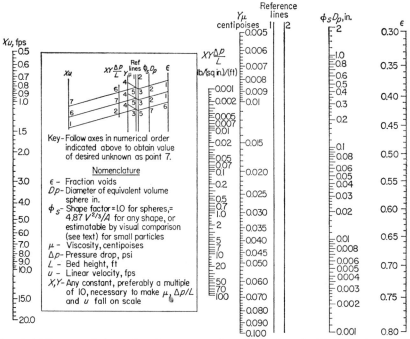

Fig. 3-4. Nomograph for estimating pressure drop through packed beds in the streamline range.

This is shown graphically in Fig. 3-3. Pressure drops are readily evaluated for the entire laminar- and turbulent-flow range. For the intermediate-flow range $10 < \mathrm{Re} < 200$, the state-of-flow factor n is evaluated from the inset and correlation (3-13) should be used. For rapid estimates in laminar and turbulent flow, nomographs of Figs. 3-4 and 3-5 may be helpful.

Generalized Equation for Compressible Fluids. Equations (3-8) and (3-13) require that the fluid density remain essentially constant as the

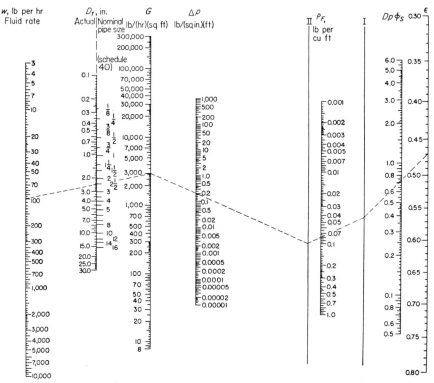

FIG. 3-5. Nomograph for estimating pressure drop through packed beds in the turbulent-flow range.

fluid passes through the bed. For isothermal flow this is always true when the fluid is a liquid. With gas flow, substantial variations in gas density may be involved when the column pressure drop is high. For such a condition the correlations would have to be applied to successive bed strata, the pressure drop obtained in one stratum would have to be used to correct the gas density in the subsequent strata, and so forth. Such a method will give near-accurate results only if the sectional heights so chosen are very small and the calculation steps are therefore numerous. It is more desirable to treat gas density as a variable and differentiate the pressure-drop equation (3-13). This has yielded[12] the following generalized correlation:

$$p_1{}^2 - p_2{}^2 = \frac{2ZRG^2T}{g_cM}\left[\ln\frac{v_2}{v_1} + \frac{2f_m(1-\epsilon)^{3-n}}{\phi_s{}^{3-n}\epsilon^3D_p}L\right] \qquad (3\text{-}14)\star$$

Equation (3-14) is applicable to isothermal flow conditions when high pressure drops or large fluid-density variations are to be anticipated.

Example 3-1. Air is passed through a bed of alumina spheres contained in a 6-in. standard pipe. The solids are supported by a stainless-steel screen and the construction is such that entrance effects may be discounted. The packed height is 6 ft, and the size distribution of the alumina is as follows:

Mesh	Weight per cent
6–8	15
8–10	75
10–14	10

The temperature inside the unit may be considered constant at 32°F. The exit pressure is to be at least 15.0 psia. Find the delivery pressure to the unit if it is desired to pass 100 cfm of air, measured at standard conditions, through the unit.

Solution. For air density at standard conditions

$$\rho_F = \frac{28.82}{359} = 0.0803 \text{ lb per cu ft}$$

and at exit conditions

$$\rho_F = \frac{0.0803 \times 15.0}{14.7} = 0.0820 \text{ lb per cu ft}$$

Air mass velocity

$$G = \frac{100 \times 0.0803 \times 144 \times 60}{6.065^2 \times 0.785}$$
$$= 2{,}400 \text{ lb/(hr)(sq ft)}$$
$$= 0.667 \text{ lb/(sec)(sq ft)}$$

AVERAGE PARTICLE DIAMETER

Mesh	d_p	X	$\dfrac{X}{d_p}$
6–8	0.110	0.15	1.36
8–10	0.078	0.75	9.62
10–14	0.055	0.10	1.82

$$\sum\frac{X}{d_p} = 12.80 \qquad \text{and} \qquad D_p = \frac{1}{12.80} = 0.0782 \text{ in.}$$

$$\text{Re} = \frac{2{,}400 \times 0.0782}{12 \times 2.42 \times 0.018} = 359$$

From Fig. 3-3, $n = 1.9$. Assuming that the surface condition of the alumina spheres is similar to that of clay, there results from Fig. 3-3 $f_m = 1.4$.

Bed voidage is evaluated from Fig. 3-7. Hence for

$$D_p/D_t = 0.782/6.065 = 0.129, \quad \epsilon = 0.41.$$

For the spherical particles $\phi_s = 1.0$. Using as a first approximation the exit-fluid density $\rho_F = 0.0820$ lb per cu ft and employing Eq. (3-13), there results

$$\Delta p = \frac{2 \times 6.0 \times 1.4 \times 0.667^2 \times (1 - 0.41)^{1.1} \times 12}{0.0782 \times 1.0^{1.1} \times 0.41^3 \times 0.0820 \times 32.2}$$
$$= 3,530 \text{ psf} = 24.5 \text{ psi}$$

This first trial, based on the desired exit-gas density, indicates that a substantial pressure drop is involved and that the density of the air along the flow path will vary quite significantly. Therefore, if it is intended to work with Eq. (3-13), it will be necessary to calculate the pressure drop for very small bed increments, say, three inches or so for this case, and evaluate the air density after each increment for the purpose of estimating the pressure drop over the next increment. Nevertheless, the result is only an approximation because the increments cannot be made infinitely small.

An exact solution is possible through use of Eq. (3-14). Data for the equation are as follows:

Compressibility factor: $Z = 1.0$
Gas constant: $R = 1,544$
Gas temperature: $T = 492°R$
Exit pressure: $p_2 = 2,160$ psf
Exit specific volume: $v_2 = 12.2$ cu ft per lb

The remaining required data are as given for Eq. (3-13). Hence:

$$p_1{}^2 - 2,160^2 = \frac{2 \times 1.0 \times 1,544 \times 0.667^2 \times 492}{32.2 \times 28.82}$$
$$\left[\ln \frac{12.2}{v_1} + \frac{2 \times 1.4 \times 6 \times (1 - 0.41)^{1.1} \times 12}{1.0^{1.1} \times 0.0782 \times 0.41^3} \right]$$

Since v_1 is a function of p_1, the solution of the equation involves a method of trial and error. However, it will be noted that $\ln (12.2/v_1)$ is indeed so small in comparison with the other term in the brackets that the logarithmic term may be neglected. Hence solution for inlet delivery pressure yields $p_1 = 31.0$ psi. The bed pressure drop will be $31.0 - 15 = 16.0$ psi. It will be noted that this is substantially less then the value calculated by the first trial with Eq. (3-13). The difference emphasizes the extent to which the density change of the air in the tower affects the over-all pressure drop.

Pressure-drop Equation of Ergun. On the basis of a fixed-bed pressure-drop analysis, Ergun[7] proposed the generalized correlation

$$\frac{\Delta p}{L} g_c = 150 \frac{(1 - \epsilon)^2}{\epsilon^3} \frac{\mu u_0}{D_p{}^2} + 1.75 \frac{1 - \epsilon}{\epsilon^3} \frac{G u_0}{D_p} \qquad (3\text{-}15)\star$$

$\mu = \text{lb/sec-ft or (centipoise} \times 0.000672)$
$G = \text{lb/sec-ft}^2 = (\rho u_0)$

With the total energy loss in fixed beds being composed of viscous and kinetic components, Ergun demonstrated that the first term of Eq. (3-15) accounts primarily for the viscous energy losses, whereas the remaining term is primarily related to kinetic losses.

Equation (3-15) may be rewritten as

$$\frac{\Delta p}{L} g_c \frac{D_p}{G u_0} \frac{\epsilon^3}{1 - \epsilon} = 150 \frac{1 - \epsilon}{Re} + 1.75 \tag{3-15a}$$

The left-hand side of Eq. (3-15a) is the ratio of the total energy losses to the term that represents the kinetic-energy loss only. Comparison with Eq. (3-13) indicates that this is essentially a modified friction factor; hence Ergun denoted it by the symbol f_k, the subscript k emphasizing its relation to the kinetic-energy component in the bed. According to Eq. (3-15a), a presentation of pressure-drop data in fixed beds suggests itself, therefore, by simply relating f_k with $D_p G/\mu(1 - \epsilon)$. This is shown in Fig. (3-6). The correlation is presented in detail because a subsequent analysis of fixed-bed mass-transfer data by Ergun,[8] presented later, is directly based on the kinetic approach. Besides this extension, the correlation affords a means of accurately calculating voidage, solids densities, and outside-particle surface areas in packed

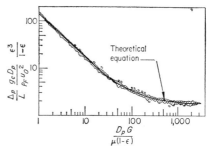

FIG. 3-6. Packed-bed pressure-drop correlation by Ergun.[7]

beds, whether the bed is composed of nonvesicular or vesicular particles. This will be taken up in a subsequent section.

As far as application is concerned, the particle diameter in Eq. (3-15) is defined by $D_p = 6/S_v$, where S_v is the surface area of the solids per unit volume of solids. All other quantities are identical with those of Eq. (3-13).

EVALUATION OF PARAMETERS FOR EQUATIONS

The correlations so far discussed may be applied to flow through packings of arbitrary shapes, provided individual packing and bed parameters are available. Besides the usually given data pertaining to flow rates, fluid properties, and apparatus dimensions, a knowledge of bed voidage, particle-shape factor, particle diameter, and possibly vesicularity and surface roughness may be required. These aspects and their evaluation will be discussed in the following section.

Voidage. Pressure drops in packed beds are highly sensitive to voidage as well as packing arrangements. Considering first the effect of packing arrangement, Martin, McCabe, and Monrad[15] investigated this phase by working with beds of relatively large spheres through which they passed water. The effects noted were considerable. Thus for a tetragonal arrangement of spheres of a voidage of 30.19 per cent the observed pressure drop for turbulent flow was more than twenty times as high as through a bed composed of the same spheres in cubical arrangement and with 47.64 per cent voids. The effect of orientation under these conditions is easily recognized when it is recalled that, with this voidage

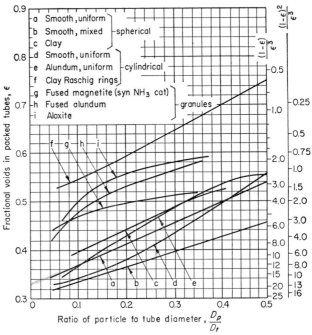

Fig. 3-7. Voids in tubes packed with various materials for various ratios of particle diameter to tube diameter.[12]

range encountered in a randomly packed bed, the pressure-drop increase would have been only about fivefold. Considerations of packing density are of course of great importance in the preparation of a catalyst bed or in the loading of packed towers for gas absorption or distillation.

For any specific packing, size, and column diameter the resulting packed-bed voidage will be largely dependent on (1) the mode of charging the vessel and (2) the surface condition of the particles. Generally, the resulting bed will be more dense as the particles are added into the column more slowly. Also, with smooth-surfaced particles, denser beds will form. The loosest arrangements are usually formed when the vessel is "packed wet," that is, if the column is first filled to some height with water and the packing is then gradually added.   The wet-packing method is not too frequently used with catalyst pellets and reactors; it is quite common with ceramic-type and similar packings used in absorption, distillation, and extraction columns.   When a unit is packed by a method that yields a loose arrangement, the bed can be expected to settle in due time.   The extent of settling is then reflected in a corresponding pressure-drop rise, which is frequently appreciable.   As contrasted to a loose arrangement obtained by packing wet, a bed of more than average density may be prepared by tapping the reactor wall during the dumping process. This is neither always convenient nor always effective with large-diameter equipment.

Voidage data may be estimated from Fig. 3-7.   The values are sufficiently accurate to be used with the pressure-drop correlations given earlier.   The graphs represent smoothed data observed with conventional shapes and materials that are normally encountered in catalytic reactors and similar packed tubes.

The particles referred to in Fig. 3-7 ranged from about 0.10 to 0.73 in. Tube diameters varied from about 0.6 to 4.0 in.   With such material and tube combinations a bed was first prepared by mere dry dumping and then a second bed was prepared by dumping and simultaneous outside pounding.   The second procedure produced beds which were denser by 3 to 5 percentage points.   The curves finally proposed in Fig. 3-7 are based on arithmetic averages between the two methods of preparation. The data have been reported in good accord with industrially observed bed densities.

Wall Effect and Velocity Distribution.   A voidage correlation in terms of D_p/D_t takes into account the "wall effect."   In order to understand what is meant by wall effect, let us imagine that a vessel of a certain diameter is being charged with particles of ever-increasing diameter. Eventually a condition for which the particles become relatively large in comparison with the radius of curvature of the vessel will be approached. For such a situation the particles must then recede from the wall and thereby tend to generate a concentric ring of higher than average bed voidage.   This phenomenon, known as "wall effect," may have a significant bearing on flow distribution in a packed tower.   For the purpose of estimating voidage in large vessels where wall effect is virtually absent, the curves of Fig. 3-7 should be extrapolated to $D_p/D_t = 0$.   For all packings except the mixed spheres, ϵ increases with D_p/D_t approximately at the same rate.   For the mixed spheres the increase is much smaller. Hence wall effect is minimized by resorting to a size spectrum, rather than a single component.   With respect to order of magnitude, the voids may be 10 percentage points higher in a reactor of $D_p/D_t = 0.25$ than in a

vessel with no wall effect. This is a consideration that must be taken
into account in scale-up.

The distribution of the voids over the cross section of a packed vessel
is really not quite as simple as may be visualized with the aid of the above-
defined wall effect. This is indicated by the work of Schwartz and
Smith,[19] who have shown that the central packed core is apparently
not of as uniform a voidage as would
appear from a strictly peripheral wall
effect. Some of the data of Schwartz
and Smith, shown in Fig. 3-8, point to
the possibility that the effect of the wall
extends at least to a depth of about two
pellet diameters into the bed. This is
true not only for spheres but for cylinders
as well. Another interesting observa-

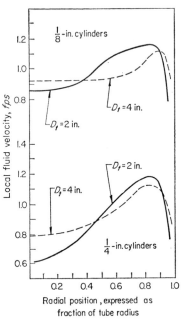

FIG. 3-9. Typical packed-tube
velocity-distribution data observed by Schwartz and Smith.[19]

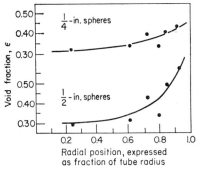

FIG. 3-8. Data of Schwartz and Smith[19]
showing variation of local voidage with
radial position for spheres in a 4-in.-
diameter tube.

tion is made from Fig. 3-8. Contrary to the belief that wall effect may
be discounted when $D_t/D_p > 8$, the data seem to indicate that even with
$D_t/D_p = 16$ the wall effect is not yet entirely dispelled.

Until relatively recently the belief has been that the velocity-distribution profile across a packed section was blunt. Thus local velocities
over the cross section were believed to be close to the average fluid
velocity. The study by Schwartz and Smith[19] has thoroughly disproven
this belief. Instead the velocity profile over a packed cross section
appears to be quite different and characteristic. Some typical velocity
profiles are indicated in Fig. 3-9; they pertain to ⅛- and ¼-in. cylinders
in 2- and 4-in. diameter pipes. In all cases local velocity relative to the
superficial average air velocity is shown in relation to radial position.
In every case there is a characteristic maximum velocity about 1½ pellet

diameters away from the wall.   Toward the center the profile decreases. The maximum near the wall is more pronounced in the small tube.   It is interesting to note that the maximum is also relatively greater for the large particles.   If the occurrence of the maxima is viewed as a consequence of the wall effect, the stated results are then corroborating.

Vesicularity.   Process studies frequently require a determination of solids density of the catalysts used in packed tubes.   When the catalysts have a dense structure and do not absorb water or other liquids, the density may in most cases be obtained with a pycnometer.   The problem becomes more complex and uncertain when the catalysts have an appreciable internal porosity that may be more or less accessible to fluid penetration.   A solid exhibiting such characteristics is known as "vesicular"; a typical vesicular material is coke.   Many catalyst carriers such as aloxite, alundum, and carborundum are vesicular to a greater or lesser extent.   Since the average pore size in a vesicular material is of a certain order of magnitude, it follows that the particle density will increase as the particle is gradually broken up into smaller pieces.   In fact the increase will become progressively more marked as the particle size approaches the average pore size.   When the particle is finally pulverized to fragments that approach the original size of the internal pores, the vesicularity will have disappeared entirely and the density is then the true density of the solid.   Hence it may be stated that particle density of a vesicular material is characteristic not of the material alone but also of particle size.

A reliable effective particle density of vesicular materials may be obtained by applying the Ergun equation (3-15) to packed-bed flow data.[6] The correlation is of the form

$$\frac{\Delta p}{L u_0} = a + bG \tag{3-15b} \star$$

Furthermore Ergun showed that

$$\rho_b = \rho_S - C_1 (\rho_b{}^2/a)^{\frac{1}{3}} = \rho_S - C_2 (\rho_b/b)^{\frac{1}{3}} \tag{3-16} \star$$

where constants C_1 and C_2 are functions of specific surface area and solids density.

From the above two equations the required procedure for evaluating the density of any solid is as follows:

1. Obtain pressure drops for a given weight of solids with the column compacted to various degrees, hence columns of various bulk densities.

2. A plot of $\Delta p/L u_0$ vs. G on cartesian coordinates will yield straight lines of intercept a and slope b.

3. Constants a and b are thus evaluated and used for computation of $(\rho_b{}^2/a)^{\frac{1}{3}}$ and $(\rho_b/b)^{\frac{1}{3}}$.

4. In accordance with Eq. (3-16) these values are plotted vs. ρ_b, again using cartesian coordinates. Evaluation of the intercept for this plot will yield ρ_S, the solids density.

A typical plot of $\Delta p / L u_0$ vs. G is given in Fig. 3-10. The data pertain to a high-temperature coke of appreciable internal porosity. For the eight separate pressure-drop tests the bulk density was varied from 0.7976 to 0.9634 g per cc. The plot of $(\rho_b^2/a)^{1/3}$ or $(\rho_b/b)^{1/3}$ vs. ρ_b is shown in Fig. 3-11. The intersection of the lines, occurring at a zero value of the abscissa, indicates an effective solids density of 1.55 g per cc. Since voidage is related to bulk density by $\epsilon = 1 - \rho_b/\rho_S$, an effective bed voidage, constituting the voidage in the bed of vesicular particles that is actually effective as far as fluid flow is concerned, may now be calculated. For

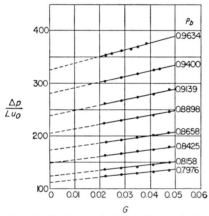

FIG. 3-10. Typical data observed by Ergun[6] for determining voidage and density of coke. (*Courtesy of Analytical Chemistry.*)

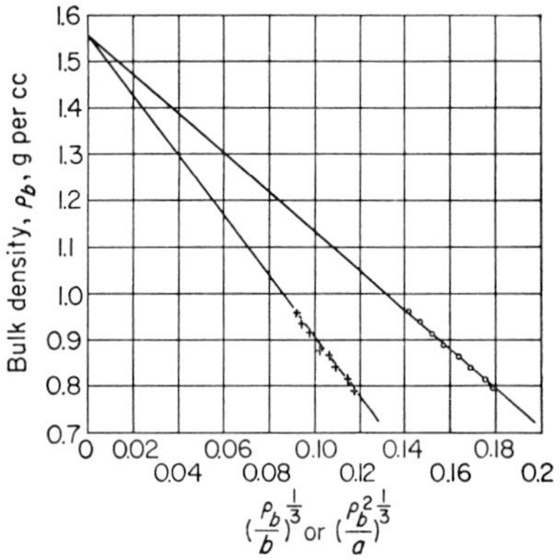

FIG. 3-11. Graphical presentation of Eq. (3-16) of Ergun.[7] (*Courtesy of Analytical Chemistry.*)

$\rho_b = 0.9634$ g per cc this is found to be $\epsilon = 0.38$. Voidages obtained by this method are the correct values to be used with the earlier proposed pressure-drop equations. The values are considerably smaller than voidages that would have been indicated by pycnometric measurements.

Surface Roughness. In flow through a duct the surface roughness is defined by the average height of the protuberances relative to the hydraulic diameter of the passage. Surface roughness of particles may be defined similarly[3,12] as long as the protuberances are small in relation to particle size. In order to illustrate this let it be assumed that a common vesicular material such as coke is available. The height of the protuberances will be determined by the average pore size. As the coke particle is reduced in size, a dimension for which pore size and particle size are of the same order of magnitude will eventually be approached.

At this point the original vesicularity will cease to add to surface roughness but will instead contribute to a modification of particle shape. Just where this division between the two effects occurs is difficult to assess. For this reason it is at the present state of the art questionable that effects observed with rough particles are due to roughness rather than shape characteristics, or vice versa. Correlations which have been proposed by Brownell and Katz[3] tend to allow for surface roughness much in the same sense as it is accounted for in open-duct flow. Typical data have also been observed with materials of various degrees of surface roughness.[12] The materials considered were glass and smooth metal packings, alundum and clay particles, and aloxite catalyst carriers, the roughest particles. These materials were tested through wide ranges in laminar and turbulent flow. For the laminar range, extending up to $D_pG/\mu = 10$, the surface roughness had no effect on pressure drop. However, for the turbulent region, as characterized by $D_pG/\mu > 100$, effects were observed. Thus in beds of alundum and clay the pressure drop was about 1.5 times as high as in glass beads, whereas through aloxite beds the factor increased appreciably to a value of 2.3.

Surface roughness has a notable effect on the density which will result in a bed when the particles are dumped. Since particles of appreciable surface roughness will tend to come to rest sooner than smooth particles when dumped into a column, resulting voidages will be appreciably higher with rough particles. This is substantiated by the data of Fig. 3-7.

Shape Factor. Let us designate the surface area of an arbitrarily shaped particle by A. The surface area of a spherical particle having the same volume as the particle of arbitrary shape will be A_p. Then by definition

$$\text{Shape factor } \phi_s = \frac{A_p}{A} \qquad (3\text{-}17)$$

Since a spherical particle is a body that will provide a given mass with the least surface area, values calculated by Eq. (3-17) will always be less than unity. Shape factors thus defined are also known as sphericity factors. Whereas shape factors may for regular geometric bodies be calculated from Eq. (3-17), it is somewhat more convenient to use the relation[12]

$$\phi_s = \frac{V^{2/3}}{0.205A} \qquad (3\text{-}18)\star$$

In addition to spherical and irregularly shaped granular particles, cylindrical and, less frequently, ring-shaped bodies may find use in catalyst beds. Shape factors for cylinders and rings are readily expressed as functions of heights and diameters of the particles. Figure (3-12) gives such data for cylindrical pellets and rings.

Granular particles usually do not permit a direct calculation of their shape factor from the dimensions. This is so because the surface area is often too irregular and complex to permit evaluation by either calculation or direct measurement. Under such conditions shape factors are best determined from pressure-drop tests. This will then require a suitable column into which the granules are to be charged. The packed height should be such that an appreciable pressure drop is indicated.

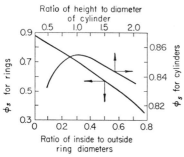

FIG. 3-12. Shape factors for cylinders and rings in relation to dimensions.

However, if the tests are made with a gas, the pressure drop should not be so high that it will materially affect the over-all gas density.

When the solids are nonvesicular, the bed voidage is simply determined by water displacement. With vesicular solids this is not feasible, and it is then suggested that the Ergun gas-flow method be used.[6] The method has already been described in detail in the section dealing with vesicularity. It is recommended that the tests be carried out in the laminar-flow range, where Re < 10. The pressure-drop equation is not only more accurate in this range but, owing to the constancy of the state-of-flow factor, handled more conveniently. It is of course desirable that the flow range be checked by evaluating the Reynolds number.

With the voidage known, pressure drop and other quantities are inserted into Eq. (3-8) and the shape factor, being the only unknown, is obtained directly.

Evaluation of the shape factor by the flow method may require considerable operational skill. In order to preclude any obvious sources of error, it is recommended that the performance of the unit be checked by comparing the data for smooth spheres with the recommended friction-factor line in Fig. 3-3. This precaution should be sufficient to indicate any serious deficiencies in the unit. The flow method is of course also suitable for evaluation of shape factors for small granular materials of the type to be used in fluidization. Shape factors for typical granules of the kind used as catalysts or catalyst carriers may range from as low as 0.5 for very irregularly shaped bodies to almost unity for nearly spherical granules. For the frequently used commercial grades of granular activated carbon and silica gels, shape factors vary from about $0.70 < \phi_s < 0.90$.

Particle Diameter. Equations (3-8), (3-12), and (3-13) have been applied to data observed with beds comprising narrow cuts as well as relatively wide size ranges. For narrow cuts composed of regular geometrically shaped particles that are in excess of about 0.125 in. the value of D_p to be taken is the diameter of the equivalent-volume sphere. For mixed-size beds composed of smaller particles the average diameter has been calculated by

$$D_p = \Sigma X d_p \tag{3-19}$$

It has been shown by Reboux[18] that the definition

$$\frac{1}{D_p} = \sum \frac{X}{d_p} \tag{3-20}\star$$

is more compatible with the concept of the hydraulic radius underlying Eqs. (3-8) and (3-12). A comparison of the two modes of average-diameter evaluation is shown by means of typical mixtures to which the equations have previously been applied. The data are given in Table 3-1.

TABLE 3-1. COMPARISON OF COMPOSITE-DIAMETER VALUES
(Mixtures of Glass Beads[12])

D_p, in.	X	D_p, in., by Eq. (3-20)	D_p, in., by Eq. (3-19)
0.172 0.228	0.507 0.493	0.196	0.200
0.172 0.228 0.388	0.2335 0.2474 0.5190	0.264	0.298
0.172 0.228 0.388 0.508	0.1655 0.1515 0.1985 0.4845	0.328	0.386
0.172 0.388 0.508 0.730	0.1280 0.1820 0.2700 0.4200	0.431	0.536

The deviations between the diameters calculated by the two methods increase with increasing complexity of the mixture. The average difference for the mixtures described in the table is about 15 per cent. The values calculated by Eq. (3-19) are consistently higher than those obtained from Eq. (3-20). Since pressure drop is inversely proportional to a function of particle diameter, use of Eq. (3-19) will tend to give low values. For this reason Eq. (3-20) is to be preferred for the evaluation of diameters of complex mixtures.

MINIMUM-FLUIDIZATION VELOCITY

The ability to predict the point of incipient fluidization reliably is of basic importance in virtually all fluidized-process studies and designs. As was learned from Fig. 2-5, the range of flow rates within which a fluidized dense phase exists is appreciable. Although fluidized reactors are usually operated at fluid rates that are well in excess of minimum-fluidization rates, there are nevertheless processes for which it may be desirable to operate essentially near or only slightly above G_{mf}. This is particularly true where some of the following conditions may prevail:

1. Bed is composed of a friable material, leading readily to attrition.
2. Charge is originally characterized by a wide size spectrum.
3. Owing to relatively small heats of reaction, heat-transfer rates between bed and environment are not required to be appreciable.
4. Required bed heights are relatively small, particles have generally good fluidization characteristics and do not lead to channeling.

In review it appears then that operation at mass velocities which are slightly in excess of G_{mf} will minimize attrition and elutriation losses. A by-product of the low fluid rates is a low solids velocity in the bed, and hence relatively low bed-wall heat-transfer coefficients. This requires, then, that heats of reaction or heats required for processing be small. Under these conditions the fluidized bed may still largely be an isothermal body. A final and obvious requirement for application of low fluid rates is that the solids have good inherent fluidization characteristics.

Elevated fluid rates are generally required where:

1. High space velocities are called for
2. Appreciable heats of reaction must be dissipated across heat-transfer surfaces
3. Essentially isothermal bed conditions are required
4. Solids mobility is demanded for the purpose of solids circulation

Operation at high fluid rates is greatly facilitated if the solids do not readily yield to attrition. If possible, size distribution should be kept within narrower limits in order to minimize the demands on the solids-recovery system.

Basic Equation. At the point of initial bed expansion the pressure drop is given by

$$\Delta p = L(1 - \epsilon)(\rho_S - \rho_F) \qquad (3\text{-}21)^\star$$

Since this is a fixed bed, pressure drop is also defined by

$$\Delta p = \frac{2f_m G^2 L (1 - \epsilon)^{3-n}}{D_p \phi_s{}^{3-n} g_c \epsilon^3 \rho_F} \qquad (3\text{-}13)^\star$$

Upon equating and recalling that, in order to permit fluidization, the bed must be at the minimum fluid voidage ϵ_{mf}, there results

$$G_{mf}^2 = \frac{D_p g_c (\rho_S - \rho_F) \epsilon_{mf}^3 \phi_s^{3-n}}{2 f_m (1 - \epsilon_{mf})^{2-n}} \tag{3-22}$$

Since most gas-solid systems begin to fluidize at rates for which Re < 10, substitution of $f_m = 100/\text{Re}$ and $n = 1.0$ into Eq. (3-22) yields

$$G_{mf} = \frac{0.005 \, D_p^2 g_c \rho_F (\rho_S - \rho_F) \phi_s^2 \epsilon_{mf}^3}{\mu (1 - \epsilon_{mf})} \tag{3-23}\star$$

Data pertaining to particle size, densities, and possibly fluid viscosity are usually available from process specifications; voidage data and, in particular, ϵ_{mf} values normally should not be expected. Furthermore, unless spherical or nearly spherical particles are used, shape factors are usually unavailable. These omissions will then seriously limit the value of the above correlation, especially since the experimental methods for evaluating shape factor and voidage may be considerably involved.

Characteristics of the minimum fluid voidage have already been discussed in Chap. 2. With nonvesicular particles a fair approximation of ϵ_{mf} is obtained when the solids are poured slowly from one container into another. The density of the particles is then evaluated from water-displacement tests, and these values may be applied to the acquired bed height. The resulting values may be a few percentage points higher than data determined from the actual expansion behavior of a bed;

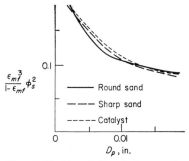

FIG. 3-13. Correlation between the product of the voidage function and the square of the shape factor with particle diameter.[13] (*Courtesy of Génie Chimique.*)

however, the high values will yield conservative G_{mf} values. Shape-factor determinations for nonvesicular as well as vesicular particles have already been described.[6]

Generalized Equation. In order to improve its usefulness, Eq. (3-23) should be reworked with the possible aim of eliminating the parameters ϵ_{mf} and ϕ_s. The clue to the method is contained in the ϵ_{mf} values themselves and their relationship to ϕ_s and D_p, as shown in Fig. 2-6. The important observation is that ϵ_{mf} increases as ϕ_s decreases. This is of course entirely compatible with the requirements for incipient fluidization.[10]

Inspection discloses that the product $[\epsilon_{mf}^3/(1 - \epsilon_{mf})]\phi_s^2$, as it appears in Eq. (3-23), may be represented as a function of D_p. This is shown in

Fig. 3-13 for three key materials used in the fluidization studies.[13] Since this relationship is unrelated to flow rate and viscosity, the product may just as well be related to the Reynolds number, and thereby dimensional homogeneity will be preserved. The resulting function may then be used in Eq. (3-23) to yield

$$G_{mf} = \frac{C D_p{}^2 g_c \rho_F (\rho_S - \rho_F)}{\mu} \qquad (3\text{-}24)$$

where C is a function of $D_p G/\mu$, as indicated in Fig. 3-14. For Re < 5.0, $C = 0.0007$ Re$^{-0.063}$. Incorporating g_c in the experimental constant then yields

$$G_{mf} = 688\ D_p{}^{1.82} \frac{[\rho_F (\rho_S - \rho_F)]^{0.94}}{\mu^{0.88}} \qquad (3\text{-}25)\star$$

This will give G_{mf} in pounds per hour per square foot if D_p is expressed in inches, ρ_F and ρ_S in pounds per cubic foot, and μ in centipoises.

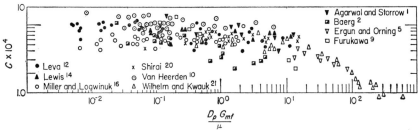

FIG. 3-14. Calculated values of C in relation to the Reynolds number.[13] (*Courtesy of Génie Chimique.*)

The data in support of the correlation cover a wide range, as indicated in Table 3-2. Virtually all readily available literature and other data were consulted. Wherever the onset of fluidization was not explicitly or otherwise specified, the fixed-bed pressure gradient was brought to an intersection with the isobaric fluidized-pressure-drop line, and the resulting flow was augmented by 10 per cent. This increase was deemed necessary to account for possible solids channeling tendencies.

As may be seen from Table 3-2, most materials considered were non-vesicular. For these particles the density obtained by water displacement will be correct and this will give correct values of G_{mf}. Some of the materials referred to in Table 3-2 are vesicular. For these particles the density should really be evaluated by the Ergun method.[6] If a fluid-displacement method must be used instead, resulting solids densities may be high, depending on the type of fluid chosen. This will then lead to somewhat high G_{mf} values.

TABLE 3-2. SUMMARY OF DATA PERTAINING TO MINIMUM FLUIDIZATION

Reference	Material	Shape	D_p, in.	ρ_S, lb per cu ft	D_t, in.	Fluid	ρ_F, lb per cu ft	μ, lb/(hr)(ft)
Agarwal and Storrow[1]	Adsorbent carbon	......	0.0124-0.0045	101	0.4 to 2.5	Air	0.074	0.043
	Geon	Spherical	0.0052	83		Air	0.074	0.043
	Sand	......	0.0305-0.0072	165		Air	0.074	0.043
	Coal	......	0.0220-0.0124	83		Air	0.074	0.043
	Broken Raschig rings	......	0.0220-0.0036	156		Air	0.074	0.043
Baerg et al.[2]	Iron powder	Sharp	0.0148-0.0077	425	Annular tube in a vessel of 5.5 in. ID	Air	0.072	0.045
	Round sand	Rounded	0.0348-0.0127	145		Air		
	Foundry sand	Sharp	0.0110-0.0063	142		Air		
	Jagged silica	Sharp	0.0290-0.0123	142		Air		
	Scotchlite beads	Spheres	0.0180-0.0024	160		Air		
	Cracking catalyst	Irregular	0.0055-0.0038	122		Air		
Ergun and Orning[5]	Glass beads	Spherical	0.0224-0.00895	156	1.0	H_2, CO_2	0.005 to 0.112	0.022 to 0.043
	Iron shot	......	0.0303-0.0186	486	1.0	N_2		
	Lead shot	Spherical	0.0396-0.0196	673	1.0	CH_4		
Furukawa et al.[9]	Activated carbon	......	0.01061-0.00531	66	3.15	Air	0.074	0.043
Leva et al.[12]	Round sand	Rounded	0.01505-0.00202	165	2.5 and 4.0	He	0.0102 to 0.112	0.034 to 0.043
	Sharp sand	Sharp	0.01268-0.00229	165		Air		
	Mixed sands	Rounded and sharp	0.01237-0.00541	165		CO_2		
	Iron catalyst	Sharp	0.01518-0.00430	312				
	Coal	Moderately sharp	0.03819-0.00658	123				

TABLE 3-2. SUMMARY OF DATA PERTAINING TO MINIMUM FLUIDIZATION (*Continued*)

Reference	Material	Shape	D_p, in.	ρ_S, lb per cu ft	D_t, in.	Fluid	ρ_F, lb per cu ft	μ, lb/(hr)(ft)
Lewis et al.[14]	Glass beads	Spherical	0.0224–0.004	147	2.4	Air and water	0.075 to 62.3	0.043 to 2.45
	Glass beads	Spherical	0.0149–0.006	155	and			
	Aerocat microspheres	Spherical	0.0063	62(?)	4.5			
Miller and Logwinuk[16]	Silicon carbide	....	0.0098–0.0038	198	2.0	Air, helium, CO₂, and ethane	0.0102 to 0.112	0.0228 to 0.0436
	Alumina oxide	....	0.0098–0.0039	243	2.0			
	Silicon dioxide	....	0.00977–0.00346	165	2.0			
	Silica gel	....	0.00977–0.00346	70	2.0			
Shirai[20,22]	Sharp sand	Sharp	0.0164–0.00406	165	1.5	Air	0.075	0.043
	Quartz	Sharp	0.0480–0.00835	160	and	Air	0.075	0.043
	Coal	Moderately sharp	0.0135–0.00559	85	3.0	Air	0.075	0.043
Van Heerden et al.[10]	Carborundum	....	0.0090–0.0033	198	3.35	Air, argon CO₂, CH₄ (H₂ + N₂)	0.0065 to 0.1130	0.0225 to 0.0540
	Coke	....	0.0260–0.0037	112				
	Iron oxide	....	0.0036	322				
Wilhelm and Kwauk[21]	Sea sand	....	0.0393–0.0147	198	3.0 and 6.0	Air and water	0.075 to 62.3	0.0435 to 2.42
	Socony beads	Spherical	0.174–0.129	72–100				
	Glass beads	Spherical	0.205–0.0113	150				
	Lead shot	Spherical	0.0505	673				
	Crushed rock	....	0.0557	165				

Equation (3-25) has been tested with beds of mixed sizes.   Originally it was suggested that the composite diameter be evaluated by Eq. (3-19). Subsequent investigations have, however, indicated that better accuracy results when the composite diameter is calculated according to

$$D_p = \frac{1}{\sum \dfrac{X}{dp}}$$

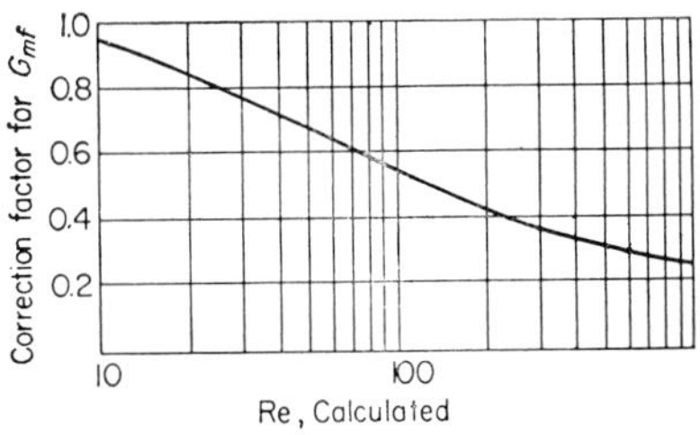

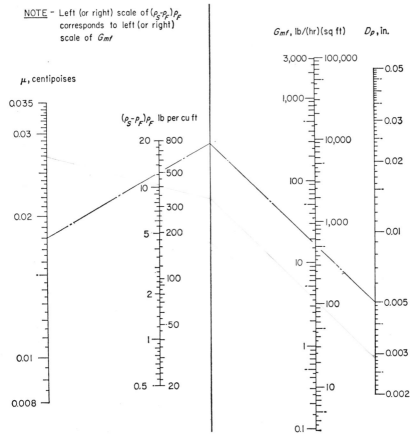

FIG. 3-15. Correction factor[13] for results obtained with Eq. (3-25) if the Reynolds number is in excess of 10.   (*Courtesy of Génie Chimique.*)

In its above form the correlation is limited to applications where Re < 10.   For this reason one must calculate $D_p G_{mf}/\mu$, after G_{mf} has

FIG. 3-15a. Nomograph of Eq. (3-25).   (*Courtesy of Génie Chimique.*)

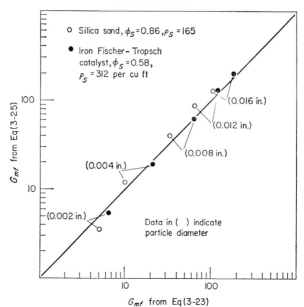

FIG. 3-16. Comparison of Eqs. (3-23) and (3-25) for predicting onset of fluidization.

been estimated, in order to check on the range of validity in relation to the problem. If the resulting $D_p G_{mf}/\mu$ is in excess of 10, G_{mf} must be

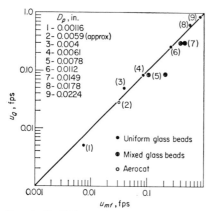

FIG. 3-17. Values of u_{mf} predicted by Eq. (3-25) and compared to u_Q, the velocity required to bring the bed into the quiescent state of fluidization.[14]

corrected by means of Fig. 3-15. For limited estimates the equation has been condensed to the nomograph, Fig. 3-15a.

Figure 3-16 gives a brief comparison of the generalized correlation with Eq. (3-23). The data pertain to materials and sizes that are frequently encountered in fluidization operations. The good agreement between the values calculated by the two equations supports the assumptions made in the derivation of the generalized form.

Lewis et al.[14] have designated the state of incipient fluidization as the quiescent quicksand condition. The fluid velocity required to induce it they termed u_Q. Their observed values of u_Q, pertaining to incipient fluidization of glass beads and aerocat particles, are compared in Fig. 3-17 with u_{mf} values predicted for those particles by the generalized correlations. It is interesting to observe that the comparison is apparently equally satisfactory for mixed beds and close cuts. For the mixed beds composite diameters were calculated by Eq. (3-20).

Other Correlations. Of the numerous relationships that have been proposed for G_{mf} estimation, only the correlations of Miller and Logwinuk,[16] van Heerden et al.,[10] Johnson,[11] Wilhelm and Kwauk,[21] and Baerg and coworkers[2] will be further discussed. Details pertaining to operating conditions, apparatus construction, and solids properties are given in Table 3-2. From the rela-

tively wide range of conditions and interpretation of results, it is not surprising that G_{mf} values predicted by the individual correlations are not in very close agreement. This is apparent from Fig. 3-18, where the individual correlations were used to predict G_{mf} for a bed of spherical glass beads fluidized in air at standard conditions. The extent of deviation between extreme values predicted is dependent on particle size. Thus for small particles of 0.002 in. the G_{mf} values predicted range from about 2 to about 12 lb/(hr)(sq ft). For particles of 0.015 in. diameter, the spread is, however, only about 2.5-

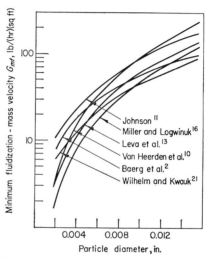

FIG. 3-18. Comparison of correlations for predicting onset of fluidization.

fold, with a lower value of 85 and a higher value of about 200 lb/(hr) (sq ft) indicated. Thus it follows that not all correlations emphasize the G_{mf}-D_p dependency to the same extent.

Miller and Logwinuk. The authors' correlation reads

$$G_{mf} = \frac{0.00125 \, D_p{}^2(\rho_S - \rho_F)^{0.9}\rho_F{}^{1.1}g_c}{\mu} \tag{3-26}$$

The equation is of the same form as Eq. (3-24). But whereas C in Eq. (3-24) is a function of D_pG/μ, the horizontal course of the Miller and Logwinuk data is readily recognized from Fig. 3-14.

The form of Eq. (3-26) was based on a consideration of dimensional analysis. Exponents were then experimentally evaluated. The exponents of the density product in the Miller and Logwinuk equation have not been reported elsewhere.

Van Heerden, Nobel, and Van Krevelen. In essence these authors used dimensional analysis and on the basis of experimental data proposed the following equation:

$$G_{mf} = \frac{0.00123 \, D_p{}^2 \rho_B \rho_F g_c}{B\mu} \qquad (3\text{-}27)$$

where B is a generalized shape factor. For the materials examined, B values are as follows:

Material	B values
Carborundum	0.62–0.78
Coke	0.39–0.58
Iron oxide	0.59

Roughly speaking, B values appeared to increase with particle diameter. D_p values were based on sieve ratings.

The quantity ρ_B is the material bulk density at the so-called maximum porosity. The latter is defined as the loosest stable arrangement wherein particles are still resting on each other in a fixed bed by mutual contact. For glass beads of 1 mm diameter this porosity was reported to be 40.6 per cent. Assuming that for all particle shapes a similar maximum porosity existed, van Heerden et al. suggested combining the porosity value with the shape belonging to it. This led then to the generalized shape factor B. The main difference between the van Heerden development and the considerations that led to Eq. (3-25) is that the Dutch workers assumed that maximum porosity, which in effect is the equivalent of the minimum fluid voidage, was independent of particle size. In reality, it is a function of D_p, as is indicated by the data of Fig. 2-6. There is a great similarity between Eqs. (3-26) and (3-27).

Johnson. The equations proposed by Johnson are as follows:

$$G_{mf} = \frac{D_p{}^2 \phi_s{}^2 g_c}{18\mu} (\rho_S - \rho_F)\rho_F \frac{\epsilon^5}{1 + 0.5(1 - \epsilon)} \qquad (3\text{-}28)$$

and

$$G_{mf} = 0.171 D_p \phi_s \rho_F \left(\frac{\epsilon}{1 - \epsilon}\right)^3 \left\{\frac{g_c{}^2 \rho_S \epsilon^6}{\mu(1 - \epsilon)[1 + 0.5(1 - \epsilon)]}\right\}^{\frac{1}{3}} \qquad (3\text{-}29)$$

The criterion of which equation is valid for a particular situation rests on the examination of the resulting Reynolds number. Thus for values of $D_p G/\mu < 2$, Eq. (3-28) holds; for higher values, Eq. (3-29) is recommended.

Briefly stated, Johnson started with an analogy between a true liquid and the fluid bed. Thus properties of bed density and bed viscosity were assigned to the solids charge. Next the bed was considered to be a medium wherein an individual particle had a characteristic free-falling velocity. With this established, Stokes' law was modified by substituting for its fluid density and viscosity terms the respective bed properties.

Specifically, bed density was introduced into the correlation by means of bed voidage and fluid and solids densities. For a definition of solids bed viscosity Johnson extended the Einstein equation for viscosity of a suspension of spheres in a liquid.

Use of the equations requires availability of particle-sphericity data and minimum-fluid-voidage values. Johnson suggested that ϵ_{mf} be taken from Fig. 2-6 and, if the case in question is a fluidization with a gas, that the ϵ_{mf} values be increased by 6 to 8 per cent. For liquid fluidization he suggested an increase of 25 to 35 per cent. The recommended increases in ϵ_{mf} values are appreciable, and they lead one to believe that Johnson may have based his incipient-fluidization observations less on bed expansion than on induced solids motion. This would also explain, at least in part, the very substantial recommended increases in ϵ_{mf} data for liquid fluidization, since liquid-fluidized columns will exhibit strong solids convection currents only at relatively elevated fluid rates. In comparing the Johnson correlation in Fig. 3-18 with the rest of the correlations, voidages as read from Fig. 2-6 were increased by 7 percentage points. Owing to the possible difference in reference state, as stated, the Johnson data could not be included in the development of the generalized correlation for G_{mf}.

Wilhelm and Kwauk. The authors correlated their data by relating values of $K_{\Delta p}$ or $K_{\Delta \rho}$ to the Reynolds number $D_p G/\mu$. By definition

$$K_{\Delta p} = \frac{D_p{}^3 \rho_F g_c \,\Delta p}{2\mu^2 L_{mf}}$$

which is the product of the Chilton-Colburn friction factor

$$f_{CC} = \frac{D_p \rho_F g_c \,\Delta p}{2G^2 L}$$

and the square of the Reynolds number, $(D_p G/\mu)^2$. The other dimensionless number is $K_{\Delta \rho} = D_p{}^3 g_c \rho_F (\rho_S - \rho_F)/2\mu^2$. This is the product of the square of the Reynolds number and the drag coefficient,

$$C_D = \frac{D_p g_c \rho_F (\rho_S - \rho_F)}{2G^2}$$

The two expressions will transform into each other by using either $\Delta p/L_{mf}$ or $(\rho_S - \rho_F)$ as the pressure gradient.

The relationship between $K_{\Delta p}$, $K_{\Delta \rho}$, and $D_p G/\mu$, as proposed by Wilhelm and Kwauk, is given in Fig. 3-19. In order to estimate the minimum-fluidization mass velocity, $K_{\Delta p}$ or $K_{\Delta \rho}$ is first evaluated. This is then brought to intersect with the incipient-fluidization line to yield the value of the Reynolds number for incipient fluidization.

The Wilhelm and Kwauk correlation shown in Fig. 3-18 appears to yield low G_{mf} values for particles of $D_p > 0.008$ in. It has not been experimentally verified for particles substantially below this size. Indi-

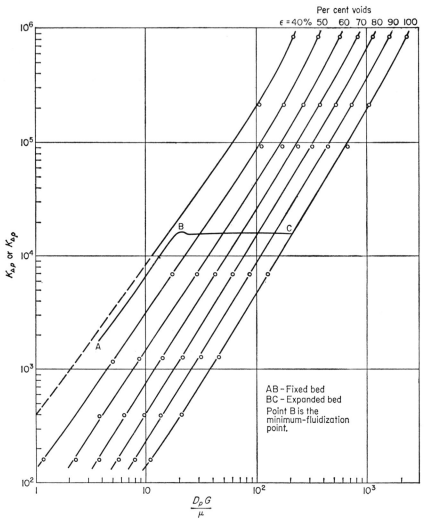

Fig. 3-19. The generalized correlation of Wilhelm and Kwauk[21] for predicting the onset of fluidization and bed expansion.

cations are that extrapolation to smaller sizes will result in the prediction of high G_{mf} values.

Baerg, Klassen, and Gishler. The correlation of these workers represented by

$$G_{mf} = 1.3 \times 10^3 (D_p \rho_b)^{1.23} \qquad (3\text{-}30)$$

was conceived in an entirely different manner from all the correlations discussed above. The authors, then primarily concerned with considerations of heat transfer between a bed and a confining wall, observed that, for all materials investigated, heat-transfer coefficients showed an abrupt increase with a characteristic fluid mass velocity. The sudden increase was attributed to the advent of particle motion in the bed, and hence the authors had established a reliable indicator and reference point for incipient fluidization. This development is important as far as theory of heat flow between fluidized solids and a retaining wall is concerned. It will therefore be discussed in greater detail in Chap. 8.

As appears from Fig. 3-18, the correlation of Baerg et al. is surprisingly well in line with the rest of the data, although some interesting deviations persist. Thus the high values predicted for small particles are perhaps due to channeling tendencies of the small-diameter solids. With such solids, then, particle motion would set in only at relatively elevated mass velocities sufficient to destroy the channels and induce normal fluidization. The correlation was found useful for flow of air through beds of a relatively large variety of solids. D_p is to be expressed in feet and ρ_b in pounds per cubic foot. Since the formula does not include fluid-property parameters, its application is largely limited to air-fluidized beds.

Example 3-2. A 4-in.-ID column with a porous-plate bottom was charged with 5.57 lb of anthracite coal. The pycnometric density of the coal with mercury as displacement fluid was 123 lb per cu ft. Size distribution and average particle size were as follows:

d_p, in.	Weight fraction X	$\dfrac{X}{d_p}$
0.036	0.20	5.56
0.030	0.29	9.67
0.025	0.23	9.20
0.021	0.25	11.90
0.018	0.03	1.67

$$\sum \frac{X}{d_p} = 38.00 \quad \text{and} \quad D_p = \frac{1}{38.00} = 0.0263 \text{ in.}$$

It is intended to fluidize this charge with air at 90°F and let the air discharge from the bed into the surrounding atmosphere under 743 mm Hg. For these conditions estimate the minimum-fluidization mass velocity.

Solution. Cross-section of fluidizing vessel

$$S = \frac{4^2 \times 0.785}{144}$$
$$= 0.0872 \text{ sq ft}$$

Fluidization pressure drop

$$\Delta p = \frac{5.57}{0.0872} = 63.9 \text{ psf}$$
$$= 23.0 \text{ mm Hg}$$

Inlet air pressure

$$\rho_F = \frac{28.82 \times 766.0 \times 492}{359 \times 760 \times 550}$$
$$= 0.0724 \text{ lb per cu ft}$$
$$\rho_F(\rho_S - \rho_F) \approx 123 \times 0.0724 = 8.87 \text{ lb per cu ft}$$

Air viscosity $\mu = 0.018$ centipoise. Using the nomograph of Fig. 3-15a,

$$G_{mf} = 240 \text{ lb/(hr)(sq ft)}$$

A laboratory test with this coal under the conditions cited[12] indicated initial bed expansion at 189 lb/(hr)(sq ft). Allowing for 10 per cent additional flow rate, which is accounted for by Eq. (3-25) and the nomograph, the coal would be observed to commence fluidization at 208 lb/(hr)(sq ft). This is in reasonably good agreement with the value of $G_{mf} = 240$ obtained by nomograph. The deviation is of course due to the considerable vesicularity of the coal. The water-displacement density was determined and found to be 148 lb per cu ft. On the basis of this value G_{mf} would have been 290 lb/(hr)(sq ft). From this observation it may be concluded that possibly even the "mercury density" of the coal was somewhat too high and that for a more precise estimate the density should be obtained by the gas-flow method of Ergun.

Example 3-3. A 6-in.-diameter glass column with a porous-plate bottom is carrying uniform catalyst beads of $D_p = 0.174$ in. and $\rho_S = 100$ lb per cu ft. The solid is intended to be fluidized with water of 1.0 centipoise viscosity. Calculate the minimum-fluidization mass velocity.

Solution. Since the nomograph does not cover the high density range characteristic of this problem, Eq. (3-25) is used directly. Data are as follows:

$$D_p = 0.174 \text{ in.} \qquad D_p^{1.82} = 0.174^{1.82} = 0.0415$$
$$\mu = 1.0 \text{ centipoise} \qquad \mu^{0.88} = 1.0$$
$$(\rho_S - \rho_F)\rho_F = (100 - 62.3)62.3 = 2,350$$
$$[(\rho_S - \rho_F)\rho_F]^{0.94} = 2,350^{0.94} = 1,470$$

Hence,

$$G_{mf} = 688 \times 0.0415 \times \frac{1,470}{1.0} = 42,000 \text{ lb/(hr)(sq ft)}$$

On the basis of this value

$$\text{Re}_{mf} = \frac{42,000 \times 0.174}{12 \times 2.42} = 252$$

and it will be noted that a correction is required. From Fig. 3-15 the correction factor will be 0.39. Hence $G_{mf} = 42,000 \times 0.39 = 16,400$ lb/(hr)(sq ft). This is in good agreement with the value of $G_{mf} = 17,000$ found by Wilhelm and Kwauk for this material fluidized under the stated conditions.

PROBLEMS

3-1. A granular oxidic nonvesicular catalyst is to be reduced by contacting with hydrogen in a reactor of 1.0 in. ID.   The average particle size of the catalyst is 0.01518 in., and the specific gravity is 5.0.   The catalyst is held in the tube by a 200-mesh stainless-steel screen, and the bed height is 18 in. with a voidage of 49.2 per cent. There is no hold-down screen on top of the bed.

The space velocity of the hydrogen through the unit is 450 volumes of hydrogen per hour, measured at standard conditions of temperature and pressure, per volume of dumped catalyst.   The temperature in the reactor during a typical run is as follows:

Position in bed, in. above base	Temp, °F	Position in bed, in. above base	Temp, °F
0	250	12	622
3	752	15	550
6	913	18	509
9	804		

Auxiliary pressure-drop tests made with air and this catalyst in a 4-in.-ID glass tube gave the following data:

Catalyst weight: 4,262 g
Bed height: 0.684 ft
Barometric pressure: 740 mm Hg
Air temperature: 84°F

Air mass velocities, lb/(hr)(sq ft)	Pressure drop, psf
21.10	13.65
48.70	31.20
84.50	56.00

It is desired to carry the reaction through in a fixed bed.   For the conditions as specified determine whether the bed may be operated with either upflow or downflow of the hydrogen.   For the evaluation of physical properties of the gas it may be assumed that the gas is pure hydrogen.

3-2.   The odor in a plant space of 40 by 80 by 20 ft is to be controlled by contacting the air with 5 cu ft of activated carbon.   The shape factor of the carbon may be taken as $\phi_s = 0.82$.   The voidage when the carbon is normally dumped will be $\epsilon = 0.52$.   Size distribution is as follows:

Mesh	Weight fraction
6–8	9
8–10	80
10–14	11

A blower that is idle in the plant is to be used for the circulation.   It has the following characteristics:

Cfm	Delivery pressure, in. H_2O	Cfm	Delivery pressure, in. H_2O
2,000	30	8,000	18
4,000	28	10,000	4
6,000	24		

In order to prevent attrition, it is essential that the unit be operated as a fixed bed, with a gas velocity of no more than 0.5 u_{mf}. For these conditions find the required bed dimensions if it is desirable to circulate the air at least five times through the carbon bed per hour.

3-3. A gas-solid contacting unit is composed of a straight cylindrical shell and an adjoining lower conical section. The shell has an inside diameter of 24 in. and a height of 48 in. The angle at the apex of the conical section is $22\frac{1}{2}°$. A 4-in. standard pipe enters the conical section through the apex, and the delivery opening is fitted with a 10-mesh screen.

The unit carries peas extending all the way into the shell up to a height of 3 ft. The average diameter of the peas is $D_p = 0.25$ in. Air is admitted into the unit through the apex at a rate of 60 cfm, measured at standard conditions. Surrounding atmospheric pressure is 735 mm Hg and the temperature is 77°F. Calculate the required delivery air pressure to the unit.

3-4. A crushed anthracite coal is contaminated with a silica sand. It has been proposed to remove the sand by subjecting the material to an upward flow of water, floating the sand out of the mixture. Solids properties are as follows:

Anthracite coal:

Mesh	Weight per cent
6–8	13
8–10	67
10–14	20

Solids density: $\rho_S = 118$ lb per cu ft

Silica sand:

Mesh	Weight per cent
35–48	5
48–65	17
65–100	38
100–150	36
150	4

Solids density: $\rho_S = 160$ lb per cu ft

The proportion of sand in the mixture amounts to 10.6 weight per cent. Available as an envisioned washer is a vessel consisting of a cylindrical shell 4 ft in diameter and 8 ft high, joined below by a conical section with an angle of 45° at the apex. The water is to be admitted through a 3-in. standard pipe in the apex.

If this equipment is fitted with proper overflow nozzles at a position 7 ft up the shell, find the required water rate which will effect the separation. (NOTE: For best separation and equipment utilization one should operate at the point at which the coal bed will just begin to fluidize; i.e., the water rate should be slightly in excess of that required for minimum fluidization.)

3-5. The effluent water from Prob. 3-4 is recovered by removing the sand in an ordinary gravity filter. Coal fines having a considerable size spectrum are carried along. Investigate the possibility of backwashing the sand for the purpose of recovering the coal fines. Establish the upper size limit of the coal particles which may just still be recovered by backwashing.

REFERENCES

1. Agarwal, O. P., and J. Anderson Storrow: *Chem. & Ind.* (*London*), 278–286 (1951).
2. Baerg, A., J. Klassen, and P. E. Gishler: *Can. J. Research*, **F28**: 287–307 (1950).

3. Brownell, L. E., and D. L. Katz: *Chem. Eng. Progr.*, **43**: 537–548 (1947).
4. Carman, P. C.: *Trans. Inst. Chem. Engrs. (London)*, **15**: 150–166 (1937).
5. Ergun, S., and A. A. Orning: *Ind. Eng. Chem.*, **41**: 1179–1184 (1949).
6. Ergun, Sabri: *Anal. Chem.*, **24**(2): 388 (1952).
7. Ergun, Sabri: *Chem. Eng. Progr.*, **48**: 89–94 (1952).
8. Ergun, Sabri: *Chem. Eng. Progr.*, **48**: 227–236 (1952).
9. Furukawa, J., T. Ohmae, and I. Ueki: *Chem. High Polymers (Tokyo)*, **8**(2): 111 (1951).
10. Heerden, C. van, A. P. P. Nobel, and D. W. van Krevelen: *Chem. Eng. Sci.*, **1**(1): 37–49 (1951).
11. Johnson, E.: *Inst. Gas Engrs. (London)*, *Rept.* 1949–1950, *Publ. No.* 378/179.
12. Leva, Max, M. Weintraub, M. Grummer, M. Pollchik, and H. H. Storch: U.S. *Bur. Mines Bull.* 504, 1951.
13. Leva, Max, Takashi Shirai, and C. Y. Wen: *Génie chim.*, **75**(2): 33–42 (1956).
14. Lewis, W. K., E. R. Gilliland, and W. C. Bauer: *Ind. Eng. Chem.*, **41**: 1104–1117 (1949).
15. Martin, J. J., W. L. McCabe, and C. C. Monrad: *Chem. Eng. Progr.*, **47**: 91–94 (1951).
16. Miller, C. O., and A. K. Logwinuk: *Ind. Eng. Chem.*, **43**: 1220–1226 (1951).
17. Moody, L. F.: *Trans. ASME*, **66**: 671–684 (1944).
18. Reboux, P.: "Phénomènes de fluidisation," Association Française de Fluidisation, Paris, 1954.
19. Schwartz, C. E., and J. M. Smith: *Ind. Eng. Chem.*, **45**: 1209–1218 (1953).
20. Shirai, T.: personal communication.
21. Wilhelm, R. H., and M. Kwauk: *Chem. Eng. Progr.*, **44**: 201 (1948).
22. Yagi, S., and T. Shirai: *Chem. Eng. (Tokyo)*, **16**(1): 2–6 (1952).

CHAPTER 4

THE EXPANDED BED

Nomenclature

b' = exponent, Eq. (4-7)

c_u = uniformity coefficient, defined on page 103

d_p = component diameter in a mixture of particles, ft; $d_p = \sqrt{d_1 d_2}$, where d_1 and d_2 are rated openings of adjacent sieves

D_p = particle diameter, ft

D_t = circular-conduit diameter, ft

f = function of

g_c = gravitational conversion factor, 32.2 (lb mass)(ft)/(lb force)(sec)(sec)

G_e = hypothetical fluid velocity required to merely expand a bed of solids, lb/(hr)(sq ft)

G_f = fluid mass velocity through a fluidizing bed, lb/(hr)(sq ft)

G_{mf} = fluid mass velocity for minimum fluidization, lb/(hr)(sq ft)

k' = constant, Eq. (4-7)

L_e = expanded-bed height, ft

L_{mf} = bed height at point of minimum fluidization, ft

m = slope, Fig. 4-14

m' = slope, Fig. 4-20

n = exponent in Richardson and Zaki correlations

r = fluctuation ratio, highest to lowest bed level in a gas-fluidized charge

R = bed-expansion ratio, i.e., L_e/L_{mf}

Re = Reynolds number, $D_p G/\mu$

S = cross sectional area of unpacked tube, sq ft

u_f = linear velocity of fluid through a fluidizing bed, fps

u_p = velocity of particles, moving "en masse," fps

u_t = terminal velocity of a particle, fps

V = volume of a spherical particle, cu ft

w = weight of solids in a bed, lb

W_e = expansion work, ft-lb

W_f = fluidization work, ft-lb

X = weight fraction of a size component in a mixture, dimensionless

β = interparticle friction factor

ΔE_{gas} = total energy given up by the fluidizing gas passing through a column of fluidizing solids, ft-lb

ΔF_{gs} = energy loss of the gas due to friction on the solids, ft-lb

ΔF_{ss} = energy loss of the gas by virtue of having induced solids friction in the bed, ft-lb

ΔKE = kinetic-energy losses of the gas, ft-lb

Δp = pressure drop, psf

ΔZ = energy loss of the gas by virtue of having imparted potential energy to a bed of solids, ft-lb

ΔZ_i = same concept as ΔZ, except that bed is assumed to behave ideally

ϵ = bed voidage

ϵ_i = ideal bed voidage

ϵ_b = interaggregate bed voidage

ϵ_e = expanded-bed voidage

ϵ_{mf} = bed-voidage fraction at point of minimum fluidization, dimensionless

ϵ_t = total bed voidage in an aggregated bed

η = fluidization efficiency

θ = time, sec or hr

μ = fluid viscosity, lb/(hr)(ft)

ρ_b = bulk density or dispersed-solids density, lb per cu ft

ρ_F = fluid density, lb per cu ft

ρ_S = solids density, lb per cu ft

ϕ_s = particle-shape factor; $\phi_s = V^{2/3}/0.205 A$, where V is volume of particle and A is particle surface area

$_{1,2}$, etc. refers to properties relative to vertical position

Abstract

In this chapter bed-expansion characteristics are discussed. The chapter is divided into two main sections; the first section deals with liquid-fluidized beds, and the second section treats gas-fluidized beds.

Liquid-fluidized expansion data are examined in the light of the earlier presented pressure-drop equation, and the limits of this treatment are ascertained. The chapter proceeds then to the correlations of Richardson and Zaki as well as other pertinent developments. Finally, bed stratification is briefly considered.

Gas-fluidized expansion data are examined from the point of view of aggregation. The effect of particle motion on the ideal expansion behavior is assessed. Generalized correlations for predicting bed expansion are given and limits of applicability of the relationships are established. A new concept, the "fluctuation ratio," is introduced. The section also examines the effect of baffles on bed expansion and discusses segregation in both freely fluidizing and baffled beds.

Introduction. The prediction of the state of bed expansion is important for specifying the height of the fluidized-bed chamber. In most cases, especially where gas-solid systems are involved, mere expansion behavior of a column of solids is, however, not sufficient to arrive at the height of the confining shell. This is so because the upper boundary of a fluidized bed may exhibit substantial level fluctuations. For specifying shell height these fluctuations must also be considered. Even with the fluctuations accounted for there are additional considerations that may be important as far as unit height is concerned. These latter aspects pertain to elutriation. Thus it is frequently required to make provision for a sufficiently high freeboard section, so that carry-over losses are minimized.

Chapter 3 started with a brief consideration of flow through empty conduits. Certain assumptions and modifications led to working equations for fixed beds which, combined with the pressure-drop–weight-gradient relationship for the fluidized column, yielded correlations for incipient fluidization. In this chapter the correlations will be extended, as far as possible, to the expanded bed. In the course of the endeavor all deviations will be noted and analyzed for their possible reasons and significance.

In the course of considering fluidized-bed properties, the apparent fundamental difference between liquid-solid and gas-solid systems has been noted. Purely from visual observation it may be concluded that particulately fluidizing liquid-solid systems resemble a fixed bed more closely than do aggregatively fluidizing gas-solid systems. With this in mind the expansion characteristics of the liquid-fluidized bed are examined first, to be followed by the apparently more complex gas-fluidized systems.

LIQUID-SOLID SYSTEMS

Expansion. The expansion of a column of solids is concurrent with an increase in average bed voidage. In the derivation of Eq. (3-6) from the generalized flow equation in empty conduits, the voidage function followed from hydrodynamic considerations. Limiting ourselves to the laminar-flow region, which appears to be characteristic of most early states of bed expansion, it remains to examine to what extent Eq. (3-6) will apply to the expanded bed. For an expanded bed of voidage ϵ_e the height will be L_e, and Eq. (3-6) becomes

$$\Delta p = \frac{200 G \mu L_e (1 - \epsilon_e)^2}{D_p{}^2 \phi_s{}^2 \rho_F g_c \epsilon_e{}^3} \tag{4-1}\star$$

If there is no slugging, the fluidized-bed pressure drop will remain constant and equal to the bed weight gradient. Replacing the expanded-bed height L_e by its equivalent $(1 - \epsilon_{mf})/(1 - \epsilon_e)$, it is seen that the validity of the Eq. (4-1) may be readily tested by simply plotting mass velocity G, or the Reynolds number, vs. $(1 - \epsilon_e)/\epsilon_e{}^3$ for various states of expansion. If the fixed-bed law applies, a log-log plot should yield a straight line of slope $m = -1.0$.

Comprehensive literature and operating data are available for examining this point. The data extend from such applications as backwashing of rapid sand filters in beds of many square feet of cross section to fluidization of hydrogenation catalysts in tubes of 1 in. diameter or less. A few data from various sources have been assembled in Fig. 4-1. Reynolds numbers extend roughly from 0.002 to 1.0, thus a substantial portion of the laminar-flow range is covered. As for voidage range, this is indicated by the interval $5 > (1 - \epsilon)/\epsilon^3 > 0.1$, corresponding to $0.47 < \epsilon < 0.92$. Lines of slope $m = -1.0$ drawn into the figure indicate that the data follow the fixed-bed equation up to a voidage of about $\epsilon = 0.80$.

For expansions beyond this voidage the experimental points fall below
the course of the equation, indicating that for an anticipated flow increase
the column expands more than should be expected from Eq. (4-1).

The voidage function in Eq. (4-1) and the related correlations of Chap.
3 are identical with the function contained in the Kozeny-Carman equation.[4]* The validity of the func-
tion as far as application to flow
through porous structures is concerned rests on the assumptions
that a modified channel flow prevails and that the flow pattern is
thoroughly tortuous. Thus the
pore spaces in the solid are considered to be a series of random channels formed by the surrounding
particles. This model is quite
satisfactory for relatively dense
structures such as are ordinarily
found in fixed beds. It is also
satisfactory in liquid-fluidized beds
up to about 80 per cent free space.
However, for values of $\epsilon > 0.80$
the particles may no longer be considered to form the walls of the
channels. Thus flow is now principally around individual particles,

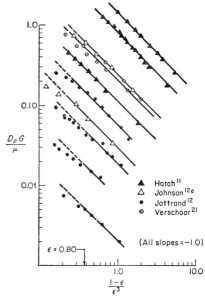

Fig. 4-1. Expansion data for liquid-solid
systems in laminar flow.

and it is due to this change in con-
ditions that the voidage function of the Kozeny-Carman equation fails
to apply to flow through porous media of $\epsilon > 0.80$. In an attempt to
analyze this type of flow, Brinkman[3] estimated how the Stokes'-law
forces are modified by the interfering effect of adjacent particles. On
this basis he proposed that, at constant pressure drop, the voidage
increase due to upward liquid flow through a column of solids follows
the relation

$$\frac{1}{1-\epsilon} + 0.75 \left[1 - \left(\frac{8}{1-\epsilon} - 3 \right)^{\frac{1}{2}} \right]$$

For a voidage range of $0.50 < \epsilon < 0.70$ the relative bed expansion proposed by the Brinkman expression is of the same order of magnitude as
that proposed by the Kozeny-Carman equation or Eq. 4-1. For the
range $\epsilon = 0.70 \rightarrow 0.80$ the agreement is somewhat better. For $\epsilon > 0.80$
the Brinkman function will give higher bed-voidage values. This has

* Superscript numbers indicate works listed in References at the end of the chapter.

been experimentally investigated by Verschoor,[21] who worked with a 74-mm-diameter column 1,450 mm long. He fluidized close cuts of sand and glass beads in water and toluene. Some of the Verschoor data are shown in Fig. 4-1. The failure of the voidage function of Eq. (4-1) to apply to the range of $\epsilon > 0.80$ is indicated. According to the Brinkman analysis, the force exerted by a fluid on a particle immersed in a dense swarm of particles is greater than the force the fluid would exert on the same particle isolated from others. Hence it follows that the liquid-fluidized bed should possess a sharply defined upper boundary, because there the magnitude of the acting force decreases suddenly. The sharply defined upper interface has been verified by Verschoor, as well as by others.[21,22] The highest voidage obtained by Verschoor was $\epsilon = 0.96$. This was for the fluidization of 100- to 120-mesh sea sand in water. An interesting set of data at very high voidages has also been reported by Happel and Epstein.[10] They employed a 3.94-in.-diameter tube which was fitted with a series of longitudinally extending rods on which 4.9-mm beads could be aligned at desired intervals. This permitted investigation of effect of porosity on pressure drop without the possible disturbances of induced particle movement. Ink-injection tests indicated that flow was laminar. For a voidage span of $0.689 < \epsilon < 0.941$ the data were in excellent agreement with the proposed correlation of Brinkman. As compared with typical water-fluidized data pertaining to small-diameter particles,[16] a deviation was noted. It appeared that under the influence of identical flow rates the fluidized

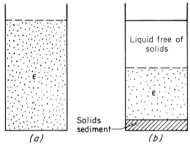

FIG. 4-2. Hindered settling. Solids were uniformly dispersed in (a); hindered settling has taken place in (b), causing the sediment below and the clear liquid, above the suspension of voidage ϵ.

solids expanded to a somewhat smaller voidage than was indicated by the flow data through the fixed arrangement of spheres.

Hindered Settling. In a sense fluid flow in hindered settling is the reverse of fluid flow through an expanded column. Whereas in free settling, particles descend as single elements in a column where $\epsilon \rightarrow 1.0$, the voidage in hindered settling may vary virtually from zero to unity itself. In order to visualize this, let Fig. 4-2a be a suspension of uniform spherical particles in a liquid. The column has been thoroughly agitated, and its voidage at the end of the agitation period is ϵ. As agitation ceases, the column will settle at a definite rate and liquid will be forced upward through the channels. Figure 4-2b shows the same column after a certain time has elapsed. The rate of settling of the interface will, in addition to the physical properties of the fluid and solids, be also dependent on the original voidage of the suspension. With an originally smaller voidage the resistance to flow through the then smaller channels would have been higher and the rate of descent of the interface would have been lower.

A comparison of a few typical hindered-settling and expansion data in water is given in Fig. 4-3. These data pertain to uniformly sized particles, and there is excellent agreement. The data of Lewis et al.[16] show the deviation beyond a voidage of 80 per cent, whereas the data of Hatch[11] are still in agreement with Eq. (4-1) up to a higher voidage of $\epsilon \approx 0.85$.

With nonuniform particles the problem of hindered settling is much more complicated: while the solids interface descends, size segregation will take place in the bed. This will in turn influence the voidage in various strata of the bed and thereby sharply affect the settling rate. In extreme cases fines might even be forcefully carried upward by fluid currents induced through the settling of the heavier components. With appreciable size distributions, one would no longer expect the similarity between hindered settling and flow through an expanded bed indicated by the data of Fig. 4-3.

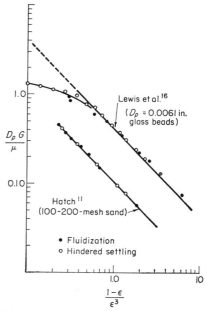

Fig. 4-3. Comparison of liquid-solid expansion and hindered settling of uniformly sized particles.

Transition and Turbulent Range. A data analysis for the transition and turbulent range by means of Eq. (3-11) becomes complicated because the state-of-flow factor does not remain constant. Thus for the range $10 < Re < 1,000$, for example, the state-of-flow factor increases from 1.0 to 1.95. From Eq. (3-11) it is seen that, for this range, not only will the value of the voidage function vary but similar variations are involved with u_0, $D_p, \rho_F \phi_s$, and μ. Thus the results of the analysis would depend heavily on the established n-Re relationship. In view of the empirical way in which this was established, prediction of expanded-bed height based on the method would be of doubtful value.

Data Presentation of Richardson and Zaki. A comprehensive theoretical development regarding the presentation and correlation of liquid-

solid expansion data has been given by Richardson and Zaki.[20] Briefly
stated, the proposed equations describe the dynamic equilibrium of
individual particles as a function of fluid-bed and apparatus properties.
By application of dimensional analysis it appeared that the following
groupings were to be anticipated:

$$\frac{u_f}{u_t} = f\left(\frac{D_p u_f \rho_F}{\mu}, \frac{D_p}{D_t}, \epsilon\right) \tag{4-2}$$

where u_f and u_t are fluid velocity and free-falling velocity of the particles
in a quiescent fluid, respectively.

Thus far, possible effects of type of flow on u_f/u_t have not been considered. Postulating that, in the laminar range, fluid-inertia effects are
negligible as compared with viscosity, fluid density is then no longer a
parameter. The situation is reversed in turbulent flow, where the effect
of viscosity becomes subordinated to fluid density. The result is that
in both instances u_f/u_t is dependent only on D_p/D_t and ϵ. For the transition range, on the other hand, both ρ_F and μ are important, thus rendering
u_f/u_t dependent on $D_p \rho_F u_f/\mu$, D_p/D_t, and ϵ.

Richardson and Zaki's theoretical development was fairly well supported by experimental data of their own, obtained for the purpose of
establishing generalizations. The fluidization tubes were of 1.5 and 2.44
in. diameter, and particle sizes ranged from about 0.01 to 0.25 in. The
ratio D_p/D_t varied from nearly 0 to about 0.5, thus wall effects could
during some tests have been quite appreciable. Spheres, cylinders, cubes,
and prismatic bodies were fluidized in water, glycerine, and some oils.

The expansion data were presented in the form $u_f/u_t = \epsilon^n$, with
$D_p u_f \rho_F/\mu$ and D_p/D_t as specific parameters. Since for any one particle
u_t is the free-falling velocity and a constant, the expansion data may be
simply correlated by plotting u_f against ϵ. With logarithmic coordinates,
n should then be the slope of the resulting line. The experimental data
were analyzed in this manner, and the following expressions for evaluation of n were suggested:

$$n = \left(4.35 + 17.5 \frac{D_p}{D_t}\right) \text{Re}^{-0.03} \qquad 0.2 < \text{Re} < 1 \tag{4-3}\star$$

$$n = \left(4.45 + 18 \frac{D_p}{D_t}\right) \text{Re}^{-0.1} \qquad 1 < \text{Re} < 200 \tag{4-4}\star$$

$$n = 4.45\, \text{Re}^{-0.1} \qquad 200 < \text{Re} < 500 \tag{4-5}\star$$

$$n = 2.39 \qquad \text{Re} > 500 \tag{4-6}\star$$

In the above expressions, the Reynolds number is defined as $D_p u_f \rho_F/\mu$,
where u_f is the superficial fluid velocity and D_p is the diameter of the
equivalent circular projected area of the particles. As this is a rather
difficult term to evaluate, it was suggested that the diameter of the

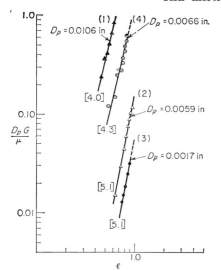

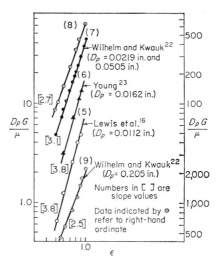

FIG. 4-4. Solid-liquid expansion data for the laminar-flow range, presented by the method of Richardson and Zaki.[20] Data in brackets are slope values of lines. NOTE: For (2), ordinate is to be multiplied by 10.

(1) Hatch,[11] (2) Johnson,[12a] (3) Jottrand,[12] (4) Verschoor.[21]

FIG. 4-5. Solid-liquid expansion data for the transition and turbulent range, presented according to the method of Richardson and Zaki.[20]

TABLE 4-1. SLOPE VALUES PREDICTED BY RICHARDSON AND ZAKI AS COMPARED WITH VALUES OBTAINED FROM INDEPENDENT DATA

Type of flow	Curve number in Figs. 4-4 and 4-5	Slope by Richardson and Zaki	Experimental slope	Average value of D_pG/μ
Laminar........	3	4.9	5.1	0.02
	2	4.8	5.1	0.06
	4	4.5	4.3	0.3
	1	4.4	4.0	0.5
Transition......	5	4.1	3.8	2.0
	6	3.6	3.8	8.0
	7	3.3	3.1	20.0
Turbulent......	8	2.5	2.7	350
	9	2.39	2.5	1,000

equivalent-volume sphere or the geometric mean of adjacent sieve ratings be used instead.

The proposed correlations of Richardson and Zaki have been subjected to rigorous tests by comparing them with extensive liquid-fluidization data from various literature sources. These data are given in Figs. 4-4 and 4-5. Since n values are dependent on flow range as characterized by $D_p G/\mu$, it is more revealing to relate ϵ with $D_p G/\mu$ than with u_f, the superficial velocity. The slopes obtained from the experimental data are compared with calculated values in Table 4-1. From the excellent agreement indicated in the table it may be concluded that the Richardson and Zaki correlation is a most reliable method for predicting expansion of liquid-fluidized beds. It should be noted that the correlations remain valid virtually up into a region where $\epsilon \to 1.0$.

Example 4-1. A sand filter employs a 29-in.-high bed of silica sand above a layer of coarse gravel. The sand is of 2.55 specific gravity, has a bed voidage of $\epsilon = 0.45$, and the following size distribution:

Size cuts, in.	Weight fraction X	$\dfrac{X}{d_p}$
0.0217	0.10	4.70
0.0217–0.0244	0.10	4.35
0.0244–0.0264	0.10	3.94
0.0264–0.0283	0.10	3.65
0.0283–0.0299	0.10	3.43
0.0299–0.0323	0.10	3.21
0.0323–0.0346	0.10	2.98
0.0346–0.0374	0.10	2.78
0.0374–0.0413	0.10	2.54
0.0413	0.10	2.42

$$\sum \frac{X}{d_p} = 34.00 \quad \text{and} \quad D_p = \frac{1}{34.00} = 0.0295 \text{ in.}$$

This sand bed is to be backwashed with 44°F water at a velocity of 0.0413 fps. Estimate the expanded height of the sand bed for this flow.

Solution. Using Eq. (3-25),

$$G_{mf} = 688 \times 0.0295^{1.82} \frac{[62.3 \times (159 - 62.3)]^{0.94}}{(1.3)^{0.88}}$$

$$= 3{,}170 \text{ lb/(hr)(sq ft)}$$

Reynolds number

$$\frac{D_p G_{mf}}{\mu} = \frac{0.0295 \times 3{,}170}{12 \times 1.3 \times 2.42} = 2.48$$

Since $D_p G_{mf}/\mu < 5.0$, no correction of G_{mf} is required. We shall now resort to the method of Richardson and Zaki. A voidage of $\epsilon = 0.45$ is given for the sand. This will probably be close enough to ϵ_{mf} to serve as a starting point.

The exponent n is calculated from Eq. (4-4). Since the cross section of the filter bed is not specified and is probably large in relation to D_p, we shall let $D_p/D_t \to 0$. The fluidization mass velocity

$$G_f = 0.0413 \times 62.3 \times 3,600$$
$$= 9,260 \text{ lb}/(\text{hr})(\text{sq ft})$$

and the corresponding Reynolds number

$$\frac{D_p G_f}{\mu} = \frac{0.0295 \times 9,260}{12 \times 1.3 \times 2.42} = 7.25$$

For this flow n is estimated from Eq. (4-4). Hence with $D_p/D_t = 0$,

$$n = 4.45 \times 7.25^{-0.10} = 3.64$$

Next the expansion line is laid out on logarithmic coordinates. It passes through $\epsilon = 0.45$ and $Re = 2.48$ and has a slope $n = 3.64$. For $Re = 7.25$ the line indicates $\epsilon = 0.60$, and the expanded bed height will be

$$29 \frac{1 - 0.45}{1 - 0.60} = 39.8 \text{ in.}$$

This is in reasonably good agreement with the observed value of 43.5 in.

Example 4-2. A spherical-bead catalyst of $D_p = 0.174$ in. is to be fluidized with water at 70°F in a 6-in.-diameter column. The catalyst has a density of 100 lb per cu ft. The originally unexpanded column height was 28 in. and the voidage associated therewith was $\epsilon = 0.37$. Find the height of the expanded bed when the solids are subject to an upward water rate of 0.408 fps.

Solution. The minimum-fluidization mass velocity is first estimated by Eq. (3-25). Thus

$$G_{mf} = 688 \times 0.174^{1.82} \times \frac{[62.3(100 - 62.3)]^{0.94}}{1.0^{0.88}}$$
$$= 42,200 \text{ lb}/(\text{hr})(\text{sq ft})$$

The Reynolds number

$$\frac{D_p G_{mf}}{\mu} = \frac{0.174 \times 42,200}{12 \times 1.0 \times 2.42} = 253$$

Hence the correction factor from Fig. 3-15 is 0.375, and $G_{mf} = 15,800$ lb/(hr)(sq ft). The method of Richardson and Zaki is now resorted to.

$$\frac{D_p G_{mf}}{\mu} = 253 \times 0.375 = 95$$
$$\frac{D_p G_f}{\mu} = \frac{0.174 \times 0.408 \times 3,600 \times 62.3}{12 \times 1.0 \times 2.42} = 549$$

An expansion line is now laid out on logarithmic coordinates starting at $\epsilon = 0.37$ and $Re = 95$ and with a slope of $n = 2.39$. For $Re = 549$ this line will pass through $\epsilon = 0.775$. Hence expanded-bed height will be

$$28 \frac{1 - 0.37}{1 - 0.775} = 78.4 \text{ in.}$$

Wilhelm and Kwauk have made such a run and found a $G_{mf} = 17{,}000$ lb/(hr)(sq ft) and an expanded height of 80 in. for the flow specified.

Auxiliary Correlations. The idea of presenting liquid-fluidized bed-expansion data by way of a power function of bed voidage was not originally conceived by Richardson and Zaki. Lewis, Gilliland, and Bauer[16] chose to present their water-fluidized glass-bead-bed data in this manner. For a Reynolds-number range extending roughly from 0.1 to 12, $G \propto \epsilon^{4.65}$, for both liquid-fluidized beds and hindered-settling operations. Richardson and Zaki report for this range an average exponent of about 4.2. The values from both investigations appear therefore in reasonably fair agreement.

A correlation along similar lines was more recently suggested by Jottrand,[12] who fluidized fine sands in water. When the logarithm of the superficial fluid velocity was plotted vs. the logarithm of the voidage of the expanded bed, the result was a series of parallel straight lines which, upon extrapolation to $\epsilon = 1.0$, terminated at the free-settling velocity of the particles. According to Jottrand, $G \propto \epsilon^{5.6}$. The data extended over the flow range $0.001 < Re < 0.4$, which was substantially lower than the range investigated by Richardson and Zaki.

Expansion Data of Lewis and Bowerman. Operating with columns of 1.5 and 2.6 in. ID, Lewis and Bowerman[15] fluidized a spherical non-uniformly sized catalyst. The size distribution was as follows:

Mesh	Weight per cent	Mesh	Weight per cent
325	19.9	100–140	25.8
200–325	21.7	80–100	7.2
140–200	22.7	80	2.7

Liquids used were n-heptane, isooctane, and a gasoline blend stock. Fluid viscosity and other physical properties varied sufficiently to be of weight in the evaluation. For the purpose of correlation the authors resorted to expressions for terminal velocity and substituted for u_t an expression of the form

$$\frac{u_f}{\epsilon} = u_t(k'\epsilon^{b'}) \tag{4-7}$$

where k' and b' are specific constants. Equation (4-7) is intended to take into account the effects that particles may exert on each other.

Since these effects should rapidly decrease as interparticle spaces increase, a relation such as the above, including bed voidage, may not seem unreasonable. This procedure and Lewis and Bowerman's experimental results led to the following expressions:

$$\epsilon = 1.39 \left[\frac{u_f \mu}{g_c D_p{}^2 (\rho_S - \rho_F)} \right]^{0.12} \quad \text{Re} < 2.0 \qquad (4\text{-}8)$$

$$\epsilon = 1.95 \left[\frac{u_f \rho_F{}^{0.29} \mu^{0.43}}{g_c{}^{0.71} D_p{}^{1.14} (\rho_S - \rho_F)^{0.71}} \right]^{0.34} \quad 2 < \text{Re} < 500 \qquad (4\text{-}9)$$

$$\epsilon = 0.907 \left[u_f \sqrt{\frac{\rho_F}{g_c D_p (\rho_S - \rho_F)}} \right]^{0.43} \quad \text{Re} > 500 \qquad (4\text{-}10)\star$$

From these correlations it follows that

$$\begin{aligned} u_f &\propto \epsilon^{8.33} & \text{Re} < 2.0 \\ &\propto \epsilon^{2.94} & 2.0 < \text{Re} < 500 \\ &\propto \epsilon^{2.33} & \text{Re} > 500 \end{aligned}$$

A comparison with other data of this kind, notably those of Richardson and Zaki, is given in Fig. 4-6. The agreement is excellent in the turbulent range, good to fair in the transition range, and unsatisfactory in the laminar-flow range. Also indicated in Fig. 4-6 are the data points of Lewis, Gilliland, and Bauer[16] and Jottrand.[12] As already pointed out, the Lewis et al. data agree with the work of Richardson and Zaki fairly well in the low Reynolds-number range. The data of Jottrand are off by an appreciable amount.

The severe deviation between the Lewis and Bowerman work and the exponent of Lewis et al. has been attributed[15] to the effect of size distribution. This explanation is possibly open to question in view of the systematic expansion data that have been observed by Andrieu.[2] Working with a variety of solids fluidized in water and salt solutions, Andrieu

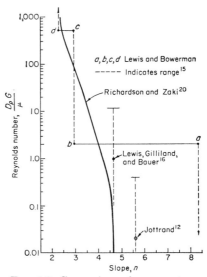

FIG. 4-6. Comparison of exponents on voidage in expanded beds.

composed special sand mixtures, containing two, three, and four size components. The expansion behavior of these beds when fluidized with water is shown in Fig. 4-7. Also shown are data which pertain to a close cut of the same sand, fluidized under identical conditions in the same equipment. All data, including the multicomponent data, fall along straight lines, and the slopes are in quite satisfactory agreement with the slopes reported by Richardson and Zaki for the Reynolds-number range in question.

Correlation of Wilhelm and Kwauk. Details pertaining to the apparatus and materials used by Wilhelm and Kwauk[22] are given in Table 3-2. The data were correlated by evaluating the two dimensionless quantities, already introduced in Chap. 3. Thus,

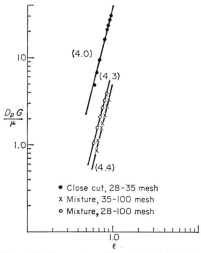

FIG. 4-7. Expansion data of Andrieu[2] observed with sand and water; data in parentheses are slopes.

$$K_{\Delta p} = \frac{D_p{}^3 \rho_F g_c \, \Delta p}{2\mu^2 L_{mf}} \qquad (4\text{-}11)$$

and

$$K_{\Delta \rho} = \frac{D_p{}^3 g_c \rho_F (\rho_S - \rho_F)}{2\mu^2} \qquad (4\text{-}12)$$

For the purpose of solving a problem in liquid-fluidized bed expansion, either $K_{\Delta p}$ or $K_{\Delta \rho}$ is evaluated, together with $D_p G/\mu$ for the particular flow rate. The respective values are brought to intersection in Fig. 3-19, which indicates the expanded-bed voidage. Relating this to the original voidage of the unexpanded bed yields state of bed expansion.

Voidage Functions. From preceding developments it was learned that expansion of liquid-fluidized beds may be described by

$$\frac{u_f}{u_t} = f(\epsilon) \qquad (4\text{-}2a)$$

This relationship was originally proposed by Richardson and Zaki, who expanded it by use of dimensional analysis. The relationship is also readily obtained by a consideration of Eq. (3-23). Thus for spherical particles and extension into the fluidization range, Eq. (3-23) becomes

$$u_f = \frac{0.005 \, g_c (\rho_S - \rho_F) D_p{}^2 \epsilon^3}{\mu (1 - \epsilon)} \qquad (3\text{-}23a)$$

The free-falling velocity of spherical particles for the laminar-flow range is given by Stokes' law, whence

$$u_t = \frac{(\rho_S - \rho_F)g_c D_p{}^2}{18\mu} \qquad (4\text{-}13)\star$$

Hence
$$\frac{u_f}{u_t} = 0.09\,\frac{\epsilon^3}{1-\epsilon} = f(\epsilon) \qquad (4\text{-}2a)$$

It follows that data presentation on the basis of Eq. (4-2a) is comparable with the developments which present bed expansion by means of Eq. (3-23a).

Voidage functions that have been proposed for defining bed expansion in the laminar-flow range are given in Table 4-2. A further comparison

TABLE 4-2. BED-EXPANSION VOIDAGE FUNCTIONS IN LAMINAR FLOW

Investigator	Voidage function
Richardson and Zaki	4.4
Lewis, Gilliland, and Bauer	4.65
Jottrand	5.6
Lewis and Bowerman	8.33
U.S. Bureau of Mines	$\dfrac{\epsilon^3}{1-\epsilon}$

is made in Fig. 4-8, which pertains only to laminar flow. Each function was evaluated at $\epsilon = 0.40$ and related to higher values. The reference state $\epsilon = 0.40$ was chosen because it is relatively close to the voidage of fixed beds before fluidization. For $\epsilon < 0.75$ the expressions of Lewis et al., Richardson and Zaki, and the U.S. Bureau of Mines give roughly equivalent values. For $\epsilon > 0.80$ the function $\epsilon^3/(1-\epsilon)$ will give low expanded heights. This has already been discussed and agrees with the theoretical analysis of Brinkman.[3] The correlation of Jottrand will predict considerably

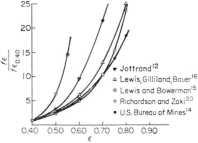

FIG. 4-8. Comparison of voidage functions for the low Reynolds-number range.

greater bed expansions through the entire range. This is even more true for the relation of Lewis and Bowerman.

Stratification. In an expanded bed of freely moving solid particles an upward fluid stream will tend to so arrange the solids in the bed that a greater proportion of fines is found in the upper-bed region than in the lower strata. This action, encountered in both liquid- and gas-fluidized beds, is known as classification or stratification. The phenomenon, known for a long time, has been reported in connection with expansion studies of sand filter beds and similar units.

The first report of stratification in liquid-fluidized beds was made by Verschoor.[21] Although his sand was of the very narrow size range 100 to 120 mesh, the range seemed sufficient to lead to stratification.

A systematic study of stratification was made by Andrieu.[2] For this purpose a column of 7.5 in. ID, carrying pressure-drop connections 201, 349, 501, 645, and 1,406 mm above the liquid distributor, was available. The column was charged with 10 kg of 35- to 48-mesh sand. The non-expanded bed height was 25.5 cm, and the average bed voidage was 48 per cent. Water was admitted at velocities ranging from 0.035 to 2.63 cm per sec. In its highest position the bed had expanded to 129 cm.

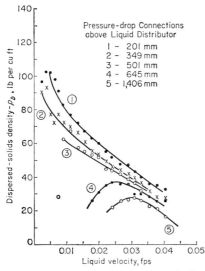

FIG. 4-9. Liquid-solid system bed-expansion data of Andrieu[2] showing density gradients through fluidized column. Curves pertain to pressure-drop taps as indicated.

Considering the second zone, for instance, its apparent bed density is

$$\rho_2 = \frac{\Delta p_2 - \Delta p_1}{(L_e)_2 - (L_e)_1}$$

and the average porosity for this zone

$$\epsilon_2 = 1 - \frac{\rho_2}{\rho_S - \rho_F}$$

Voidages for the other zones were obtained similarly.

Apparent-density data for the individual zones are shown in Fig. 4-9 in relation to water velocity. The data for zones 3 to 5 do not extend to the low fluid velocities because the bed had not yet expanded sufficiently to register a pressure drop. The maximum bed density observed in zones 3 to 5 is due to the gradual rise of the solids into the zone and the subsequent expansion of this portion of the bed. As expected, there is a gradual density decrease as the top of the bed is approached.

Although the bed considered by Andrieu was composed of the rather close cut 35 to 48 mesh, the limiting dimensions of individual pieces were nevertheless between 0.0112 and 0.0076 in. If for the sake of simplicity the particles are considered spherical, particle volumes V and terminal velocities u_t will be as follows:

D_p, in.	$V \times 10^{-6}$, cu in.	u_t, fps
0.0112	0.735	0.114
0.0076	0.230	0.076

Since the over-all expansion behavior of the sand bed followed Eq. (3-23a), the increase in voidage in the upper strata indicates that the values of u_t for the sand contained in those strata are smaller than the u_t for the average diameter. Hence it must follow that the smaller particles have to some extent moved to the top of the column.

From the density variation of the bed along the vertical axis the variation of voidage has been found to be as shown in Table 4-3.

TABLE 4-3. VARIATION OF BED VOIDAGE WITH BED ALTITUDE, DATA OF ANDRIEU

Position	Bed altitude, in. above bed support	Bed voidage
1	8	0.853
2	14	0.865
3	20	0.890
4	26	0.896
5	56	0.920

Summary. Analysis of liquid-solid expansion data has led to the following conclusions:

1. Bed expansion up to a voidage of $\epsilon \approx 0.80$ may be predicted by an equation of the Kozeny-Carman type, provided the liquid flow is laminar as indicated by $D_p G/\mu < 10$. Under these conditions the equation will also apply to hindered settling if the solids are essentially a close cut.

2. The expansion behavior of liquid-solids columns may be predicted through the entire laminar- to turbulent-flow range by the generalized correlation of Richardson and Zaki. Their relationships were found valid for voidages ranging from conventional fixed-bed values of $\epsilon \approx 0.40$ to the limit of expansion, where $\epsilon \rightarrow 1.0$.

Estimation of the expanded height of a liquid-fluidized solids bed involves the following steps:

a. Estimate G_{mf} by Eq. (3-25).

b. Establish the value of ϵ_{mf} from Fig. 2-6 and locate the point (ϵ_{mf}, G_{mf}) on log-log coordinates.

c. The value of $D_p G_{mf}/\mu$ will then be a clue to the correct relationship of Richardson and Zaki to be used.

d. Slope n is evaluated, and a straight line of that slope is drawn through point (ϵ_{mf}, G_{mf}). The expanded-bed voidage may then be readily obtained for any operating mass velocity. This will then yield the expanded-bed height.

3. Liquid-fluidized solids will tend to become stratified. Thus after some time of operation a greater proportion of fines will be found near the top than in the bottom section. Considerable vertical density gradi-

ents were discovered in such beds. Thus for a typical case the voidage was near $\epsilon = 0.85$ in the bottom, whereas in the top it was $\epsilon = 0.92$. Density gradients of this kind are entirely compatible with the observed stratification phenomena.

GAS-SOLID SYSTEMS

By far the greatest number of fluidized installations involve the contacting of solids with gases. This may be for the purpose of achieving physical, chemical, or catalytic changes. Whatever the nature of the individual application may be, certain fundamental questions require attention in all instances. One of these questions, already considered in the preceding chapter, involves prediction of the onset of fluidization. Other questions are concerned with specifying fluid rates for desired bed expansions and performance. The following section will deal primarily with problems of this sort.

Although gas-solid applications are more extensively found in the field than are liquid-solid applications, the mechanics of the gas-solid fluidized state are not as well understood as those of the liquid-solid state. The reason for this is the greater complexity and lesser mechanical stability which are inherent in the gas-solid fluidized state. Thus, whereas with a liquid it is possible to expand a bed of solids quite smoothly almost to a voidage of $\epsilon = 1.0$, that is by no means achieved by using a gaseous fluid. Somewhere along the course of the expansion the gas-solid system will reach a point of mechanical instability which has so far defied every attempt at an exact exploration.

Aggregation. As already observed, the function $(1 - \epsilon)/\epsilon^3$ will describe expansion of liquid-solid systems up to about $\epsilon = 0.80$. The function was based on an assumption of modified channel flow through packed solids. In order for it to apply, two requirements had to be met: (1) The average pore dimension had to be of the order of magnitude of the particles, so that the particles could in essence form the confining channel wall. (2) The bed had to be of a randomized pore texture assuring tortuous flow. Both requirements are met in liquid-solid systems where $\epsilon < 0.80$. For higher voidages, modified channel flow no longer prevails and the flow resistance offered by such a bed tends to approach the resistance which individual particles will offer to the liquid. Since this finite resistance will prevail as $\epsilon \to 1.0$, any correlation postulating that $\Delta p \propto (1 - \epsilon)/\epsilon^3$ will fail to describe conditions correctly in the limiting case.

As for gas-solid dense-phase systems, they will under ordinary circumstances not attain a voidage of $\epsilon > 0.80$ where modified channel flow ceases. Hence in order to examine the applicability of the function

$(1 - \epsilon)/\epsilon^3$ to such systems, only the questions of the randomness of the pore texture and the tortuosity of flow through the interstices need be answered. As has already been learned, gas-solid systems are notorious for possessing a nonhomogeneous and labile pore texture. This is largely due to the formation of aggregates of particles. As pointed out by Carman,[4] the total gross voidage in an aggregated bed of particles is always higher than if the same particles were distributed in a truly randomized pattern in the bed. In order to visualize this, let sketch a of Fig. 4-10 be a column of a given mass of nonaggregated, homogeneously distributed spherical particles of voidage ϵ_i. Sketch b shows another column, containing the same mass of spherical particles; however, for some reason the particles are now aggregated. Let us suppose that the voidage within individual aggregates is still ϵ_i and that the voidage between aggregates is ϵ_b; the total voidage will then be $\epsilon_t = \epsilon_b + \epsilon_i(1 - \epsilon_b)$.

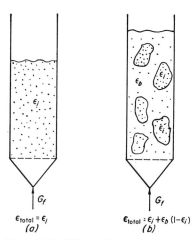

$\epsilon_{total} = \epsilon_i$
(a)

$\epsilon_{total} = \epsilon_i + \epsilon_b(1 - \epsilon_i)$
(b)

FIG. 4-10. Effect of aggregation on total voidage in gas-solid system. Note that, although both columns contain the same mass of the same material and gas rates are identical, the total voidage in the aggregated bed exceeds that in the nonaggregated bed.

The extent of the possible difference between beds a and b may be visualized from some typical data. Thus let us assume that in bed a the solids are distributed at random and that the ideal voidage for a given mass of spherical particles is $\epsilon_i = 0.40$. Column b contains the same mass of solids, but now for some reason the particles are so aggregated that the voidage within the aggregates is still $\epsilon_i = 0.40$ and the interaggregate average voidage is, say, $\epsilon_b = 0.30$. The total gross voidage will then be $\epsilon_t = 0.30 + 0.40(1 - 0.30) = 0.58$. This is significantly larger than the ideal voidage ϵ_i. As a matter of interest it should be pointed out that a bed in which $\epsilon_b \to 0$ is conceivable; for that case, the ideal dispersion would be approached. Obviously such a bed would have only a few interaggregate gas pockets; they could be either homogeneously distributed through the bed or localized.

Qualitative Considerations. If a column of entirely randomized solids, as indicated by sketch a, Fig. 4-10, were to behave ideally as the solids became fluidized, the intraparticle void space would increase by such an amount that, for the then-expanded bed, pressure and weight gradients would remain equal. Moreover, the rate of expansion of the void space would have to be uniform in all regions of the charge, and the bed in its expanded form would be entirely homogeneous. In a sense such a system, traversed by a fluid, would constitute a reservoir of a definite fluid holdup. The amount of holdup would be in accord with the new voidage. Whereas this situation is closely approached with liquid-solid systems, the fluid holdup in gas-solid systems is always in excess of the ideal. This is well known from the formation of gas bubbles in gas-fluidized solids. Although such systems may approach ideal behavior at incipient fluidization, the beds tend to become less homogeneous at elevated flow rates.

Thus the gas bubbles and their paths through granular solids may be considered as constituting the boundary region between solids aggregates.

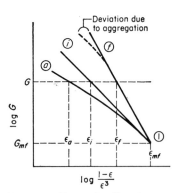

Fig. 4-11. Expansion lines in gas-solid systems.

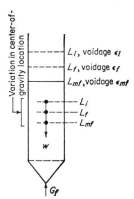

Fig. 4-12. Fluidized column.

The gross voidage of such a bed is in excess of the ideal conceived. It will be instructive to investigate how this condition will manifest itself when, as shown in Fig. 4-11, the logarithm of the mass velocity pertaining to such a bed is plotted vs. the logarithm of the voidage function $(1 - \epsilon)/\epsilon^3$. The point defined by the coordinates G_{mf} and $(1 - \epsilon_{mf})/\epsilon_{mf}^3$ may be predicted by a suitable correlation for minimum fluidization such as Eq. (3-23). Proceeding to higher flow rates, the relation should initially be such that the slope $m = -1.0$. However, if because of aggregation the rate of voidage increase will be greater than would occur in the ideal bed, a curve for which the slope range is $0 > m > -1.0$ should result. Above the curve 1-a there is the line of ideal behavior 1-i of $m = -1.0$.

No mention has so far been made of particle motion. Let Fig. 4-12 be a bed of solids fluidized by a gas at a mass velocity G_f. A consideration of the total energy given up by the gas, as it passes through the solids bed, is as follows:

$$\Delta E_{gas} = \Delta Z + \Delta F_{gs} + \Delta F_{ss} + \Delta KE$$

where ΔZ = potential-energy increase of solids due to bed expansion

ΔF_{gs} = energy required to overcome friction of gas on all solids surfaces

ΔF_{ss} = energy demanded to sustain solids motion inside bed

ΔKE = variation in kinetic energy of gas that may occur because of path restrictions or enlargements

All these energy terms must add up to the energy lost by the gas, which is $\Delta E_{gas} = G_f S \, \Delta p / \rho_F$.

Let us assume now that the bed will behave ideally. Under the influence of the flow rate G_f, it will expand from an original voidage of ϵ_{mf} to ϵ_i. This path of ideal expansion is indicated in Fig. 4-11 by line 1-i. In accordance with ideal behavior the particles must be assumed immobile, hence there are no collisions. This will then eliminate the term ΔF_{ss} in the above energy balance. Since in the ideal case the bed is also entirely homogeneous as far as voidage is concerned, there is no kinetic-energy variation due to flow-path restrictions or enlargements. Hence only ΔZ and ΔF_{gs} remain. The latter is primarily a function of the sum of all surface areas in the bed. Since the mass of the bed and its state of subdivision into individual particles will remain unchanged throughout, ΔF_{gs} will be considered constant. Moreover, because the term represents the friction between a solid and a gas at low velocities, it may be considered negligible. There results then for the ideal expansion

$$\Delta E_{gas} = \Delta Z = \Delta Z_i$$

If the weight of the bed is w, it is readily seen that ΔZ_i becomes proportional to the bed expansion, $L_i - L_{mf}$.

Considering now an expansion under actual operating conditions where aggregation and internal collisions prevail, experiments have shown that, for the same solids mass, the bed will expand only to a height L_f. Hence ΔZ will be smaller than ΔZ_i by a definite amount. Before one can interpret the difference between the two terms, it is necessary to find out if the energy lost by the gas in the ideal expansion is the same as that lost in the nonideal expansion. Barring any extraneous effects such as slugging or bed lifting, the evidence shows that the pressure drop associated with fluidization under low gas mass velocities is independent of solids aggregation. Hence the energy lost by the gas while passing through the now-aggregated bed is the same as that given up during passage through the ideally behaving bed. The difference between ΔZ and ΔZ_i must therefore be found elsewhere. From the first of the above energy balances it follows that the term ΔF_{ss}, representing particle-to-particle friction, must now become important. Moreover, since the bed is now no longer homogeneous throughout, the term ΔKE, representing the kinetic-energy variation of the gas while passing through the bed, can no longer be equal to zero.

Summing up the analysis, it appears that the energy required for moving the particles must have been provided at the expense of the potential energy of the bed. Hence the nonideal bed, in which the particles are endowed with motion, must be of lesser voidage than the ideally behaving bed. This is indicated by voidage ϵ_f in Fig. 4-11, and the course of the expansion of the entire nonideal bed is given by the course of line 1-f. As far as the ideal bed 1-i is concerned, the conditions under which it exists are highly labile and transformation to the more common situation as represented by line 1-f is in agreement with the second law of thermodynamics.

Experimental Data. Considerable gas-solid expansion data have been reported in the literature.[5,7,8,11,12 14,16−19,22] Only a few typical values are shown in Fig. 4-13. For the largest particles, expansion curves are similar to curve 1-a of Fig. 4-11, for which slope $m > -1.0$. As particle size decreases, the slopes become more negative, and for the smallest diameters the expansion data proceed almost vertically. At this point it is well to recall that neither curve 1-a nor 1-f represents ideal conditions. The deviation of 1-a from the ideal curve is due to aggregation, whereas the deviation of 1-f is due to particle motion. Since the two phenomena are graphically shown on opposite sides of the ideal curve, a particle-size range for which the effects of aggregation will essentially cancel the effects of particle motion should be anticipated. For this range, which happens to be near 0.015 to 0.018 in., the slope m of the expansion curve is indeed close to -1.0. It must, however, be understood that this by no means indicates an ideal expansion behavior of this particle size of solids.

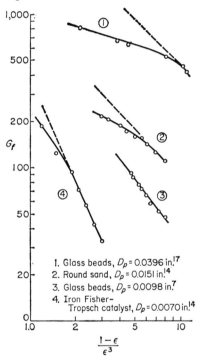

1. Glass beads, $D_p = 0.0396$ in.[7]
2. Round sand, $D_p = 0.0151$ in.[4]
3. Glass beads, $D_p = 0.0098$ in.[7]
4. Iron Fisher-Tropsch catalyst, $D_p = 0.0070$ in.[4]

FIG. 4-13. Typical gas-solid expansion data. Aggregation sets in where data begin to deviate from dashed lines.

Closer examination of Fig. 4-13 reveals that the effects of aggregation are felt in every instance, to a greater or lesser degree. This is indicated by the fact that the data in the higher flow regions will actually align *along curves, rather than along straight lines.* In the immediate vicinity of G_{mf} the data tend to correlate along a straight line, indicating little or no aggregation. At elevated flow rates, slopes m become in all instances less negative, which indicates that aggregation becomes more prevalent at the higher flow rates. It is instructive to observe that small-particle beds may be expanded over substantially wider flow ranges than large-particle beds before aggregation sets in. This is indicated by the fact that, with small particles, departure from the straight line occurs at higher values of the reduced mass velocity than with large particles.

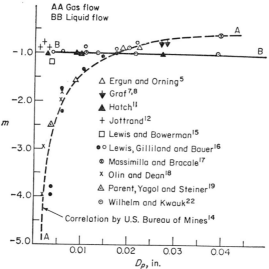

Fig. 4-14. Slope values from gas- and liquid-fluidized data in relation to particle diameter.

As far as practical methods of correlation are concerned the data may in most cases be satisfactorily presented by straight lines. This yields the relationship between slopes and particle size indicated in Fig. 4-14. The correlation is based on virtually all of the available bed-expansion-literature data.

Fluidization Efficiency. From the preceding discussion it has been learned that the slope of the line that relates $\log G_f$ with $\log (1 - \epsilon)/\epsilon^3$, for a given bed expansion, is dependent on (1) the particle diameter and (2) the state of bed aggregation. For low values of reduced mass velocity—that is, near the point of incipient fluidization—bed aggregation is relatively unimportant, and the slope of the line is then predominantly influenced by particle diameter and the prevailing particle-motion–energy relationship in the bed. Considering therefore an expanded bed of low values of G_f/G_{mf}, as indicated in Fig. 4-15, line mf-e is termed the expansion line and mf-f the fluidization line of the solid. For a definite state of bed expansion, as indicated by voidage ϵ_f, the energy for fluidization

(which constitutes bed expansion *and* particle movement) is given by
$W_f = G_f S \, \Delta p / \rho_F$, and similarly for mere bed expansion, $W_e = G_e S \, \Delta p / \rho_F$.

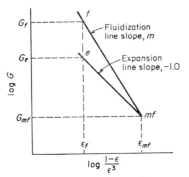

The energy required for particle movement is then

$$W_f - W_e = \frac{S \, \Delta p}{\rho_F} (G_f - G_e)$$

and the fraction of the energy, in terms of total energy expended, that is useful for particle motion is given by

$$\eta = \frac{W_f - W_e}{W_f} = \frac{G_f - G_e}{G_f} \quad (4\text{-}14)\star$$

FIG. 4-15. Fluidization and expansion lines for gas fluidization; method is applicable to particles of $D_p <$ 0.015 in.

This is the definition of fluidization efficiency.

Estimation of Fluidization Efficiency. The usefulness of fluidization efficiency has so far been demonstrated by a consideration of bed-wall heat-transfer phenomena, as well as particle velocities along the confining wall of a bed.[13] Heat transfer is discussed in detail in Chap. 8. As far as establishing the link between fluidization efficiency and vertical particle velocities is concerned, results are so far available only for small-diameter vessels carrying sands and silica gel particles. The solids were fluidized by moderate air velocities; small portions of dyed solids of the same kind were then rapidly placed on top of the fluidizing columns, and their travel time to the base of the bed was noted. With the bed of weight w being fluidized by a gas mass velocity G_f, the following equality may be written:

$$G_f \frac{S \, \Delta p \eta}{\rho_F} = \beta u_p w \quad (4\text{-}15)$$

where u_p = average particle velocity, observed along wall of vessel
β = interparticle friction factor, characteristic of properties of material fluidized

Since $S \, \Delta p \approx w$ and $u_p = L_{mf} R / \theta$, there results

$$\frac{G_f \eta}{\rho_F} = \beta \frac{L_{mf} R}{\theta} = u_f \eta \quad (4\text{-}16)$$

The interparticle friction factor β is readily evaluated from experimental data if η can be estimated from expansion data. This may generally be accomplished with sufficient accuracy for particles of $D_p < 0.012$ in. With β known for a particular material, values of η may then be calculated for sizes for which the graphical procedure based on the data of Fig. 4-14 would become too inaccurate.

A generalized correlation of fluidization efficiency in terms of reduced mass velocity is given in Fig. 4-16. The solidly drawn curves extend over the experimentally verified range of conditions. The dotted extrapolations are primarily based on heat-transfer observations.

Bed Expansion. In order to specify reactor height, one must understand the expansion characteristics of the fluidized charge. At very low reduced mass velocities the top of gas-fluidized beds will remain almost motionless. At higher reduced mass velocities, however, the top of the charge may fluctuate considerably. Hence for a reliable prediction of reactor height one must first estimate the anticipated bed expansion and then account separately for possible fluctuation of the top. In most cases

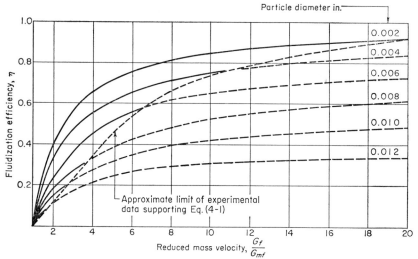

FIG. 4-16. Fluidization efficiency vs. reduced mass velocity.

additional reactor shell must then also be provided to minimize losses due to elutriation. This last consideration will be discussed in detail in Chap. 5.

Gas-fluidized Beds. The key to prediction of expanded-bed height of gas-fluidized solids is provided by Figs. 4-14 and 4-15. With D_p known, m may be evaluated from Fig. 4-14. With ϵ_{mf} known from Fig. 2-6, G_{mf} is evaluated next and the fluidization line is drawn on logarithmic coordinates. The line will provide the expansion of the charge at any desired mass velocity.

Bed-expansion calculations in gas-fluidized systems are further simplified by Figs. 4-16 and 4-17. Thus in order to arrive at bed expansion, one may proceed as follows:

1. Calculate G_{mf}, either by Eq. (3-25) or nomograph 3-15a.
2. Calculate the reduced mass velocity G_f/G_{mf}.

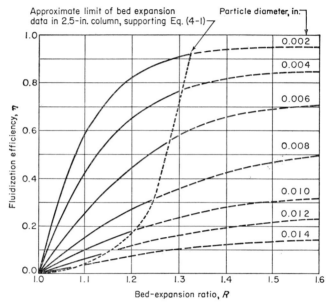

FIG. 4-17. Fluidization efficiency vs. expansion ratio.

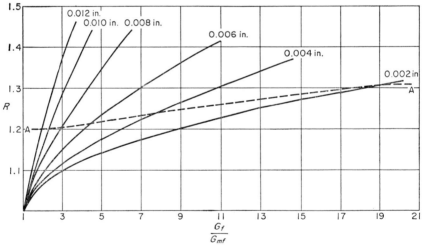

FIG. 4-18. Expansion ratio in relation to reduced mass velocity, generalized correlation. The parameter is the particle diameter. Dashed line AA represents recommended expansion limits for close cuts.

3. Figure 4-16 will then yield the fluidization efficiency and this is used in Fig. 4-17 for evaluating the bed-expansion ratio R.

Another chart, Fig. 4-18, relates reduced mass velocity directly with bed-expansion ratio. It may be used whenever the fluidization efficiency is not desired.

Limits of Gas-fluidized Bed Expansion. As already pointed out, the expansion line is in reality a curve beyond a certain value of mass velocity. It has generally been observed that slugging and generally poor fluidization performance set in beyond the point of linearity of the data. For this reason it is important to know the upper limit of linearity. A correlation of this effect is given in Fig. 4-19, which relates values of the limiting reduced mass velocities, beyond which the fluidization line is

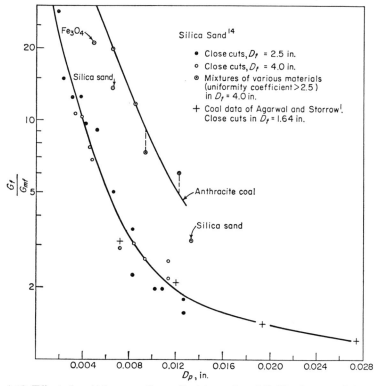

FIG. 4-19. Effect of particle properties on limiting value of G_f/G_{mf} for gas-solid systems.

curved, with particle diameter. The data pertain to sands, iron oxide, and anthracite coal. As would be expected, limiting G_f/G_{mf} values increase as particle size decreases. A tube-diameter increase from 2.5 to 4.0 in. appears to have little effect. However, size distribution is very important. A few data for anthracite coals and silica sands, which were composed of several size components, have become available. The size distribution for these solids is merely indicated by the value of the uniformity coefficient. By definition the uniformity coefficient $c_u = d_{60}/d_{10}$, where d_{60} and d_{10} are the sieve openings that allow passage of 60 and 10 per cent, respectively, of a typical sample. The mixtures referred to in Fig. 4-19 had a value of $c_u > 2.5$, and for these the limiting values of G_f/G_{mf} are substantially higher than for close cuts of comparable particle size. The higher limiting reduced mass velocities observed with mixtures are of course in accord with lesser tendencies of these solids to slug and form aggregated beds. Thus the finding is entirely in line with the generally better fluidization performance obtained with mixed-size solids. Figure 4-19 includes also the data which Agarwal and Storrow[1] reported for close cuts of coal, data referred to in Chap. 2. Static-bed height for all data shown varied from 10 in. to about 2.5 ft.

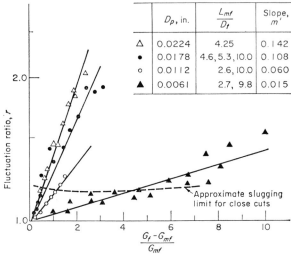

	D_p, in.	$\frac{L_{mf}}{D_f}$	Slope, m'
△	0.0224	4.25	0.142
●	0.0178	4.6, 5.3, 10.0	0.108
○	0.0112	2.6, 10.0	0.060
▲	0.0061	2.7, 9.8	0.015

FIG. 4-20. Data of Lewis, Gilliland, and Bauer[16] showing fluctuation ratio for uniform glass beads in relation to $(G_f - G_{mf})/G_{mf}$.

Fluctuation Ratio. Under conditions of high gas flow, the top of a fluidized charge may fluctuate considerably. The extent of the fluctuations and their estimation may become important when a fluidized-reactor height must be specified. Quantitatively the fluctuations may be defined by the ratio of the highest and lowest levels which the top occupies for any particular gas flow rate. This concept has been termed the fluctuation ratio of the system.

Fluctuation ratios evaluated from literature data have been correlated with the ratio $(G_f - G_{mf})/G_{mf}$. The data of Fig. 4-20 indicate that the particle diameter is the chief variable. It is surprising to find that no coordinated effect of the bed height to column diameter ratio is indicated. The data are tentatively correlated by

$$r = e^{m'(G_f - G_{mf})/G_{mf}} \qquad (4\text{-}17)$$

The slope m' is related to particle diameter, as shown in Fig. 4-21, which includes some data of Wilhelm and Kwauk[22] as well as data of

Massimilla and Bracale.[17]   For mixed sizes the slopes tend to be lower than for narrow cuts.   This indicates less fluctuation of the top of the bed and hence smoother fluidization.

In a sense the fluctuation ratio is a manifestation of the labile character of the gas-fluidized aggregative bed.   Thus with the bed level at a high position one may assume a large gas holdup between the solids aggregates.   The sudden collapse of the level indicates that a portion of the interaggregate holdup has been released, and a new holdup formation cycle begins.   It is tacitly assumed that, during all these level changes, the voidage within the solids aggregates remains essentially constant.   This does not necessarily have to be so, however, and voidage readjustments within the aggregates may occur simultaneously with the interaggregate voidage variations.

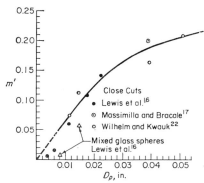

FIG. 4-21. Slope m' in relation to D_p, for evaluation of fluctuation ratio.

Beyond certain limiting values of $(G_f - G_{mf})/G_{mf}$ the top oscillations are also caused by slugging.   The approximate locus of the slugging boundary, as determined from Fig. 4-19, has been indicated in Fig. 4-20. The fluctuation ratios pertaining to the slugging zone follow smoothly from the nonslugging range.   In view of the general continuity of phenomena, this is not unexpected.   It is, however, surprising that the fluctuation ratios should be independent of the aspect ratio of the fluidized bed.   Since slugging is known to be affected by this ratio of dimensions, additional confirmation would appear desirable.

Baffled Gas-fluidized Beds.   A systematic investigation of the effect of baffles on the expansion behavior of gas-fluidized systems was reported by Massimilla and Bracale.[17]   The fluidized chamber was of 90 mm ID, and glass spheres ranging from 0.7 to 3 mm were fluidized.   The baffles consisted of disks of wire mesh mounted in series vertically on a central shaft and inserted into the beds.

Comparison with unbaffled beds of the same materials indicated (1) the considerably greater flow range to which the baffled system could be subjected and (2) an appreciable improvement in fluidization performance, strikingly reflected by a significant lowering of the fluctuation ratio.

Fluctuation ratios of the solids investigated in both baffled and non-baffled beds are shown in Fig. 4-22 in relation to the reduced mass velocity.   With the beds composed of relatively large particles and operating at appreciable reduced mass velocities, substantial fluctuation ratios prevail in the unbaffled state. With baffling, on the other hand, fluctuations have been almost entirely eliminated, reflecting—as reported by the authors—a considerable improvement in fluidization.

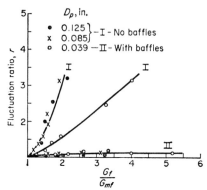

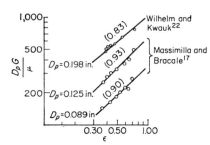

FIG. 4-22. Effect of baffling on fluctuation ratio. (*Data of Massimilla and Bracale.*[17])

FIG. 4-23. Aggregative-fluidization data of Massimilla and Bracale[17] compared with aggregative-fluidization data of Wilhelm and Kwauk.[22] All data pertain to gas-solid systems.

This improvement of fluidization performance is also apparent when the expansion data of Massimilla and Bracale are presented in the already familiar way, as suggested by Richardson and Zaki. It is well to recall that their method was developed solely from liquid-fluidized systems.

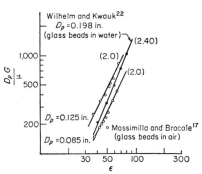

FIG. 4-24. Baffled (aggregative) gas-solid data of Massimilla and Bracale[17] compared with unbaffled (particulate) liquid-solid data of Wilhelm and Kwauk.[22] Slope values are indicated in parentheses.

If their method of plotting is applied to the present unbaffled gas-fluidization data of Massimilla and Bracale, considerably smaller slopes are obtained than would result if the same material were fluidized in a liquid. This is indicated in Fig. 4-23. Also shown for comparison are typical aggregative gas-fluidization data of Wilhelm and Kwauk. Since particle sizes are of the same order of magnitude, the fair agreement of the slopes suggests that this may be a method for describing the aggregative behavior of gas-fluidized systems quantitatively. Let us now consider the expansion behavior of the solids of Massimilla and Bracale, but baffled this time, and compare it with the expansion behavior of the same-size glass beads of Wilhelm and Kwauk, but now water-fluidized, as indicated in Fig. 4-24. Considering first the data of Wilhelm and

Kwauk, the slope has increased to 2.40, in agreement with the value predicted by the correlation of Richardson and Zaki.[20] For this condition Wilhelm and Kwauk report typical particulate fluidization. Examining now the slopes of the baffled gas-fluidized bed data, their values have also increased from about 0.92 to 2.0. This would certainly suggest that the baffles tend to induce particulate fluidization.

Segregation during Fluidization. From a consideration of liquid-fluidized solids it has already been learned that, during bed expansion, size segregation will occur in nonuniform beds. An investigation by Fleming,[6] as well as various other data,[9] indicates that size segregation is

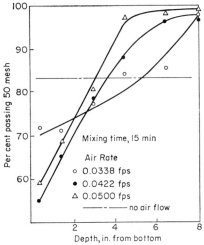 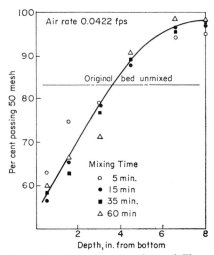

FIG. 4-25. Desegregation data of Fleming[6] in relation to fluid rate; the original bed composition is indicated by the broken line.

FIG. 4-26. Desegregation data of Fleming[6] showing effect of mixing time.

also encountered in gas-fluidized systems if the solids are not of uniform size or density.

Fleming worked with a 9.5-in.-diameter glass vessel. Air entered through a perforated pad in the base, and provision was made to collect samples from various positions above the bottom of the bed. As a charge, 10.8 lb of soda ash of 66 microns average diameter was mixed with 2.2 lb of tripolyphosphate of +50 mesh. Solids densities were, for both materials, close to 158 lb per cu ft. Typical observed results are given in Figs. 4-25 and 4-26. Figure 4-25 relates the percentage of solids through a 50-mesh screen to the position in the charge. The data are for a running time of 15 min and three air velocities. Whereas at the lowest air velocity of 0.0338 fps little had occurred, segregation became quite appreciable at 0.0422 fps and even more significant at the highest rate of 0.050 fps. A possible reason for the small effect observed at the low air flow may be that the bed was still too close to incipient fluidization.

In Fig. 4-26 the percentage of solids through a 50-mesh screen is again related to bed height, but this time for the constant air velocity 0.0422 fps, with time of aeration being the variable. For a bed depth of about 4 in. from the bottom an increase in aeration time from 5 to 60 min had apparently no effect on segregation. This would then indicate that the entire observed size segregation for the bottom part of the bed is accomplished in less than 5 min. For the top section an increase in aeration time from 5 to 60 min tends to further segregation.

The mechanism by which segregation takes place lends itself readily to observation. The originally homogeneous bed will first fluidize in such a way that virtually the entire charge participates. Soon thereafter small channels appear, and an upward movement of solids through them is observed. The particles moving upward are a portion of the fines, and the segregation process has started. As it proceeds, the bottom portion of the bed may become sufficiently depleted of fines to cause fluidization there to cease. The bottom part will now collapse somewhat and will merely serve as a fluid distributor to the upper, now highly segregated layer, which in most cases will fluidize briskly. Once the bottom portion has ceased to fluidize, it may still contain a substantial percentage of fines; however, these will now be conveyed upward only at a very slow rate. For all practical purposes the segregation process has now ceased.

Segregation will of course also occur in beds where there are differences in density instead of differences in size. Qualitative observations have been made for such a system.[14] The mixed bed consisted of sand and magnetite particles, and the density variation was almost twofold. With such a bed it was difficult, if not impossible, to define a minimum-fluidization mass velocity. For any mass velocity for which the entire bed seemed initially fluidized it was almost impossible to prevent segregation. When the mixed beds were operated at low mass velocities, segregation was markedly promoted by outside vibrations. The segregation process with mixed-density solids is similar, as already described for beds composed of mixed sizes.

Effect of Baffles. Effects of baffles on segregation have been observed by Hall and Crumley.[9] The data are of value because they describe some pertinent problems that are frequently met in pilot-plant studies; they are also of special interest to the present discussion because they emphasize some rather unexpected results observed in baffled beds. Whereas baffles are frequently employed to facilitate fluidization of a bed that may ordinarily not be fluidized, it is well to remember that baffles may hinder certain solids mixing patterns in a bed. This action can become so pronounced that segregation may actually be induced.

Hall and Crumley worked with a 1-in.-diameter reactor which carried a bed of Fischer-Tropsch iron catalyst to a depth of 5 ft. In the course of their studies they found that the fluidization and expansion characteristics of the slender column were greatly improved by the use of internal baffles. Thus by the use of the baffles the tall column was apparently broken up into a great number of small sections, each of which seemed to fluidize quite satisfactorily. Although fluidization was thus greatly promoted, the baffled bed was then segregated, as shown in Table 4-4.

TABLE 4-4. DATA OF HALL AND CRUMLEY OBSERVED WITH A FRESH FISCHER-TROPSCH IRON CATALYST IN A DEEP BAFFLED BED

Size, British standard sieves	Distribution of particles, %, at following bed levels				
	Bottom to 12 in.	12 to 24 in.	24 to 36 in.	36 in. to top	Avg of whole bed
170	100	99.3	94.8	74.1	92.1
170–240	...	0.4	2.6	4.5	1.8
240	...	0.3	2.6	21.5	6.1

The segregation data of Table 4-4 are of the same character as those reported by Fleming for a shallow nonbaffled bed. The segregation effect of the baffles was pursued further, and for this purpose Hall and Crumley employed a used Fischer-Tropsch iron catalyst that was carbon-containing. The effect of baffle characteristics on such a catalyst is shown in Table 4-5.

TABLE 4-5. EFFECT OF BAFFLES ON BED DENSITY IN A FISCHER-TROPSCH PILOT REACTOR

Type of baffle...............	None	10-mesh steel gauze			Brass strip cross piece
Distance apart, in.............	....	6	4	2	2

Bulk density of catalyst, lb per cu ft

Top of bed...................	54.8	53.5	47.2	41.6	57.2
Center of bed...............	56.6	56.6	56.0	52.2	59.7
Bottom of bed...............	55.4	66.5	61.0	76.0	63.4
Max difference.............	1.8	13.0	13.8	35.4	6.2

As expected, the least-dense section is near the top. The steel-gauze data indicate that baffles can indeed impede internal solids mixing and thereby be effective promoters of segregation.

Qualitatively speaking, the data are in agreement with the observations made by Andrieu[2] in liquid-fluidized columns. It will be recalled that Andrieu also reported density and size segregations.

Example 4-3. A jagged silica sand is poured into a 4-in.-diameter cylindrical vessel, and air is admitted into the bottom through a porous plate. Data are as follows:

Sand:

   Weight: 20 lb
   Specific gravity: 2.65
   Size: 100–150 mesh
Air:
   Temperature: 70°F
   Outlet pressure: 14.7 psia
   Flow rate: 40 cu ft per hr

For the above data and conditions determine:

1. Whether fluidization will occur. If it will occur, estimate (a) the expanded bed height, (b) the fluctuation ratio, and (c) the fluidization efficiency.

2. The upper limiting mass velocity under which the bed will be operated essentially free of slugging.

Solution

1. The nomograph of Fig. 3-15a will be used for evaluating G_{mf}.

$$(\rho_S - \rho_F)\rho_F = (165 - 0.0750)0.075 = 12.4$$
$$\mu = 0.018 \text{ centipoise}$$
$$D_p = \sqrt{0.0041 \times 0.0058} = 0.00488 \text{ in.}$$
and
$$G_{mf} = 15 \text{ lb/(hr)(sq ft)}$$
$$G_f = \frac{40 \times 0.075}{0.0872} = 34.4 \text{ lb/(hr)(sq ft)}$$

Since $G_f > G_{mf}$, the charge will fluidize.

To estimate the expanded height of the bed, we shall use generalized correlation Figs. 4-16 and 4-17.

$$\frac{G_f}{G_{mf}} = \frac{34.4}{15} = 2.30$$

From Fig. 4-16, $\eta = 0.34$, and from Fig. 4-17, $R = 1.10$.

Next a bed voidage will have to be found. For a jagged sand of $D_p = 0.00488$ in., $\epsilon_{mf} \approx 0.55$ and the static bed height is

$$L = \frac{20}{2.65 \times 62.3 \times 0.45 \times 0.0872} = 3.08 \text{ ft}$$

The expanded-bed height will then be $1.10 \times 3.08 = 3.39$ ft.

The fluctuation ratio is now found by first evaluating the slope m' from Fig. 4-21. For $D_p = 0.00488$, $m' = 0.03$, and

$$r = e^{0.03(2.30-1.0)} \approx 1.04$$

Hence the top of the bed should be almost without fluctuation.

2. The upper limiting mass velocity as found from Fig. 4-19 is $G_f/G_{mf} = 8.0$. For this value the fluctuation ratio becomes 1.24, significantly higher than for the above lower operating mass velocity.

Summary. Gas-fluidized solids have a tendency toward aggregation, which is another way of saying that gas-fluidized solids beds are not homogeneous. It could be shown that, in a bed in which aggregation prevails, the over-all voidage is higher than in a nonaggregated, or homogeneous, bed. Aggregation is one reason why the expansion behavior of a gas-fluidized column does not follow an ideal path. Another reason for deviation from ideal behavior is found in the motion of the particles in the bed. The characteristics of actual gas-solid expansion data could be interpreted by these two deviations from the ideal case.

The expansion behavior of gas-solid beds is described, and methods for estimating expanded-bed height are outlined. Briefly stated, the method first requires estimation of G_{mf} for the particular particle size. Dividing this into the operating gas mass velocity yields the reduced mass velocity, which may be used directly to obtain the bed-expansion ratio by means of design charts. Of course these charts are applicable only to gas-solid systems and only up to a certain limiting value of the reduced mass velocity; beyond this limiting value, aggregation effects become so severe in the beds that the design charts would predict short columns. Hence a correlation which permits estimation of the limiting reduced mass velocity in terms of particle diameter is proposed.

A new concept, the so-called "fluctuation ratio," is introduced. It is a number which describes the extent of oscillation to which the upper boundary of a gas-fluidized system may be subjected.

The effect of baffles on fluidization character is discussed. The available data indicate that insertion of baffles modifies the expansion behavior of gas-fluidized columns severely. A comparison of baffled gas-solid beds with nonbaffled liquid-solid beds suggests that insertion of baffles in the aggregatively fluidizing column tends to promote particulate-fluidization behavior.

Gas-fluidized systems will have a tendency toward size segregation in the bed in very much the same sense as was observed with liquid-fluidized columns. Typical segregation data are presented for a case without baffles, as well as for instances in which baffles were employed. Whereas baffles have generally been found effective for promoting fluidizability of a powder, they have also been recognized as favoring segregation in a bed.

PROBLEMS

4-1. A fluidized-bed catalytic reactor of 24 in. ID operates under a space velocity of 300 volumes of fresh gas per volume of catalyst per hour, measured on inlet conditions. The dumped catalyst volume in the non-fluidized state is 3.0 cu ft. The catalyst is nonvesicular, and its specific gravity is 5.00. Independent pressure-drop tests with the catalyst yielded $\phi_s = 0.62$. Data pertaining to the fluid as it passes through the reactor are as follows:

Parameter	Inlet	Exit
Density, lb per cu ft..............	0.963	1.144
Viscosity, lb/(hr)(ft)..............	0.062	0.067

For these conditions:

1. Find the maximum particle diameter $D_{p_{max}}$, that may just be fluidized

2. Employing a $D_p = 0.40 D_{p_{max}}$, specify the required height of the reactor shell.

NOTE: Assume that the gas contraction rate is linear with reactor bed height.

4-2. A coal washer is composed of a conical lower section with an angle of 60° at the apex and an upper cylindrical section, 8 ft high. The shell diameter is 2 ft. The coal to be washed has a water density of 69.5 lb per cu ft and conforms to the following size distribution:

Mesh	Weight fraction	Mesh	Weight fraction
4–6	0.18	8–10	0.32
6–8	0.38	10–14	0.12

The washer contains 325 lb of coal, and water at 60°F is admitted through a 1½-in. standard pipe in the apex of the cone. The wash water leaves the unit from the top, overspilling from a spout into a gutter. Establish the maximum water rate at which the unit may be operated without loss of coal.

4-3. A nonvesicular bead catalyst of 98.3 lb per cu ft density is water-fluidized in a column of 48 in. height. Provision has been made to measure the pressure drop for four consecutive shell sections. The lowest pressure-drop tap is placed slightly above the fluid inlet, and the remaining four taps follow in 12-in. intervals. For a given flow, pressure drops between the base and the various positions are as tabulated.

Position	Δp, mm H_2O	Position	Δp, mm H_2O
1	64.0	3	156.0
2	112.0	4	187.0

With these data on hand, establish the voidage gradient through the bed.

4-4. Sharp silica sand weighing 2.5 lb is poured into a 2-in.-diameter column which is fitted in its lower end with a porous plate. While the sand is fluidized with air, 0.25 lb of sodium chloride crystals is added to the top of the column. If the air mass velocity is equal to 40 lb/(hr)(sq ft), estimate the time required for the first salt crystals to reach the bottom of the bed. Data are as follows:

Sand:

    $D_p = 0.00488$ in.

    $\rho_S = 155$ lb per cu ft

    $\epsilon_{mf} = 0.55$

Air:

    $\rho_F = 0.075$ lb per cu ft

    $\mu = 0.018$ centipoise

The particle size of the salt is close to that of the sand. Fluidization characteristics may also be assumed to be similar.

4-5. Extensive data pertaining to liquid-fluidized columns were obtained by Wilhelm and Kwauk.[22] A typical set of operating data was as follows:

Bed diameter: D_t = 2.97 in.   Solids density: ρ_S = 164 lb per cu ft
Bed height: L = 4.21 in.   Fluid density: ρ_F = 62.3 lb per cu ft
Bed voidage: ϵ = 40.7 per cent   Fluid viscosity: μ = 1.0 centipoise
Particle diameter: D_p = 0.0147 in.

The column began to expand when the fluid velocity was 0.00474 fps, and for a fluid velocity of 0.104 fps a voidage of 86 per cent was reported, corresponding to an expanded-bed height of 17.7 in. Examine how this bed expansion compares with values that would be predicted by:

1. An equation of the Kozeny-Carman-type; for instance, Eq. (4-1)
2. The expansion function of Brinkman
3. The proper correlation of Lewis and Bowerman
4. The correlation of Richardson and Zaki
5. The correlation of Wilhelm and Kwauk

REFERENCES

1. Agarwal, A. P., and J. Anderson Storrow: *Chem. & Ind. (London),* 278–286 (1951).
2. Andrieu, R.: Ph.D. thesis, University of Nancy, France, 1956.
3. Brinkman, H. C.: *Appl. Sci. Research,* **A1**: 27 (1947).
4. Carman, P. C.: "Flow of Gases through Porous Media," Academic Press, Inc., New York, 1956.
5. Ergun, S., and A. A. Orning: *Ind. Eng. Chem.,* **41**: 1179–1184 (1949).
6. Fleming, R. J.: M.S. thesis, Stevens Institute of Technology, 1950.
7. Graf, Ernst: Ph.D. thesis, Eidgenössische Technische Hochschule, Zürich, 1955.
8. Graf, E., A. Guyer, Jr., and A. Guyer: *Helv. Chim. Acta,* **38**: 473–484 (1955).
9. Hall, C. C., and P. Crumley: *J. Appl. Chem. (London),* **2**, Suppl. Issue 1, S47–S55 (1952)
10. Happel, J., and N. Epstein: *Ind. Eng. Chem.,* **46**: 1187–1194 (1954).
11. Hatch, L. P.: *Trans. Am. Geophys. Union,* **24**: 537–547 (1943).
12. Jottrand, R.: *J. Appl. Chem. (London),* **2**, Suppl. Issue 1, S17–S26 (1952).
12a. Johnson, E.: *Inst. Gas Engrs. (London), Rept.* 1949–1950, *Publ. No.* 378/179.
13. Leva, Max, and M. Grummer: *Chem. Eng. Progr.,* **48**: 307–313 (1952).
14. Leva, Max, M. Weintraub, M. Grummer, M. Pollchik, and H. H. Storch: U.S. *Bur. Mines Bull.* 504, 1951.
15. Lewis, E. W., and Ernest W. Bowerman: *Chem. Eng. Progr.,* **48**: 603–610 (1952).
16. Lewis, W. K., E. R. Gilliland, and W. C. Bauer: *Ind. Eng. Chem.,* **41**: 1104–1117 (1949).
17. Massimilla, L., and S. Bracale: *Ricerca sci.,* **26**: 487 (1956).
18. Olin, H. L., and O. C. Dean: *Petrol. Engr.,* **25**(3): C23–C32 (1953).
19. Parent, J. D., N. Yagol, and C. S. Steiner: *Chem. Eng. Progr.,* **43**: 429–436 (1947).
20. Richardson, J. F., and W. N. Zaki: *Trans. Inst. Chem. Engrs. (London),* **32**: 35 (1954).
21. Verschoor, H.: *Appl. Sci. Research.,* **A2**: 155–161 (1950).
22. Wilhelm, R. H., and M. Kwauk: *Chem. Eng. Progr.,* **44**: 201–218 (1948).
23. Young, R. J.: *J. Appl. Chem. (London),* **2**, Suppl. Issue 1, S55 (1952).

CHAPTER 5

ELUTRIATION

Nomenclature

C = fines concentration in two-component bed at time θ, per cent or lb per lb

C_0 = fines concentration in two-component bed at time $\theta = 0$, per cent or lb per lb

C_R = residual fines concentration in two-component bed, per cent or lb per lb

C_D = drag coefficient, dimensionless

D_b = particle diameter of bed component, ft

D_f = particle diameter of fines component, ft

D_p = particle diameter, ft; for granular solids $D_p = \sqrt{d_1 d_2}$, where d_1 and d_2 are adjacent sieve openings

F_D = drag force on a particle, lb force

F_g = gravitational accelerating force, lb force

g_c = gravitational conversion factor, 32.2 (lb mass)(ft)/(lb force)(sec)(sec)

G = gas mass velocity, lb/(hr)(sq ft)

k = elutriation-velocity constant, $\min^{-1}$

K = 0.843 log $(\phi_s/0.065)$

L_{mf} = height of unfluidized bed, ft

m = constant of proportionality

Re = Reynolds number, $D_p G/\mu$

u_f = superficial air velocity through fluidizing bed, fps

u_t = terminal velocity of solid particles falling in a fluid, fps

y = solids concentration in the gas phase, lb solids per lb gas per hr

θ = time, min

μ = fluid viscosity, lb/(hr)(ft)

ρ_F = fluid density, lb per cu ft

ρ_S = solids density, lb per cu ft

ϕ_s = particle sphericity; $\phi_s = V_p^{2/3}/0.205A$, where V_p is the displacement volume of the particle and A is its geometrical surface area

Abstract

The chapter starts with a definition of elutriation, followed by a discussion of the principal factors which affect elutriation. A possible mechanism that may underlie the phenomenon is then proposed. The available literature and research data are presented and examined in the light of the proposed mechanism. Correlations are suggested as far as possible, and present limitations are briefly pointed out.

DEFINITION

The formation of fines in fluidized beds is encountered in many diversified applications. Regardless of the reasons for particle breakdown, the

114

fines will eventually require removal from the unit. One obvious method of fines removal is to subject the bed to certain gas flow rates which will in effect fractionate the charge and drive the small components overhead in the gas phase. Thus elutriation may be defined as an operation whereby a mixture of finely divided solids is separated into its individual size components by subjecting the mixture to the action of a rising current of fluid.

Broadly speaking, a system of solids which is susceptible to elutriation consists of a fraction of relatively large size and another fraction that is significantly smaller. The large-size fraction will in most instances be the original charge, and thus it will probably comprise the bulk of the bed. It will therefore be designated the "bed component." The small component may either have been present originally or have formed during the operation. It will be termed the "fines component." Solids beds used in processes frequently conform to specific initial size distributions, but the distributions may not prevail for long, once the process is in operation. It is therefore to be borne in mind that solids beds, generally encountered, will comprise wide size distributions in both the bed and the fines component. One of the questions that arise is how much of the bed, as far as particle size is concerned, requires removal. The answer is probably given by the process. However, when it comes to rates of removal, the answer will relate to elutriation. The amount which is removed will be designated as the "blow-over," and the remainder of the bed will be termed the "residue."

FACTORS AFFECTING ELUTRIATION

Application of elutriation to a solids-separation problem requires an understanding of how elutriation rates are affected by system variables. Factors of importance may be apparatus-born, involve the characteristics of solids and fluids, or both.

Apparatus Effects. Effects of apparatus construction appear complicated; so far they have not been studied quantitatively enough to permit formulation of final correlations. The principal factors involved are:

1. Fluid distribution and bed height
2. Column diameter
3. Freeboard above the solids bed

Method and quality of fluid distribution into the base of a column of solids are known to affect the entire contacting efficiency. Since solids removal by elutriation must be dependent on contacting efficiency, methods of initial fluid distribution and resulting fluid dispersion must play an important role. Since the quality of fluid dispersion will vary with bed height, it is reasonable to expect elutriation rates to be bed-height dependent. Hence it follows that, because the quality of fluid dispersion deteriorates in higher bed strata, elutriation rates should, under certain conditions, be inversely proportional to some function of bed height. All this has indeed been confirmed for beds composed of more than one component. For single-component beds, height has apparently no effect on elutriation rates[2]* if bed height is not permitted to decrease below a certain critical value.

Column diameter affects fluidization behavior; hence elutriation rates may be expected to be dependent on column diameter. Results observed

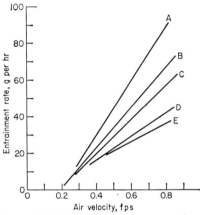

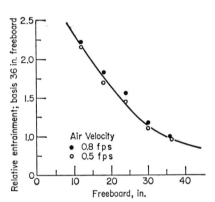

FIG. 5-1. Effect of freeboard on fines elutriation from closely sized coal (−200 mesh) in 2-in.-diameter tube, observed by Jolley and Stantan.[3] (*Crown copyright reserved. Reproduced by permission of the Controller, Her Majesty's Stationery Office.*)

FIG. 5-2. Effect of freeboard on fines elutriation at two air velocities; data of Jolley and Stantan[3] for −200 mesh coal in 2-in.-diameter tube.

in this respect are obscure and conflicting. Thus, Hyman[2] reports essentially the same entrainment rate when 60- to 80-micron glass beads are subjected to an air velocity of 1.5 fps in either a 2- or 3-in.-diameter column. However for an air velocity of 1.9 fps in both columns, the entrainment rate in the 2-in. column was about twice that observed in the 3-in. column. Retaining the air velocity of 1.9 fps but substituting 60- to 80-micron ground catalyst particles for the glass beads gave a threefold entrainment rate in the 3-in. column over that observed in the 2-in. column.

The effect of freeboard is readily demonstrated and understood. Typical data on the effect have been reported by Jolley and Stantan.[3] Their observations were made with a close cut of −200 mesh coal; they are shown in Fig. 5-1. Entrainment rates, expressed as grams of solids per

---

* Superscript numbers indicate works listed in References at the end of the chapter.

hour, are related to air velocity for various heights of freeboard. The column diameter was 2 in. and the original bed height about 25 in. The lines, pertaining to a freeboard ranging from 12 to 36 in., converge near an air velocity of 0.2 fps, for which the elutriation rate is zero. Presumably this value is near the terminal velocity of the particles in the bed. The particles were reported to be smaller than 0.003 in. Assuming $\rho s = 80$ lb per cu ft and using Stokes' equation, a terminal velocity of 0.75 fps results. The discrepancy would indicate that the average fines were only about 0.0015 in. instead of 0.003 in. The data of Fig. 5-1 have been cross-plotted for two air velocities, 0.5 and 0.8 fps. All data have been referred to a freeboard of 36 in. (Fig. 5-2). For the single-component bed used by Jolley and Stantan[3] the effect of freeboard on elutriation rates is essentially unaffected by the air velocity. The data trend indicates existence of a limiting value of freeboard beyond which elutriation becomes independent of freeboard.

Effects of Fluids and Solids. The effects of fluid and solids characteristics upon elutriation rates have been noted with more precision than the apparatus effects discussed above. Specifically investigated were influence of:

1. Superficial gas rate through beds
2. Particle size of fines component
3. Particle size of bed component

Data, though of a less comprehensive character, have also become available on the effect of solids density and particle shape of the fines component. Fluid density and viscosity effects have been investigated in a preliminary way.

Without exception, elutriation rates were observed to increase sharply as the gas velocity was increased beyond the terminal velocity of the component to be elutriated. Hence it follows that, with gas velocity remaining constant, elutriation rates will increase with decreasing fines diameter.

The effect of size of the bed component is much smaller than the effect of the fines component. The relatively scant data of this type that have become available indicate that for otherwise constant conditions elutriation rates increase as the bed-component particle size is increased.

Effect of solids density of the bed component has not been investigated, but an increase of solids density of the fines component will for otherwise constant conditions decrease elutriation rates. Elutriation rates will also decrease as the particle shape of the fines becomes more irregular. Regarding effect of fluid viscosity, the few available data indicate that, for the same linear velocities, the gas having the higher viscosity will yield the higher elutriation rates. The effects mentioned are summarized in Table 5-1.

Consideration of the various effects will permit the formulation of a probable mechanism by which the elutriation of fines from a bed of larger sizes may be explained.

ELUTRIATION MECHANISM

It is readily demonstrated that one component of the driving force that is operative in elutriation is the gas velocity. The other component of the driving force, and opposed to the action of the gas velocity, is the terminal velocity of the fines component. Hence the net driving force is the difference between the two velocities. The gas velocity has the function of inducing partial bed stratification. It is, then, through the

TABLE 5-1. QUALITATIVE EFFECTS OF VARIABLES ON ELUTRIATION

Variable	Variation in elutriation rate
Fluid distribution	Should increase as fluid distribution improves
Bed height	Should decrease with increasing bed height
Column diameter	Effects so far observed are conflicting
Freeboard	Decreases as freeboard increases; becomes independent beyond limiting value of freeboard
Superficial gas rate	Increases sharply with gas rate
Fines diameter	Increases rapidly with decreasing fines diameter
Bed-component diameter	Appears to increase as bed-component size increases
Solids density of fines component	Increases as, for constant linear velocity, fines density decreases
Solids density of bed component	Not yet investigated
Particle shape of fines	Decreases as shape becomes more irregular
Particle shape of bed	Not yet investigated
Fluid viscosity	Increases as, for constant linear velocity, viscosity increases

action of the difference of the gas velocity and the terminal velocity of the fines that the latter can be picked up from the upper boundary of the bed and conveyed through the freeboard out of the system.

Some typical stratification data have already been given in Chap. 4. Specific data pertaining to materials for which elutriation was investigated have been observed by Osberg and Charlesworth.[10] The data, graphically shown in Fig. 5-3, indicate that a considerable enrichment of fines has occurred at the uppermost boundary of the bed.

It is known that stratification in a fluidized bed may occur over a considerable range of fluid mass velocities. However, the action is probably most efficient at mass velocities which are slightly in excess of the one required to initially fluidize the largest component. Since these optimum-stratification mass velocities will in most instances be lower than the terminal velocity of the component to be elutriated, it may be inferred that the most favorable mass velocities for stratification will hardly coincide with those required for material transport out of the bed. Thus the mass velocity required for pickup of the fines component will in many cases be probably too high to effectively stratify the bed. Since particle pickup is dependent on prior stratification, it must be borne in mind that a condition may arise for which the extent of stratification just is not sufficient to provide a fines build-up in the top strata great enough so that elutriation can continue at an originally observed rate. On the other hand the fines may be so plentiful in the bed that ready

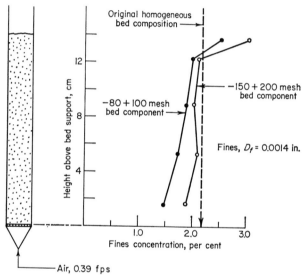

FIG. 5-3. Typical bed-stratification data observed by Osberg and Charlesworth.[10]

pickup from the upper boundary will proceed regardless of what the interbed transport rate of the fines to the upper boundary may be. Acceptance of such a mechanism should then foretell (1) a condition for which, at a given fluid velocity, the rate of entrainment will be proportional to fines concentration in the bed and (2) that, at certain limiting low values of fines concentration, complete elutriation of the fines component from a system may not be achievable regardless of gas flow rates employed. It may be stated that experimental data in support of both phenomena have been observed.

From the proposed fines-transport mechanism through the bed, prior to removal from the upper boundary, it follows that elutriation rates should increase as bed heights decrease.

Regarding the effect of the bed component, there are two reasons why elutriation rates should increase as bed-component particle size increases.

First, in beds of large particles the order of magnitude of the individual voids is greater, and hence the flow paths are less tortuous than in beds of small particles. Consequently the fines are transported more readily through the bulk of the bed to the upper boundary. Second, as for a given size of fines the size of the bed component increases, the ratio of the two sizes increases. This will lead more readily to size segregation, the basic requirement for elutriation from the upper boundary of the bed.

The fact that elutriation rates increase as, for otherwise constant conditions, particle size and solids density of the fines components are decreased is of course also compatible with the mechanism. Similarly, elutriation rates should increase with increasing fluid viscosities. For all these instances the terminal velocity of the particle is decreased, which in effect increases the over-all driving force through the bed, namely, the difference between the operating gas velocity and the terminal velocity of the fines.

TERMINAL VELOCITY

For the purpose of illustration let us consider an upright large-diameter cylinder, filled with a liquid. Just below the surface a small spherical particle is held in suspension. The liquid is at rest and the particle is released. Initially at zero, its velocity will increase; if the cylinder is of sufficient height, the particle will acquire a certain limiting velocity. The limiting velocity is called the terminal velocity of the particle in the liquid. As will be seen from the following presentation, the terminal velocity is dependent on the diameter, shape, and density of the particle as well as on the properties of the fluid.

The constant terminal velocity will have been attained when the gravitational accelerating force

$$F_g = \frac{\pi}{6} D_p{}^3 (\rho_S - \rho_F) g_c \qquad (5\text{-}1)$$

is counterbalanced by the resisting upward drag force

$$F_D = \frac{1}{2} C_D \rho_F \frac{\pi D_p{}^2}{4} u_t{}^2 \qquad (5\text{-}2)$$

In Eq. (5-2)

$$C_D = \frac{4}{3} \frac{D_p g_c (\rho_S - \rho_F)}{u_t{}^2 \rho_F}$$

and this is known as the drag coefficient. Similarly to the already presented modified friction factor for packed beds, it may be expressed as a function of the modified Reynolds number. The relation for spherical

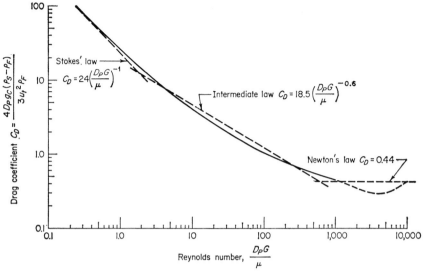

FIG. 5-4. Drag coefficient vs. Reynolds number.

particles is given in Fig. 5-4. For individual ranges C_D may be approximated as follows:

$$C_D = \frac{24}{\mathrm{Re}} \qquad \mathrm{Re} < 2.0$$
$$= 18.5\,\mathrm{Re}^{-0.6} \qquad 2.0 < \mathrm{Re} < 500$$
$$= 0.44 \qquad 500 < \mathrm{Re}$$

Equating (5-1) and (5-2) and replacing C_D by the above expression results in

$$u_t = \frac{(\rho_S - \rho_F)g_c D_p{}^2}{18\mu} \tag{5-3}\star$$

$$= 0.152\,\frac{D_p{}^{1.14}g_c{}^{0.714}(\rho_S - \rho_F)^{0.714}}{\mu^{0.428}\rho_F{}^{0.285}} \tag{5-4}\star$$

$$= \left(3g_c D_p\,\frac{\rho_S - \rho_F}{\rho_F}\right)^{0.5} \tag{5-5}\star$$

Equation (5-3) is known as Stokes' law; it is applicable for $D_p G/\mu < 2.0$. Equation (5-5) is known as Newton's law; it applies when $D_p G/\mu > 500$. Equation (5-4) is the so-called intermediate law, valid for the Reynolds-number range $2 < D_p G/\mu < 500$. The equations may be used to calculate the terminal velocity for spherical particles. A nomograph, originally proposed by Reboux[12] and shown in Fig. 5-5, may be found convenient for rapid use. Use of the equations will generally require a final check on the modified Reynolds number in order to assure that the correct form was used.

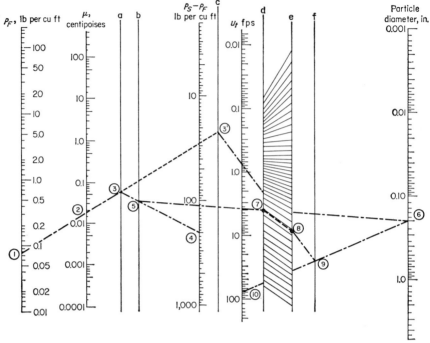

P_F, lb per cu ft
μ, centipoises
a b
$P_S - P_F$ lb per cu ft
u_t fps
d e f
Particle diameter, in.

FIG. 5-5. Nomograph for evaluation of particle terminal velocity.[12] (*Courtesy of Association Française de Fluidisation.*)

In the above forms the equations apply only to spherical particles. In a relatively recent study Pettyjohn and Christiansen[11] have extended terminal-velocity considerations to nonspherical particles. Accordingly, Stokes' law is modified to read

$$u_t = K \frac{(\rho_S - \rho_F)g_c D_p^2}{18\mu} \qquad (5\text{-}6)\star$$

where $K = 0.843 \log \dfrac{\phi_s}{0.065}$

In the expression for K, ϕ_s is the particle sphericity, or shape factor, as defined in Chap. 3. Modifications have also been proposed for the intermediate- and turbulent-flow range. For those ranges it is suggested that the original paper be consulted.[11] The subject of terminal velocity has been given here only as far as required for manipulation of the presented fluidization and related correlations. For a more detailed discussion the reader is referred to work of Korn,[5] Lapple and Shepherd,[7] and Dallavalle.[1]

Example 5-1. Spherical particles of $D_p = 0.24$ in. and $\rho_S = 200$ lb per cu ft are subject to an upward air velocity of 150 fps. The air has a density $\rho_F =$

0.075 lb per cu ft, and its viscosity is 0.018 centipoise. For this condition estimate the average particle velocity.

Solution. We shall use the nomograph of Fig. 5-5 for obtaining the values of u_t. The starting point is 1, the density of the air. Alignment with the proper viscosity value yields points 3 and 3' on axes a and c. Continuing with 3 we align with $\rho_S - \rho_F$ and obtain reference point 5. Connection is then made with the particle-diameter scale to yield 6. This yields point 7 on axis d. The direction of the pattern then yields point 8 on axis e, to be connected with the earlier obtained point 3'. This yields point 9 on axis f and finally the desired point 10. The result for our problem is $u_t = 75$ fps; hence the particle velocity will be 75 ft, upward. Application of Newton's law yields $u_t = 72$ and an upward velocity of 78 fps. The value of the nomograph is better appreciated when the intermediate law is involved in an estimate.

DATA AND CORRELATIONS

Only three data sources that might be used for possible development of a correlation existed at the time of writing. The earliest reported U.S. Bureau of Mines[8] study pertained to elutriation of a Fischer-Tropsch iron catalyst from a bed component of the same material. A few runs with sands mixed into the catalyst were also reported. The experimental column was of 1.32 in. diameter. The system was only of two components, that is, a fines component and a bed component. The ratio of the particle diameters of bed to fines ranged from 4.7 to 2.6. The elutriating gas was air.

A subsequent and more comprehensive study was reported by Osberg and Charlesworth.[10] As solids they used spherical glass beads. The ratio of bed-to-fines particle diameters varied from 8.1 to 1.63. The elutriating column was of 3 in. diameter. Air was the principal elutriating gas, though a few runs were made with helium, carbon dioxide, and Freon-12. As already reported, Osberg and Charlesworth also examined the stratification of some of their beds in an effort to learn something about mechanism. As far as fines concentrations in the charges were concerned, their beds contained less than 5 weight per cent of fines component, whereas the U.S. Bureau of Mines study[8] adhered to initial concentrations of about 20 weight per cent.

Additional elutriation data with glass beads of 69 microns diameter in bed components of 425 and 125 microns were reported by Hyman.[2] The elutriation unit was of 3 in. diameter. Initial fines concentration ranged from 95 to 50 weight per cent. In addition to these two-component data, Hyman secured some single-component data with glass beads and other materials. Moreover, he used his equipment to verify generally known effects of freeboard. His observations regarding chamber diameter have already been mentioned. The data of Hyman, as originally reported, are not in a form which permits comparison with the data treatment suggested earlier;[8] however, a slight reworking of the experimental values indicated a gratifying measure of agreement.

The work of Hyman has been continued by Richards[13] and also by Lang,[6] both of whom worked wholly with single-component systems. Unfortunately the situation in single-component beds seems entirely different from that in two-component systems, so that the reported conclusions may hardly be applied to the more complex two-component data.

Elutriation data were also reported by Kehat,[4] who used fluidization chambers of 0.86 and 1.81 in. diameter. Particles used were round quartz, sands, Scotchlite, and polystyrene spheres. Bed weights ranged from 2 to 200 g, and the systems investigated were one- and two-component. In the latter the size ratios ranged from 1:1.3 to 1:9. For the two-component systems a plot of the fines concentration change with time gave curves consisting of two branches, each of which could be represented by a first-order rate equation. On the whole the data did not lend themselves to a generalized correlation.

Elutriation data have also been reported by Jolley and Stantan.[3] The data were not the result of an elutriation study as such, but rather originated from a general investigation of the fluid characteristics of coal. Nevertheless the findings, already referred to, are of considerable interest.

Rate Equation. The first step toward data correlation involved the plotting of fines concentration changes vs. time for constant gas velocities.[8] Typical graphs, obtained from the principal data sources, are shown in Fig. 5-6. The logarithm of the ratio C/C_0, the instantaneous to the original fines concentration, is shown in relation to elutriation time. Despite the considerable differences in system properties and gas velocities, all graphs have in common (1) an initial linear portion of negative slope, (2) a point where linearity ceases, and (3) an upturn of the correlation, away from the time axis.

For the straight-line portion, extending from $C/C_0 = 1.0$ to point a, the data are expressed by

$$\log \frac{C}{C_0} = -k\theta \qquad (5\text{-}7)$$

or
$$C = C_0 e^{-k\theta} \qquad (5\text{-}8)\star$$

In this equation, which is the law of first-order chemical reactions, the slope of the straight line k is termed the elutriation-velocity constant.

If Eq. (5-7) is differentiated, there results

$$\frac{dC}{d\theta} = -kC \qquad (5\text{-}9)$$

which tells that the elutriation rate $dC/d\theta$ is proportional to the instantaneous fines concentration C in the bed. This is in agreement with the proposed mechanism.

At point a the line deflects away from the time axis. In other words, beyond this point the rate of fines depletion will proceed at a lesser rate.

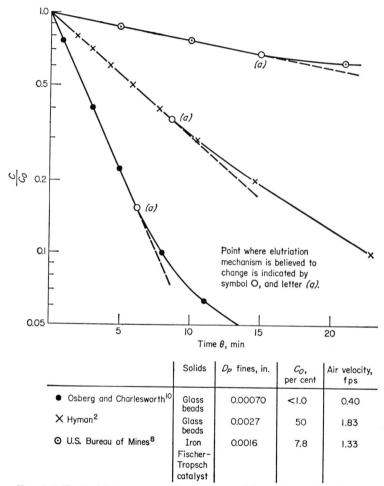

	Solids	D_p fines, in.	C_0, per cent	Air velocity, fps
● Osberg and Charlesworth[10]	Glass beads	0.00070	<1.0	0.40
✕ Hyman[2]	Glass beads	0.0027	50	1.83
⊙ U.S. Bureau of Mines[8]	Iron Fischer-Tropsch catalyst	0.0016	7.8	1.33

FIG. 5-6. Typical bed-concentration changes of fines during elutriation.

Point a has earlier been termed "break point."[8] But since there appears no definite break, but rather a gradual change, the term is not suitable. Instead it is suggested that, in accord with the proposal of Trawinski,[14] the concentration pertaining to point a be termed the "critical concentration," because it apparently represents that value of fines concentration at which the interbed transport velocity of the fines to the upper bed boundary becomes rate controlling.

A critical point has been noted for most of the Fischer-Tropsch iron-catalyst data observed at the U.S. Bureau of Mines.[8] It has been confirmed by virtually all of the data of Hyman.[2] Osberg and Charles-worth,[10] on the other hand, report such a condition for only a portion of their data. In fact they presented some runs for which the deflection at the critical point is toward the θ axis, rather than away from it, as more universally noted. Of course no explanation can presently be given for these deviations. However, despite the fact that Osberg and Charles-worth seem to have taken every precaution to eliminate and minimize electrostatic effects and other disturbing influences, irregularities along these lines might nevertheless have been responsible for the apparently unusual deviation.

It would of course be highly desirable to have a means of defining advent of the critical concentration, so that the limits of validity of Eq. (5-8) could be properly assessed. Unfortunately the available data are too fragmentary to permit generalizations. An interesting speculation regarding the physical significance of the critical concentration has been proposed by Trawinski.[14] Referring to the fluid-bed viscosity data of Matheson, Herbst, and Holt[9] discussed in Chap. 2, Trawinski points out that, as a bed is depleted of a certain fraction of its fines, particle mobility deteriorates very suddenly. Thus once this condition is reached, rate of transport of fines to the upper boundary will be greatly impeded and elutriation rates will therefore decrease. Trawinski succeeded in deriving an analytical expression that apparently permits prediction of the critical fines concentration, at least in respect to order of magnitude. This is discussed in more detail in Chap. 2.

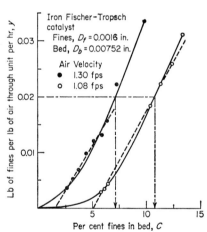

FIG. 5-7. Typical elutriation data showing equilibrium conditions between gas and solids phases.[8]

Bed–Gas-phase Equilibria. Analysis of elutriation data has revealed[8] that for a given system and gas flow rate the concentration of fines in the gas phase bears a relation to the fines concentration in the residue. This is graphically indicated in Fig. 5-7. The data pertain to elutriation of the already-mentioned Fischer-Tropsch iron catalyst.[8] The fines concentration y in the gas phase, expressed as pounds of fines in the air per poind of air per hour through the system, has been plotted vs. C, the average fines concentration in the dense phase, expressed as per cent.

Two sets of data are shown; they pertain to 1.08 and 1.30 fps air velocities. It is interesting to observe that, at the high air velocity, the fines concentration in the gas phase is higher than it is at the low air velocity. One may possibly visualize equilibrium conditions to exist between the phases. Considering, for instance, a dilute phase of concentration $y = 0.02$, equilibrium could be created either by letting an air velocity of 1.08 fps operate on a parent bed containing 10.62 per cent of fines or by allowing a higher air rate of 1.30 fps to contact a more dilute parent bed with only 6.8 per cent of fines.

There is a question how the data will proceed in the region of a low fines concentration in the bed. From the earlier proposed mechanism it follows that a residual fines content in the bed—in equilibrium, so to speak, with pure air leaving the bed—is a possibility. Residual solids concentrations C_R thus obtained by extrapolation would be about 1.2 per cent for 1.30 and near 5 per cent for 1.08 fps air velocity. The general equation of the lines is then

$$y = mC + C_R \qquad (5\text{-}10)$$

This is recognized as a modified form of Henry's law. Slope m is analogous to the Henry's law constant.

Correlation of k Values. From the proposed mechanism, as well as empirically, it has been learned that elutriation rates will increase with increasing driving rates $u_f - u_t$ increasing bed-component particle size D_b, decreasing fines-component size D_f, and decreasing bed height. Although not conceived on the basis of the presented mechanism, Osberg and Charlesworth[10] suggested that

$$k \propto \frac{(u_f - u_t)^{1.7} D_b^{0.7}}{D_f^2 L_{mf}^{1.4}} \qquad (5\text{-}11)$$

It is to be noted that this is based on some of the principal quantities that are operative in the elutriation model. The form of the Osberg and Charlesworth correlation has been found extremely useful, as the following discussion will show.

Since the fines are sufficiently small to obey Stokes' law, once they are at the upper bed boundary and thus outside the fluidized bed, it follows that

$$u_t = \frac{(\rho_S - \rho_F) g_c D_f^2}{18\mu} \qquad (5\text{-}12)$$

Hence for our condition D_f^2 may in the Osberg and Charlesworth correlation be replaced by u_t.

The next step toward correlation involves evaluation of the velocity ratio $(u_f - u_t)/u_t$ for those data for which D_b and L_{mf} remain constant. Plotting on logarithmic coordinates k values vs. the velocity ratio is the

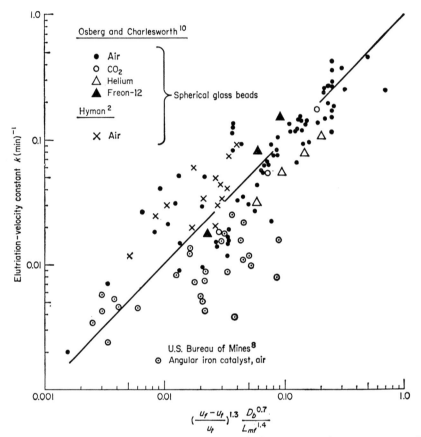

FIG. 5-8. Generalized correlation of elutriation-velocity constants for two-component systems.

next step. This yields the generalized form given in Fig. 5-8. The proposed line is represented by

$$k = \left(\frac{u_f - u_t}{u_t}\right)^{1.3} \frac{D_b^{0.7}}{L_{mf}^{1.4}} \tag{5-13}$$

With D_b expressed in inches and L_{mf} in feet it is found that a satisfactory line can be passed through the coordinates 1-1, thus yielding a value of 1.0 as a convenient constant of proportionality.

Considering the wide diversification of the data and the differences in experimental conditions and solids concentrations, the proposed correlation appears encouraging for the present time. The iron-catalyst data seem reasonably well correlated in the low-flow region. At the higher flow rates the deviation is more severe. The disagreement is believed to be chiefly due to effect of particle shape on the numerical value of the terminal velocity.

Examination of the dimensional correlation (5-13) indicates that dimensional homogeneity may be achieved if $g_c^{0.5}$ is introduced and if the exponent 0.7 of D_b is increased to a value of 0.9. It is believed that these steps would tend to oversimplify the situation and cover up the scope of the problem. Since really no new variables would thus be introduced, the resulting dimensionless equation would not be any broader in its application than the present dimensional form is. Any attempt to achieve a dimensionless correlation must therefore be based on new experimental data. In particular it appears that the geometry of the elutriation unit is not yet sufficiently investigated. This must certainly be true of the effects of vessel diameter and fluid-inlet device, which at present are still wholly obscure.

Example 5-2. A solids bed is composed of coarse and fines fractions of angular magnetite of specific gravity 5.00. The sphericity of the particles has been determined by prior pressure-drop tests and found equal to $\phi_s = 0.58$. The bed originally contained 20 per cent of fines of $D_f = 0.001595$ in. The coarse component had a diameter $D_b = 0.00532$ in. Sixteen pounds of the mixture is subject to an air velocity of 1.08 fps in a 4-in.-diameter tube. The column height at the onset of fluidization was recorded as 1.182 ft. The pressure was atmospheric and the temperature 70°F. For an aeration time of 60 min estimate:

1. The fines concentration in the bed
2. The solids concentration in the gas phase in equilibrium with the concentration in the bed

Solution. The constant correcting Stokes' law for sphericity becomes

$$K = 0.843 \log \frac{0.58}{0.065} = 0.802$$

and
$$u_t = 0.802 \frac{(5 - 0.075) \times 62.3 \times 32.2 \times 0.001595^2}{144 \times 0.018 \times 2.42 \times 18 \times 3,600^{-2}}$$
$$= 0.65 \text{ fps}$$

The elutriation-velocity constant is next evaluated from Fig. 5-8:

$$\left(\frac{u_f - u_t}{u_t}\right)^{1.3} \frac{D_b^{0.7}}{L_{mf}^{1.4}} = \left(\frac{1.08 - 0.65}{0.65}\right)^{1.3} \frac{0.00532^{0.7}}{1.182^{1.4}} = 0.0118$$

and from Fig. 5-8, $k = 0.0118$ min^{-1}.

It will now be assumed that, for the initial fines concentration and the resulting fines concentration range, Eq. (5-8) will apply and k will remain constant. Hence

$$C = 0.20 \times e^{-0.0118 \times 60}$$
$$= 0.0980$$

Therefore, after 1 hr of elutriation, the fines concentration in the bed will be 9.80 per cent.

The rate of solids transfer from the bed after 60 min of operation is then found to be $0.0118 \times 9.80 = 0.1160$ per cent of the weight of the bed per minute. With a bed weight of 16 lb, the solids carried over amount to $16 \times 0.1160/100 = 0.0186$ lb per min. Since the weight of air passed through the 4-in.-diameter unit is $1.08 \times 60 \times 0.075 \times 0.0872 = 0.424$ lb per min, the solids concentration in the air at the termination of the elutriation is 0.0186 lb of solids per 0.424 lb of air, or 4.39 weight per cent.

SUMMARY

Elutriation of fines from fluidized systems constitutes a complex problem. In practice, the size spectrum of elutriated fines may extend over wide ranges. Similarly, the composition of the bed component which is normally not elutriated is ordinarily characterized by a wide size distribution. Since experimental data have been obtained only for so-called "two-component systems"—i.e., beds which are composed of a relatively coarse bed component and a much smaller fines component—it may be stated that the problems that attend elutriation in a broad sense are virtually unexplored. Nevertheless some important observations have been made; they are as follows:

In a two-component system the fines concentration C after an elutriation time θ is given by

$$C = C_0 e^{-k\theta}$$

In this equation C_0 is the initial fines concentration and k is the elutriation-velocity constant. The law has been found valid over a wide range of fines concentration. Below a certain value of C, referred to as the critical concentration, the rate of elutriation becomes smaller than predicted by the law. This has led to the conception of a certain elutriation mechanism. According to this mechanism the bed is first partly stratified, and thereby the upper region of the bed is enriched in fines. Removal of the fines from the upper boundary occurs simultaneously. The stratification in beds subjected to elutriation has been verified.

A start has been made toward understanding how the elutriation-velocity constant is related to typical system variables, such as fluid velocity, terminal velocity of the fines component, size of the bed component, and bed height.

Still unexplored remain effects of column diameter and gas-inlet device. Of course the most important point is to examine whether, and if so, how, k values will vary if the bed to be elutriated contains more than one fines component.

PROBLEMS

5-1. A used granular magnetite catalyst is contaminated with fines that have formed during a reaction. The original particle size was 0.00488 in., and the original solids density was 312 lb per cu ft. The fines have an average density of 145 lb per cu ft and range from 0.0021 in. to subsieve dimensions. The subsieve sizes are to be removed by passage through a 325-mesh screen. The remainder of the fines, amounting to 21 per cent of the original catalyst charge, are to be removed by elutriation with air at 70°F and atmospheric pressure. A 4-in.-diameter column is available for the work, and 7.5 lb of catalyst are to be treated. Specify the air rate required so that the separation may be completed in one hour. Assume that the elutriation-equilibrium constant remains constant during the operation and that the fines removal follows the first-order reaction law, as expressed by Eq. (5-8). The magnetite has a shape factor of $\phi_s = 0.60$ and a value of $\epsilon_{mf} = 0.58$.

5-2. It is desired to produce a solids concentration of 5 per cent by weight in an air stream by allowing the air to elutriate the fines from a two-component bed. The available solids consist of a bed component of $D_b = 0.00752$ in. and a fines component of $D_f = 0.0016$ in. The density of solids is 160 lb per cu ft. The contacting unit is to be of the continuous type; that is, solids rich in fines are introduced into the middle portion of the bed and an equivalent amount of solids is removed from the base of the column, so that the bed height remains constant. A 4-in.-diameter column is available for the work. If it is desired to generate 7.2 cfm of the solids-carrying air, specify the required fines concentration in the feed as a function of bed height at the point of minimum fluidization.

REFERENCES

1. Dallavalle, J. M.: "Micromeritics," Pitman Publishing Corporation, New York, 1948.
2. Hyman, Daniel: Ph.D. thesis, MIT, Cambridge, 1952.
3. Jolley, L. J., and J. E. Stantan: *J. Appl. Chem. (London)*, **2**, Suppl. Issue 1, S62–S68 (1952).
4. Kehat, E.: M.S. thesis, Israel Institute of Technology, 1955.
5. Korn, A. H.: *Chem. Eng.*, **57**: 108 (1950); **58**: 178 (1951).
6. Lang, Peter M.: Ph.D. thesis, MIT, Cambridge, 1955.
7. Lapple, C. E., and C. B. Shepherd: *Ind. Eng. Chem.*, **32**: 605 (1940).
8. Leva, Max: *Chem. Eng. Progr.*, **47**: 39–45 (1951).
9. Matheson, G. L., W. A. Herbst, and P. A. Holt 2d: *Ind. Eng. Chem.*, **41**: 1099–1104 (1949).
10. Osberg, G. L., and D. H. Charlesworth: *Chem. Eng. Progr.*, **47**: 566–570 (1951).
11. Pettyjohn, E. S., and E. B. Christiansen: *Chem. Eng. Progr.*, **44**: 157–172 (1948).
12. Reboux, P.: "Phénomènes de fluidisation," Association Française de Fluidisation, Paris, 1954.
13. Richards, R. L., Jr.: Ph.D. thesis, MIT, Cambridge, 1955.
14. Trawinski, H.: *Chem. Ingr. Tech.*, **25**(4): 201–203 (1953).

CHAPTER 6

DILUTE PHASE AND MOVING SOLIDS

Nomenclature

A = open cross section in a conduit, not occupied by solids, sq ft

A' = function of dimensionless group, Eq. (6-3)

c = angle-of-approach correction factor for gravity flow of solids

c_0 = wall-effect correction factor for gravity flow of solids

C_D = drag coefficient

C_s = dimensional constant, Eq. **(6-13a)**

d_p = diameter of a component in a mixture of sizes; $d_p = \sqrt{d_1 d_2}$, where d_1 and d_2 are adjacent sieve openings

D_o = orifice or conduit diameter, in. in correlations (6-12) and (6-14) to (6-17)

D_p = particle diameter, ft

D_t = tube or conduit diameter, ft

f_g = gas friction factor

f_m = modified gas friction factor of Happel, Eq. (6-20)

f_p^* = solids friction factor in pneumatic systems with particles fully accelerated

f_s = solids friction factor in flow system of high solids-to-air ratio

g_c = gravitational conversion factor, 32.2 (lb mass) ft/(lb force)(sec)(sec)

G_g = gas mass velocity, lb/(hr)(sq ft)

G_p = solids mass velocity in pneumatic system with individual particle movement, lb/(hr)(sq ft)

G_s = solids mass velocity in flow system of high solids-to-gas ratio where solids flow in mass rather than as individual particles

k = dimensional constant in correlation (6-2)

k' = function of dimensionless group, Eq. (6-3)

L = bed height, or duct height, ft

n = number of size components in a granular charge

n' = exponent in correlation (6-2)

R = solids-to-gas weight ratio

u_c = choking velocity, fps

u_g = superficial gas velocity in pneumatic conveying or high solids-to-air ratio flow, fps

u_0 = superficial gas velocity in moving bed, fps

u_p = particle velocity in pneumatic system, fps

u_p^* = fully accelerated particle velocity in pneumatic system, fps

u_s = solids velocity (moving en masse) in high solids-to-air ratio flow, fps

u_{slip} = slip velocity; that is, $u_g - u_p^*$

V = total volume of conveying duct, cu ft

W = weight rate of solids flow in pneumatic or high solids-to-air ratio flow, lb per hour or lb per sec. For Fig. 6-4 the dimension is lb/(sec)(sq ft). In Eq. (6-10) and Fig. 6-7 W denotes solids holdup, expressed in pounds.

W_a = weight rate of solids flow by gravity into air, lb per hour or lb per sec
W_F = weight rate of solids flow by gravity into any fluid, lb per hr or lb per sec
X = weight fraction of solids of a given diameter in a bed of mixed sizes
α = pressure-drop ratio $(\Delta p_s + \Delta p)/\Delta p$, where Δp_s = pressure drop due to solids flow and Δp is due to air alone
β_a, β_F = angle of repose of solids in air or any other fluid
Δp_t = total pressure drop, that is, $\Delta p_t = \Delta p_s + \Delta p$, psf
Δp_s = pressure drop due to solids flow only, psf
Δp = pressure drop due to air alone, psf
ϵ = voidage in bed
ϵ_s = voidage at slugging point
ρ_b = bulk density of solids, lb per cu ft
ρ_{dg} = dispersed-gas density, lb per cu ft
ρ_{ds} = dispersed-solids density, lb per cu ft
ρ_F = density of fluid, lb per cu ft
ρ_{ods} = density of apparent over-all solids-gas mixture, lb per cu ft
ρ_S = density of solids, lb per cu ft
ψ = function of
μ = fluid viscosity, lb/(hr)(ft)

Abstract

The discussion of the dilute phase and moving solids given in this chapter is divided into three sections.

The first section considers the fluidized-phase diagrams and demonstrates how the dense and dilute phases in fluidization are related. It defines choking and saltation velocities and considers details pertaining to the slugging zone. A review of most literature data pertaining to pneumatic solids flow is then given, and correlations are presented for estimation of the accelerating section in horizontal pneumatic-transport lines, maximum solids velocities attained, and pressure drops attending gas-solid flow in such systems.

The second section considers high ratio solids-gas flow in horizontal lines. This mode of conveying solids is fundamentally different from pneumatic transport, chiefly because the solids-gas ratios are much higher and the fluid velocities considerably lower than in pneumatic handling. Correlations permitting evaluation of pressure drops for typical systems of this kind are presented.

In the third section, beds employing gravity flow of solids are treated. The section is divided into two parts. The first part reports on gravity flow of solids without gas flow; the remaining part examines the moving-solids bed with simultaneous concurrent or countercurrent gas flow.

Introduction. From the experiments of Wilhelm and Valentine[27]* already described in Chap. 2 it has been learned that the fluidized state comprises a dense phase and a dilute phase. Basic characteristics of the dense phase are (1) a comparatively low bed voidage of the order of magnitude of, say, 50 to 70 per cent and (2) the fact that the solids bed as a whole is fixed relative to the wall of the confining vessel.

* Superscript numbers indicate works listed in References at the end of the chapter.

In the systems to be discussed in this chapter the particles will always display a net movement relative to the wall of the confining vessel. Moreover, in the case of the dilute phase, voidages will always be in excess of 90 per cent. Systems of moving solids in which the voidages are of the order of magnitude of the dense phase will also be considered. These systems are known as moving-solids beds.

Fluidized-state Phase Diagram

A schematic qualitative presentation of the various phases encountered in fluidization and their relation to each other has been given by Zenz.[28]

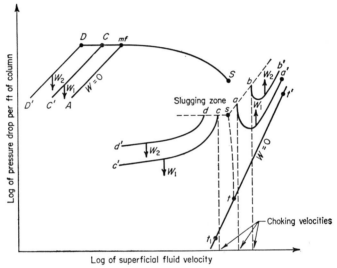

FIG. 6-1. Schematic fluidized-state phase diagram of Zenz[28] for upward fluid flow.

It is indicated in Fig. 6-1. Line A-mf pertains to a packed bed in which the solids flow rate $W = 0$. Hence this states merely the relation between fluid flow and pressure drop in a fixed bed. Upon proceeding along the line, and assuming that the bed is at ϵ_{mf}, fluidization sets in at point mf. The pressure drop is then at its maximum. With further flow increases, the pressure drop per unit bed height decreases, reflecting progressive bed expansion. In the vicinity of mf there is quiescent fluidization. The bed becomes more agitated as gas rates increase, and slugging is finally induced at point S. At this point the curve stops. The reason for the discontinuation is that conditions in the system are now of such instability and are so sensitive to gas flow that no coordinated analysis of the range has so far been possible. However, with sufficiently high gas rates, the zone may be passed over. Smooth operation manifests itself again at point s. At this point the solids concentration is suddenly found much smaller than at S. In fact the solids concentration is now of the order of magnitude found in a typical dilute phase. Hence the zone Ss, still largely an unknown, represents the transition from the dense to the dilute phase.

Now as the gas velocity is increased further, the pressure drop decreases very markedly. This is so because the inventory of the solids in the conduit must now decrease very rapidly. In fact the decrease is so fast that the resulting reduction in head loss and gas-particle friction exceeds the greater wall friction due to an increase in superficial gas velocity. Proceeding along this path, the solids dilution progresses steadily until at point t there is only one single particle in suspension. This should occur when the gas velocity is equal to the terminal velocity of the particles. Since at point t we have only one single particle in the "bed," the pressure drop must now be that normally encountered between the flowing gas and the wall of the conduit, hence the value predicted by the Fanning equation.

The gas velocity is now increased further, and the pressure drop follows the line t-t'. Our single particle was found at rest at point t, because there the gas velocity u_g was just equal to its terminal velocity u_t. As the gas velocity is increased beyond u_t, the particle must move upward with a velocity $u_p = u_g - u_t$. The difference $u_g - u_p$ is also known as the slip velocity of the particle.

DISPERSE-PHASE CHARACTERISTICS

In a discussion of disperse-phase flow, individual considerations of vertical and horizontal systems are desirable.

Vertical Systems. Let us now increase the gas velocity along line tt' (Fig. 6-1) to a value u_g. At this point the base of the conduit will be continually fed by homogeneously sized solids for which $u_t < u_g$. Hence the solids will be supported and transported upward; let their rate be equal to W_1. Because of the solids head now present and the newly induced solids-fluid friction, caused by the slip velocity, the pressure drop will rise to a'. The system thus created comprises a typical disperse phase. It is identical in every respect with the well-known pneumatic-transport systems.

As will be learned from later quantitative considerations, the gas rates, solids rates, and pressure drops under which a pneumatic system may operate will depend primarily on the size and density of the solids to be conveyed. The particle characteristics may, of course, vary appreciably. As far as solids concentration in the carrier gas is concerned, it will rarely exceed 5 volume per cent in pneumatic systems. Hence the voidage in such a system will be about 95 per cent.

Choking Velocity. As the gas rate is now decreased from a' along the curve, there occurs a decrease in pressure drop. With the conduit still carrying solids at the rate W_1, and the slip velocity now decreased, it follows that the solids inventory in the conduit must increase. As the gas rate is decreased further, such a value of pressure drop is reached that the reduced friction loss of gas and solids is exactly balanced by the increase in pressure drop due to increasing solids head. Beyond the resulting minimum a further decrease in gas rate increases the solids holdup at such a rate that the new solids head exceeds the reduction in frictional resistance. It then appears that the conduit will fill entirely with solids as the flow is further decreased by a nominal amount. In this condition the conduit is essentially choked with solids. The point a representing this state is known as the "choking point," and the fluid velocity at which choking occurs is defined as the "choking velocity." A choking point may of course occur at higher gas rates and pressure drops for a conduit that carries initially higher solids rates, such as W_2, for instance. Choking for this solids feed rate is observed at point b.

Let us now return to point t where only one single particle was suspended in the tube at its terminal velocity. We now decrease the gas flow to t_1, and the particle drops out of sight. At t_1 we introduce into the top of the column a continuous stream of solids for which $u_t > u_g$. The rate of solids feed is W_1. The solids descend, and again, because of the solids head and the fluid-particle friction, the pressure drop rises to c'. As the gas rate is now increased, with W_1 remaining constant, the solids inventory must increase. This causes a pressure-drop rise. For continued flow-rate increases a condition such that the conduit is choked with solids is reached in this case also. The choking point for a system with descending solids is given by point c. For a system of higher solids flow rate, say W_2, a similar choking point occurs at d. Thus it is found that the locus of all choking points for downward or upward solids flow at various rates is represented by the boundary lines dcs and sab.

Slugging-zone Voidage Range. The slugging zone extending upward from lines dcs and sab has so far defied detailed study. However, the approximate voidage over which slugging extends has roughly been established. The upper limit of voidage as approached by reducing gas flow rate in a disperse system has been estimated by Zenz[29] by using the equation

$$W\uparrow = \rho_S(1 - \epsilon_s)(u_c - u_{\epsilon_s}) \qquad (6\text{-}1)$$

In this equation $W\uparrow$ is the upward solids flow at which the conduit will choke when operated under a choking gas rate u_c. As a probable value for u_{ϵ_s}, the velocity of the gas when the bed is at the choking voidage, the terminal particle velocity was used. With the solids density ρ_S known, solution for the bed voidage at choking ϵ_s yielded values

· ranging from 0.943 to 0.987. These are compared with dense-bed slugging data in Table 6-1.

TABLE 6-1. REPORTED SLUGGING LIMITS IN DILUTE AND DENSE PHASES

No.	Dilute-phase ϵ_s	Dense-phase ϵ_s	D_p, in.	ρ_S, lb per cu ft	ρ_S/ρ_F
1	Not reported	0.6	0.205	146	1,920
2	0.943	Not reported	0.066	68	895
3	Not reported	0.7	0.0393	164	2,150
4	0.987	Not reported	0.0366	165	2,165
5	0.983	Not reported	0.0231	155	2,040
6	Not reported	0.7	0.0201	156	2,050
7	Not reported	0.8	0.011	156	2,050
8	0.978	Not reported	0.0066	131	1,720
9	Not reported	0.75	0.0065	165	2,156

With particle diameter and solids density being possible influencing factors, Table 6-1 permits no more than three comparisons. Thus comparing 3 with 4, 5 with 6, and possibly 8 with 9, it may merely be stated that the slugging zone extends roughly over the voidage range $0.95 > \epsilon_s > 0.75$. Indications are that the range tends to narrow as particle size decreases. All data pertain to air fluidization. For fluidization with a heavier fluid smaller ρ_S/ρ_F values would result. This would in all likelihood affect the slugging-zone range.

Horizontal Systems, Saltation Velocity. Flow in horizontal disperse-phase systems cannot be coordinated into the generalized phase diagram. However, the limitations attending solids flow in horizontal conduits may be recognized and analyzed much in the same manner as in vertical conduits.

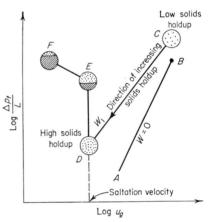

FIG. 6-2. Saltation velocity in horizontal solids flow system.[29]

In a horizontal-flow system the point of initial choking is known as the "saltation point." The attending fluid rate is designated as the "saltation velocity." The physical significance of the parameters becomes apparent from a brief consideration of typical pneumatic-flow data.

In the lower part of Fig. 6-2 let AB represent the pressure drop for a horizontal empty conduit in relation to fluid velocity. Operating this line at a fluid velocity u_B, homogeneously sized solids are continually fed into the duct. The solids feed rate will remain constant at W_1. Because of the drag on the particles and the solids friction, the pressure drop increases to a point C. As the fluid rate is now decreased along path CD, the particle velocity is reduced, and because the solids feed rate remains constant at W_1, the solids inventory increases. At point D such a condition is reached that, with the prevailing gas rate and the imposed solids feed rate W_1, all the solids in the conduit can just still be conveyed ahead. Hence point D represents the state in which the system still operates in a steady state, but at a maximum solids inventory. If the gas velocity should have only a nominal tendency to decrease, solids would have to precipitate and thus would no longer take part in any disperse-phase movement. The precipitated solids would then decrease the flow passage by such an amount that steady-state operation could continue further over the now smaller flow cross section, should no further fluctuations in gas flow rate occur. Because such fluctuations may, however, not be precluded, it must be borne in mind that a steady-state operation at D is not thinkable and that solids must continually precipitate from the disperse phase and be picked up again. For this reason the condition at D is known as the "point of saltation," and the fluid rate which attends this condition is known as the "saltation fluid velocity." Hence a slight decrease in fluid rate will result in a substantial deposition of solids, as is indicated by point E. With fluid rates decreasing further, solids flow will be partly by way of suspension above the solid layer

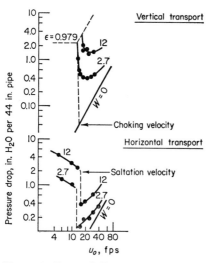

FIG. 6-3. Data of Zenz[28] pertaining to homogeneously sized solids in small-diameter vertical- and horizontal-transport lines. Note that choking and saltation occur at the same fluid rates for this case. (*Courtesy of Industrial and Engineering Chemistry.*)

and also by way of slug flow in the solid layer itself. This is represented by branch EF in Fig. 6-2.

As far as effect of pipe roughness on the onset of saltation is concerned, the available data are not conclusive. There may be a tendency for saltation to begin at points of excessive roughness.[28]

Prediction of Choking and Saltation Velocities. Figure 6-3 shows some pneumatic-transport data of Zenz[28] for flow of glass beads in vertical and horizontal conduits. For equal feed rates of the homogeneously sized particles choking and saltation occur in both vertical and horizontal lines at the same fluid velocities. For mixed sizes, however, choking and saltation velocities may differ substantially.

A correlation of choking and saltation velocities has been proposed by Zenz.[29] It is based on his earlier observed data[28] when relatively small diameter particles were passed through a 1.75-in.-diameter tube, 44 in. long. For the purpose of correlation the dimensional group $u_c{}^2/g_c D_p \rho_s{}^2$ has been related to the solids-to-gas ratio R. Shown in Fig. 6-4, the Zenz data are compared with some data of Lewis, Gilliland, and Bauer[18] pertaining to vertical transport as well as some horizontal-transport data

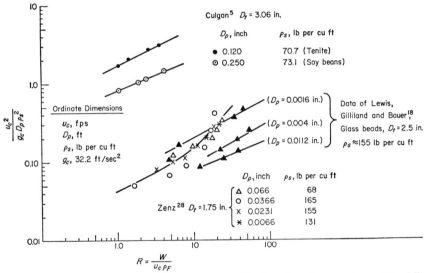

FIG. 6-4. Correlation of solids transport proposed by Zenz[29] and comparison with additional data.

of Culgan.[5] The Lewis et al. data are in reasonably good order-of-magnitude agreement with the Zenz data, which pertain to both vertical and horizontal lines.

There is no agreement between the Culgan data and the rest of the measurements. This may perhaps be due to the fact that Culgan used horizontal conduits of about 30 ft length, whereas the other data refer to sections of only a few feet. The short sections might not have been of length sufficient for full acceleration of the solids, whereas in the larger conduit used by Culgan, higher gas velocities at choking were realized. Aside from this deviation, a decided particle-diameter effect is apparent for the data of Culgan and Lewis et al. but is not indicated by the Zenz data.

For estimation of minimum carrying velocities in horizontal and vertical pneumatic-transport lines, Dallavalle[6] proposes

$$u_c = k \frac{\rho_S}{\rho_S + 62.3} D_p{}^{n'} \qquad (6\text{-}2)\star$$

where ρ_S is the solids density of the particles in pounds per cubic foot and D_p is the particle diameter, expressed in feet, of the largest particle to be conveyed. The limiting velocity u_c, which is in reality the choking or saltation velocity, will be in feet per second when constants k and n' are as follows:

Constant	Vertical	Horizontal
k	910	270
n'	0.60	0.40

Equation (6-2) is based on particles of 4 to 6 and 14 to 20 mesh. Densities of the materials were less than 187 lb per cu ft. Solids loadings were generally light, that is, below about 5 to 8 lb/(sec)(sq ft), and for such light loading conditions the minimum solids-carrying velocity appears to be independent of solids loading. There is, at present, no correlation that permits prediction of the minimum carrying velocity when solids loads are appreciable.

It will be noted that, according to Dallavalle, the limiting fluid velocity will be much higher in vertical- than in horizontal-transport lines. This is not in agreement with Zenz,[28] who on the basis of small-scale experiments concludes that choking and saltation velocities, hence limiting carrying velocities for uniform particles, are the same.

Loadings in individual systems will of course vary, depending on the solids to be conveyed. For grain and granular cellulose material and the like Dallavalle[6] suggests that 25 lb of material be conveyed by 1,000 cfm of air. This should occur through such a conduit that the linear air velocity is about 65 to 70 fps.

Example 6-1. Spherical particles of $D_p = 0.072$ in. diameter are to be conveyed with air in a horizontal pneumatic-transport line. If the solids-to-air ratio is desired to be 5.0, find the smallest air velocity at which it can be accomplished. The solids density may be taken as 70 lb per cu ft.

Solution. For a solids-to-gas ratio of 5.0 the ordinate from Fig. 6-4 becomes

$$\frac{u_c{}^2}{g_c D_p \rho_S{}^2} = 0.096$$

Hence
$$u_c = \sqrt{0.096 \times 32.2 \times 0.006 \times 70 \times 70}$$
$$= 9.54 \text{ fps}$$

Using the Dallavalle correlation,[6]

$$u_c = 270 \frac{70}{70 + 62.3} 0.006^{0.40} = 18.5 \text{ fps}$$

This is substantially higher than the value predicted by Zenz.[29] With the higher value proposed by Dallavalle, the particles are probably fully accelerated, whereas this might be questioned with the shorter conduits used by Zenz.

Experimental Data and Correlations

The earliest applications of pneumatic transport involved the conveying of many types of grains and seeds. Hence it is not surprising that in the first experimental studies such materials were studied primarily. The emphasis was then not so much on developing basic information which could be useful for design of pneumatic-transport systems as it was on providing more specific data for a class of related applications.

Because of the development of fluidization and its application to the process industries, the need for more quantitative and basic correlations pertaining to pneumatic transport has arisen. Thus it is primarily since the middle 1940s that more systematic efforts along this line have been reported.

In one of the earliest studies Gasterstädt[9] conveyed wheat and defined the ratio of the pressure drop of the solid suspension to the pressure drop for air alone at the prevailing mass velocity by a quantity α. Defining a specific loading ratio R as the weight ratio of solids flow to air flow, he concluded that a linear relationship existed between α and R, the slope of the resulting line being a function of air velocity. This basis for correlation has been repeatedly reconsidered after Gasterstädt, and the evidence so far accumulated has disproven its correctness.

The dimensionless pressure-drop ratio α proposed by Gasterstädt was employed by Vogt and White,[25] and they suggest that

$$\alpha - 1 = A' \left(\frac{D_t}{D_p}\right)^2 \left(\frac{\rho_F}{\rho_S} \frac{R\mu}{D_p u_g \rho_F}\right)^{k'} \tag{6-3}$$

Constants A' and k' are functions of the dimensionless group $[(\rho_S - \rho_F)\rho_F g_c D_p{}^3/3\mu]^{0.5}$, which is the product of the square root of the drag coefficient for spherical particles under free settling conditions and the Reynolds number. The correlation contains no particle-velocity term.

Particles used by Vogt and White were sands, steel shot, clover seed, and wheat. Mean particle diameters ranged from 0.0080 to 0.158 in., and solids densities were from 77 to 430 lb per cu ft. Experiments were conducted in a loop composed of $\frac{1}{2}$-in. standard pipe. Thus data could be obtained simultaneously in horizontal and vertical test sections. Regarding location of pressure taps from the dimensions indicated, it appears that the acceleration section provided was perhaps insufficient to assure steady-state conditions at all times. There was interference from an effect of surface roughness, since during the first 19 runs, pressure drops decreased as time progressed.

According to Eq. (6-3) the specific pressure drop is dependent on the ratio of conduit diameter to particle diameter. This is questioned in a subsequent paper by Belden and Kassel,[4] who examined vertical pneumatic transport of spherical catalysts approximately 0.04 to 0.08 in. in diameter. Transfer-line diameters were 0.473 and 1.023 in. By a proposed correlation, the total pressure drop is a function of a static portion, based on densities in the transfer line, and another part related to particle friction. There may be evidence that the data were not wholly corrected for acceleration effects.

Pressure-drop independence of the conduit-to-particle diameter ratio has also been mentioned by Korn.[16] He suggested that transport may occur in any one of three possible ways: In the case of relatively large particles in currents of low fluid density and low velocities, particles may advance by alternate leaps and saltations. With less-dense materials and in the presence of steep fluid-velocity gradients, there may be little contact with the pipe wall and the main portion of the solids may be carried by the central high-velocity fluid core. Finally, with very small particles, true suspension flow may be obtained with only an insignificant slip between particles and surrounding fluid.

Using a silica-alumina catalyst with a size spectrum extending from 10 to 220 microns, Farbar[7] investigated pneumatic flow in a pyrex-tube section of 17 mm ID and 2 ft length. Air velocities ranged from about 50 to 150 fps, and in this connection the effectiveness of a number of solids-feed nozzles was examined. One of the important findings of Farbar is that the Gasterstädt[9] pressure-drop ratio α is not linear in R, the solids-to-gas weight ratio.

Transport of uniformly sized silica-alumina catalysts and sand ranging from 0.0043 to 0.0198 in. were investigated by Hariu and Molstad[12] in vertical conduits of 0.267 and 0.532 in. diameter. The importance of particle velocity, for the purpose of data correlation, was recognized. Thus by referring measured disperse-density values to the equation of the continuity of flow, solid-particle velocities were calculated. For correlation purposes it was assumed that the total pressure drop was the sum of the pressure drop caused by the gas and a solids component. Important observations resulting from the study were as follows:

1. The pressure drop due to solids acceleration was a significant portion of the entire pressure drop.

2. The final velocity attained by the solids, which may be termed equilibrium velocity, was independent of solids loading.

3. The average final velocity of most materials was approximately one-half the surrounding gas velocity.

4. A correlation of drag coefficients vs. Reynolds number could be materially improved by including a sphericity factor in the calculated drag-coefficient values.

Experimental data for a 3-in.-diameter pipe have been observed by Culgan.[5] Solids were Tenite and alundum particles, soybeans, and cottonseed. Specific gravity of the particles was nearly unity, and particle size ranged from about 0.03 to 0.33 in. Among the more important observations made were the following:

1. The conduit length required to allow particles to reach their equilibrium velocity may be more appreciable than has hitherto been realized.

2. The equilibrium particle velocity is independent of solids loading but greatly dependent on the carrier-air velocity.

3. Observation on the effect of pipe roughness seemed to indicate that solids-air pressure drops are affected to a greater extent by pipe roughness than by flow of air alone.

The data were correlated in an empirical manner by means of a mixture friction factor and Reynolds-number relation.

Another pneumatic-transport study was made by Hinkle.[13] Like other workers,[5,9,12,16] he recognized the importance of the particle velocity for the purpose of developing useful working correlations; hence he obtained such data by using high-speed motion pictures.

As flow channels, 2-in.- and 3-in.-diameter glass pipes were used. The entire test section was 30 ft long, and pressure drops were measured at intervals of 5 ft. Particle velocities were determined photographically at various stations along the test section. Solids examined were Tenite pellets, alundum catalyst spheres, Catalin spheres, and polystyrene particles. Physical properties pertaining to these particles are given in Table 6-2.

TABLE 6-2. SOLIDS PROPERTIES OF MATERIALS INVESTIGATED BY HINKLE

Property	Tenite	Alundum	Catalin	Polystyrene
Particle density, lb per cu ft......	70.5	113	69.7	65.5
Bulk density, lb per cu ft........	45.5	71	49.0	40.0
Particle diam, in................	Mixture of sizes	......	0.25	
Mean particle size, in............	Mixture of sizes	0.33	.....	0.008–0.014
Max particle size, in............	0.12	0.36	.....	0.035
Sphericity.....................	0.93	1.00	1.00	0.96

Photographically observed particle velocities were empirically correlated for horizontal ducts by

$$u_{\text{slip}} = 1.41 u_g D_p^{0.3} s^{0.5} \qquad (6\text{-}4)$$

where $u_{\text{slip}} = u_g - u_p^*$, the difference between the carrier-gas velocity and the fully accelerated particle velocity; s is the specific gravity of the solid; and the other quantities are already known. A more convenient expression results if u_{slip} is replaced in Eq. (6-4) by its value $u_g - u_p^*$, where u_p^* is the equilibrium solids velocity, and if the solids density is introduced instead of specific gravity. Thus

$$u_p^* = u_g \left[1 - 1.41 D_p^{0.3} \left(\frac{\rho_S}{62.3} \right)^{0.5} \right] \qquad (6\text{-}5)\star$$

The fully accelerated solids velocity u_p^* will be in feet per second if u_g is in feet per second, D_p is in feet, and the solids density ρ_S is in pounds per cubic foot. The range of variables of the underlying data is as follows:

Air velocity: 66 to 119 fps
Particle diameter: 0.014 to 0.33 in.
Solids density: 65.5 to 113 lb per cu ft
Solids loading: Up to about 5 lb solids per lb air

For evaluating the total pressure drop due to combined gas and solids flow in a horizontal circular conduit, Hinkle proposes[13]

$$\Delta p_t = \frac{2 f_g u_g^2 \rho_F L}{g_c D_t} \left(1 + \frac{f_p^* u_p^*}{f_g u_g} R \right) \qquad (6\text{-}6)\star$$

where f_g is the Fanning-equation friction factor and f_p^* is a solids-flow friction factor prevailing under fully accelerated flow conditions. The latter may be estimated from a knowledge of the final solids velocity u_p^* as obtained from correlation (6-5) and the following equation:

$$f_p^* = \frac{3 \rho_F C_D D_t}{2 D_p \rho_S} \left(\frac{u_g - u_p^*}{u_p^*} \right)^2 \qquad (6\text{-}7)\star$$

C_D is the drag coefficient and is obtained from Fig. 5-4, since the value of $D_p u_g \rho_F / \mu$ is known.

Requirements for providing a sufficient accelerating section in a horizontal conduit were also studied. As already reported by Hariu and Molstad[12] as well as by Culgan,[5] Hinkle found that the equilibrium velocity attained was independent of solids loading. However, the rate at which the final particle velocity was established was greater in systems with low solids loads. This is indicated by the data of Fig. 6-5. For the material studied and the prevailing air velocity, about 30 ft of conduit were required to achieve complete particle acceleration.

The available vertical-pneumatic-transport data pertain to much shorter ducts than the data provided by Hinkle for horizontal transport. Hence there is the strong possibility that the vertical-transport pressure drops may be afflicted by particle-acceleration effects. Nevertheless Hinkle has extended his correlation, and he suggests for vertical systems

$$\Delta p_t = \frac{2 f_g u_g{}^2 \rho_F L}{g_c D_t} \left(1 + \frac{f_p^* u_p^*}{f_g u_g} R + \frac{2 g_c D_t}{f_g u_g u_p^*} R \right) \qquad (6\text{-}6a)$$

It will be noted that what is merely a term for solids head has been added in the parentheses. Although Eq. (6-6a) has been applied with

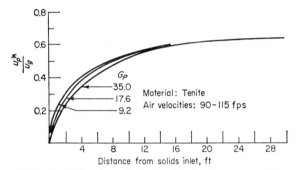

Fig. 6-5. Data of Hinkle,[13] showing effect of solids loading on particle acceleration in horizontal transport.

good results to the data of Hariu and Molstad,[12] additional confirmation in longer ducts should be desirable. In longer ducts, acceleration effects may be discounted and the validity of correlation (6-5) and its extension to vertical systems may be checked.

Example 6-2. A material of $\rho_S = 93.4$ lb per cu ft and $D_p = 0.24$ in. is to be conveyed by air through a horizontal, circular, 3-in.-ID smooth duct. The air-solids mixture leaves the duct at 14.7 psia and 70°F. The exit-air velocity is 50 fps. Find the pressure drop over 100 ft of duct for a solids-to-gas ratio of $R = 2.0$, assuming that the solids have been fully accelerated.

Solution. The fully accelerated particle velocity is found first. Hence

$$u_p^* = 50 \left[1 - 1.41 \times 0.02^{0.3} \left(\frac{93.4}{62.3} \right)^{0.5} \right] = 23.2 \text{ fps}$$

As a first approximation it will be assumed that the pressure drop is small and that the air density may be calculated on the basis of the exit pressure; hence $\rho_F = 0.075$.

$$\frac{D_p u_g \rho_F}{\mu} = \frac{0.02 \times 50 \times 0.075}{0.018 \times 0.000672} = 6{,}200$$

and from Fig. 5-4 $C_D = 0.44$

$$f_p^* = \frac{3 \times 0.075 \times 0.44 \times 3}{2 \times 0.02 \times 93.4 \times 12} \left(\frac{50 - 23.2}{23.2}\right)^2 = 0.00880$$

and from Fig. 3-1 $f_g = 0.00450$. Hence

$$\Delta p_t = \frac{2 \times 0.0045 \times 50^2 \times 0.075 \times 100}{32.2 \times 0.25 \times 144} \left(1 + \frac{0.0088 \times 23.2}{0.0045 \times 50} \times 2.0\right)$$
$$= 1.28 \text{ psi}$$

The inlet pressure then becomes $14.7 + 0.409 = 15.1$ psia. This will be sufficiently close, and no further correction for density variation of the air is required.

Summary

The relationship between the fluidized dense phase and disperse phase may be effectively described by means of a so-called fluidized-state phase diagram.

For gas-fluidized systems the fluidized dense phase is separated from the disperse phase by the slugging zone. This zone is an unstable region in which bed density is extremely sensitive to gas flow rate. Chiefly because of the experimental difficulties involved, the slugging zone is virtually unexplored. The voidage range that defines the zone has been roughly estimated to extend from 75 to 95 per cent.

Choking and saltation velocities are limiting fluid velocities for which solids will precipitate in either vertical or horizontal transfer lines. The physical significance of these limiting velocities is readily demonstrated by the fluidized-state phase diagram. As far as prediction of the limiting velocities is concerned, the relatively scant available data have resulted only in uncertain correlations. At best, limiting velocities may be only approximated for instances where the solids flow is less than about 10 lb/(hr)(sq ft).

Systematic investigations of solids transport in horizontal lines have disclosed that length of duct required to achieve full particle acceleration may be appreciable. Maximum particle velocities attained are independent of solids loading; however, rate of acceleration to the maximum velocity was slower with greater solids loads.

A knowledge of individual-particle velocities was recognized as the key to correlations for pressure drop in gas-solids transport systems. Hence an empirical correlation is suggested, one that permits evaluation of maximum solids velocity for a range of conditions usually encountered in pneumatic conveying.   Various correlations for pressure drop in gas-solids transport lines have been suggested.

HORIZONTAL HIGH-RATIO SOLIDS-GAS FLOW

It was pointed out in Chap. 2 that the apparent viscosity of aerated solids may be small enough that the granular material will flow by gravity through openings into pipes and ducts.   This property has been utilized, and a so-called fluidized feeder has been suggested.[1]   In such a unit the charge is simply aerated and a portion of the aerated charge is withdrawn by a proper side stream.   Large-scale units of this type have not yet been proposed, but the potential possibilities of this type of feeder and conveying system, as compared with the usual pneumatic conveying systems, may justify further consideration.

Solids-to-gas Ratio.   The essential difference between this mode of solids conveying and pneumatic transport is best understood from a comparison of the solids-to-gas ratios.   Whereas in pneumatic conveying solids-to-gas loading ratios are of the order of magnitude of 0.5 to 5.0, horizontal-transport lines using fluidized feeders may operate with solids-to-gas loading ratios of 25 to 100 or more.   Conversely, pneumatic-transport lines operate with gas velocities of perhaps 50 fps or more, whereas in high-ratio solids-gas flow, linear velocities in excess of 25 fps are seldom encountered.   More detailed comparative data for the two types of solids transportation are given by Koble, Jones, and Koehler.[15]

Qualitative Observations.   High-ratio solids-gas flow in horizontal-transport lines has been investigated in detail by Wen.[26]   In pneumatic conveying, the particles are entrained in the gas and thereby moved along through the conduit.   In a sense this is similar to the transport of solids by suspension in liquids.   Whereas in pneumatic conveying the individual-particle velocities over the duct cross section do not appear to vary greatly, the velocity pattern in dense-phase solids-gas flow is thoroughly nonuniform.   There may possibly be three modes of flow by which the solids will travel.   In the immediate vicinity of the fluidized feeder the particles appear to be still uniformly dispersed in the conveying tube.   In the subsequent zone the particles tend to settle and will fill only a fraction of the conveying duct.   There has, then, been compaction of the solids and a general increase in bulk density.   Finally there is a third zone in which the particles have formed dunes at periodic intervals.   With dune formation the solids have the highest bulk density, hence the solids velocity is smallest.

The main section of the conveying tube is usually occupied by the dunes.   Solids flow will then primarily be from dune to dune.   The distance between dunes and dune amplitude relative to the hydraulic dimensions of the duct are presumably functions of gas flow rate, solids feed rate, and physical properties. In high-velocity flow, though, dunes have either not been reported at all or exist merely at the exit of the duct. At lower flows the frequency and height of the dunes increase. For a still further decrease in fluid rate the dune height will approach the diameter of the conduit. For this condition, then, solids will merely move along shallow ripples on top of a solid layer which is itself essentially without motion. This condition may then eventually lead to a complete blocking of the line.

From the fact that the solids in dense solids-gas transport move more or less in bulk, it may be concluded that the effect of individual-particle properties upon pressure drop and rate of flow becomes obscured. It is therefore more logical to talk in terms of the velocity of the entire mass, rather than the velocity of individual particles. All this is reflected by the fact that parameters such as pressure drop and flow rates were found independent of such solids properties as particle shape and size and material density.[26]

Experimental Data. Virtually the only systematic data for this type of flow are those of Wen.[26] Earlier measurements of others[2,3] made in tubes ranging from $\frac{3}{16}$ to $\frac{1}{2}$ in. in diameter were too fragmentary to permit correlation. The apparatus of Wen was in essence a fluidized feeder with solids-feed hopper attached above, a test section 10 ft long, a solids-gas disengaging vessel, a scale, and the necessary instrumentation. As test sections, 1-, 0.75-, and 0.5-in.-ID pyrex-glass pipes were used. Each end of the glass pipe carried a quick-operating plug valve, and the pressure drop across 10 ft of the pipe was recorded by a Foxboro differential-pressure recorder. The air for fluidization and conveying had been dried by passage through an activated silica gel drier. Flow properties of powdered coal and spherical glass beads were investigated. Particle size and physical properties are given below.

During a typical run the charge in the feeder was fluidized with a predetermined amount of air. When constancy of operation was apparent, solids flow was diverted through the test section. After steady-state conditions were established, the solids were allowed to empty into the solids-gas disengaging vessel on the scales and the air proceeded to a dry test meter. Holdup in the test section was determined by simultaneously closing both plug valves. Having recognized the importance of full particle acceleration prior to entry into the test section proper, Wen investigated the matter in some detail. Contrary to pneumatic transport, only a few feet of pipe ahead of the test section were needed to accelerate the particles fully. From the weighings and the dry-test-meter readings, solids-gas ratios were obtained. The range of variables investigated was as follows:

Particles:

Coal, D_p, in.	Glass beads, D_p, in.
0.0297	0.0110
0.0197	0.0058
0.0044	0.0028

Solids density:

Coal: 81 lb per cu ft

Glass beads: 156 lb per cu ft

Test sections: 1.0-, 0.75-, 0.50-in.-ID glass tubing and 0.364-in.-ID steel pipe

Solids-to-air ratio: About 50:1 to 850:1

Air velocity: 0.50 to 50 fps, based on the open tube cross section

These limits should be helpful in defining the range of conditions for which the empirical correlation of the data is valid.

Correlation. Observation indicated that the total pressure drop Δp_t was much greater than that calculated for air flow alone through the empty conduit. Hence $\Delta p_t \approx \Delta p_s$.

A solids-phase friction factor was defined by

$$f_s = \frac{\Delta p_s \, g_c D_t}{2 G_s u_s L} \tag{6-8}$$

where G_s is the solids mass velocity, referred to the entire flow cross section. Solids velocity is defined by

$$u_s = \frac{G_s}{\rho_{ds}} \tag{6-9}$$

where ρ_{ds} is the density of the solids, hypothetically dispersed throughout the entire cross section of the conduit.

Using these quantities and resorting to the above approximation between Δp_t and Δp_s, solids-phase friction factors were evaluated from the experimental data and plotted in relation to solids velocity as shown in Fig. 6-6. The fact that the data correlate satisfactorily simply vs. u_s, and do not require the Reynolds number, emphasizes that in this type of flow individual-particle size plays a minor role.

The dispersed-solids density ρ_{ds} is defined by

$$\rho_{ds} = \frac{W}{AL} \tag{6-10}$$

where A is the solids-free cross section and L the length of the conduit. If this value is related to the apparent over-all solids-gas mixture, as given by $\rho_{ods} = W/V$, where V is the total unit volume, one can properly

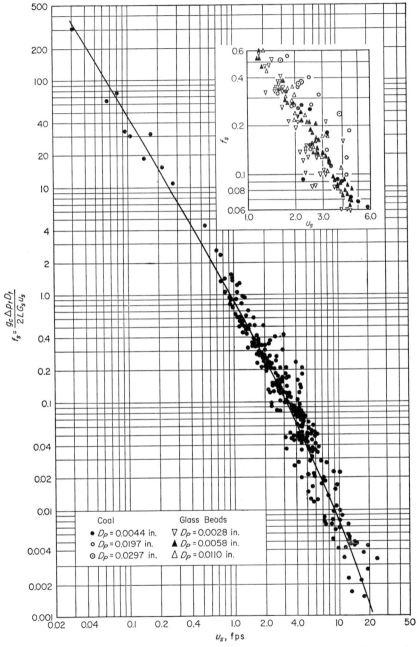

F<small>IG</small>. 6-6. Correlation of friction factors with particle velocity for high-solids-ratio flow in horizontal pipes.[26]

150

assess the amount of slip that occurs in this type of system. This may be seen from Fig. 6-7, where ρ_{ds} is given in relation to ρ_{ods} for a substantial data portion. It follows from the data that the velocity of the gas is just about twice that of the solids, when progressing in bulk. A similar observation has been reported by Hariu and Molstad[12] for true pneumatic systems.

Slip velocity can be related to pressure drop through a drag coefficient–like expression. Thus Fig. 6-8 shows $g_c \, \Delta p_s \, D_t / 2L\rho_{ds}(u_g - u_s)^2$ plotted vs. $u_g - u_s = \Delta u_s$. Values of u_g were obtained from $u_g = G_g/\rho_{dg}$, where G_g, the gas mass velocity, refers to the entire conduit cross section. However, ρ_{dg} is defined by $\rho_{dg} = (1 - \rho_{ds}/\rho_s)\rho_g$, and refers only to the volume

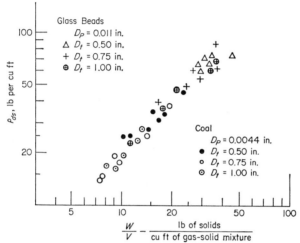

FIG. 6-7. Data of Wen[26] showing dispersed-solids density and apparent over-all gas-solids mixture density. Note that the dispersed-solids density is just about twice the over-all gas-solids mixture density.

that is actually occupied by the gas. Hence u_g is the true gas velocity above the solids.

Comparison of Figs. 6-6 and 6-8 indicates that for values of $u_s = u_g - u_s$ there result essentially the same numerical values on the ordinates. Hence for this type of flow and the solids employed

$$u_g \approx 2u_s \qquad (6\text{-}11)\star$$

which, being an important criterion for this type of flow, has already been observed from the dispersed-density data of Fig. 6-7.

Another empirical correlation between solids flow, solids density, and conduit diameter is given in Fig. 6-9. It relates $G_s D_t^{0.7}$ to $u_s\rho_s$ and permits evaluation of solids velocity for use with Fig. 6-6.

Effect of Pressure, Application and Limitations. Conveying data

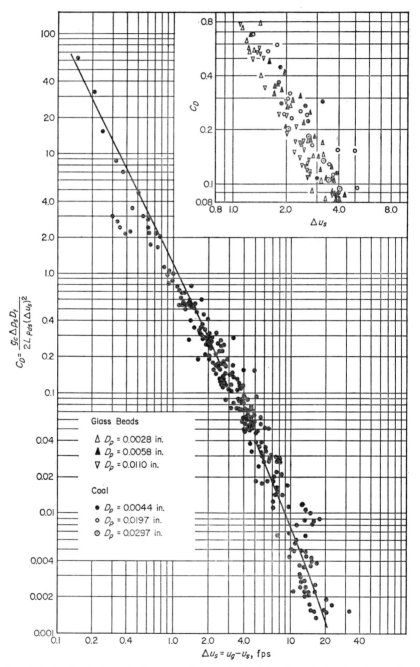

Fig. 6-8. Data of Wen[26] relating a drag coefficient to slip velocity for dense-phase solids flow in horizontal pipes.

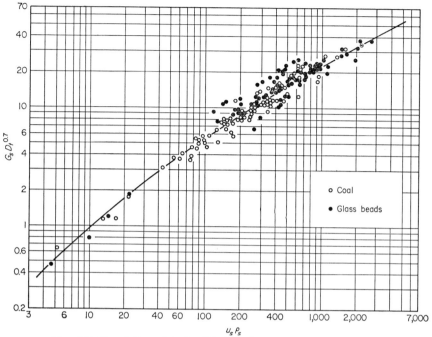

FIG. 6-9. Correlation plot of solids-flow data in horizontal pipes.[26]

for a 200-mesh coal have been reported by Barker et al.[3] for operating pressures ranging from atmospheric to 165 psia. The data, shown in

Fig. 6-10, pertain to a conveying tube of $\frac{3}{16}$ in. diameter. All tests were conducted at approximately 0.1 fps linear gas velocity, measured under the existing pressure in the fluidizer and 60°F. Thus when expressed on a weight basis, the solids-to-gas ratio is inversely proportional to the gas density. Hence from the point of view of air consumption it is most favorable to work at as low an operating pressure as is feasible. A few of the data of Longhouse et al.,[19]

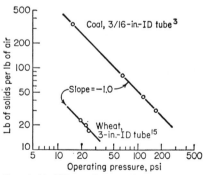

FIG. 6-10. Effect of operating pressure on solids-to-air ratio in horizontal pipes.

pertaining to the conveying of wheat under similar conditions in a 3-in.-diameter tube, lead to the same conclusion.

In order to utilize the dense-phase conveying mechanism, a so-called **fluidized feeder** has been proposed for delivering the solids-gas mixture to the conveying tube.   As has been pointed out,[3] the ease with which the solids will enter a conveying tube from such a device will depend on specific design features.   Thus funnel-shaped inlets have been reported to give improved results under some conditions of flow.   Of course once the solids and the gas are in the conveying tube it should no longer matter what the charging mechanism was.   Thus it is conceivable that a simple feed-hopper–air-injection system might be just as serviceable.   Of course care should be taken that the resistance upward through any solids valve and the solids in the hopper is always in excess of that through the conveying tube.

As far as limitations of the correlations are concerned, they are in accord with the range of variables already stated.   Although the data obtained with the 0.364-in.-diameter commercial steel pipe correlate with the remainder of the data, the earlier reported flow data of Koble et al.,[15] Barker et al.,[3] and Albright et al.[2] pertaining to $\frac{3}{16}$- to $\frac{1}{2}$-in. tube diameters correlated only poorly.   Perhaps differences in experimental manipulation were the chief reason for the disagreement.

There are doubtlessly effects of conduit surface roughness.   This is especially likely because the solids-friction component was apparently the major contributor to the pressure drop.   Thus with the correlation based on flow in smooth conduits, higher pressure drops may possibly be experienced in large-scale commercial steel equipment.

Since air was the only conveying gas, fluid-property effects could not be assessed.   In addition to the gas-density effect, already reported, an effect of gas viscosity may perhaps be anticipated.

Example 6-3.   A catalyst powder of $D_p = 0.0058$ in. particle size and solids density $\rho_S = 100$ lb per cu ft is to be transported from a storage hopper to a reaction vessel.   Dense-phase, high solids-to-gas ratio flow is contemplated through 50 ft of essentially horizontal 1-in.-ID glass tubing.   A solids flow rate of 50 lb/(sec)(sq ft) would be desirable.   The pressure at the discharge end of the tube is essentially atmospheric, and the temperature is 63°F.   For these conditions find:

1. The air pressure required at the conduit inlet
2. The necessary loading ratio
3. The volumetric air rate required

Solution.   From Fig. 6-9

$$G_s D_t^{0.7} = 50 \times 0.176 = 8.80$$
$$\rho_S u_s = 200 = 100 u_s$$
$$u_s = 2.0 \text{ fps}$$

From Fig. 6-6 $f_s = 0.27$.   Neglecting pressure drop due to gas flow,

$$\Delta p_t = \frac{2 \times 0.27 \times 50 \times 2.0 \times 50}{32.2 \times 0.0833 \times 144} = 7.00 \text{ psi}$$

Hence the air pressure at the inlet of the conduit will be

$$14.70 + 7.00 = 21.70 \text{ psia}$$

Next the dispersed-solids density is obtained as

$$\rho_{ds} = \frac{50}{2.0} = 25 \text{ lb per cu ft}$$

The dispersed-gas density then becomes

$$\rho_{dg} = \left(1 - \frac{25}{100}\right) 0.076 = 0.057 \text{ lb per cu ft}$$

Since it has been shown that for a system of this kind $u_g \approx 2u_s$, the air velocity becomes

$$u_g = 2 \times 2.0 = 4.0 \text{ fps}$$

Air mass velocity is then

$$G_g = u_g \rho_{dg} = 4.0 \times 0.057$$
$$= 0.228 \text{ lb/(sec)(sq ft)}$$

Hence the loading ratio will be

$$R = \frac{50}{0.228} = 219 \text{ lb of solids per lb air}$$

The air mass velocity was found to be $50/219 = 0.228$ lb/(sec)(sq ft). Hence one requires $(0.228 \times 3,600 \times 0.785)/144 = 4.48$ lb per hr of air. This is equivalent to 59.8 std cu ft per hr, measured at 70°F and 1 atm.

Summary

In high-ratio solids-gas flow in horizontal-transport lines the solids-to-gas ratios may vary from 25 to 100 or more. Air velocities are seldom in excess of 25 fps. In these respects this mode of solids transport differs fundamentally from pneumatic transport, where solids-to-gas ratios are rarely in excess of 5 or gas velocities often higher than 50 fps.

In lines operating under high solids-to-gas ratios the solids tend to move in mass rather than as individual particles. Thus this type of flow and its interpretation are much less dependent on particulate velocities than was found to be the case in true pneumatic transport.

Experimental data have been reported for coals and glass beads. Tube diameters ranged from 0.364 to 1 in. ID. The data analysis disclosed the important observation that air velocities were roughly twice as large as the velocity of the solids mass. This is reasonable and provided the key to data correlation.

Effects of gas properties have not been noted, though some data indicate that, from the point of view of air consumption, it is more favorable to work at the lowest possible pressure. Effects of gas viscosity have not been investigated. Pipe roughness may have an effect on transport rate. This too, as well as the effect of larger pipe diameters, is still to be investigated.

This mode of solids transport has so far been investigated only in horizontal-flow lines. It is conceivable that it might apply with modifications to slightly inclined ducts. However, this has not been considered.

GRAVITY FLOW OF GRANULAR SOLIDS

Gravity flow of granular solids is probably most commonly encountered in connection with solids handling and storage. A more specific application pertains to moving-bed catalytic cracking units, commonly known as TCC units. A moving-bed contactor is a unit in which granular solids move downward under the influence of gravity. As the movement progresses, the relative position of the particles in the charge remains essentially unaltered. Hence the flow of solids through such a vessel proceeds in an essentially rod-like fashion. If gases are passing upward, their limiting velocity must not exceed that required to expand the charge. Flow rates required to achieve such an expansion are discussed in Chap. 3. If the gas flow is downward, there is of course no such limitation. Regarding the moving bed itself, it has been found that its bulk density corresponds closely to the loosest packing arrangement for fixed beds. The size of particles composing moving beds is usually of the order of magnitude of $\frac{1}{8}$ to $\frac{1}{4}$ in., although in specific installations larger particles may be involved.

Gravity flow may also be the method by which granular solids are conveyed through a pebble heater. These are primary heaters or heat-reclaiming units in which hot broken solids contact flowing vapors or gases. The hot solids descend in the heat-exchange chamber, and gas flow may be either countercurrent or concurrent. The solids used in the pebble heater are usually of more than 0.5 in. diameter, and hence are substantially larger than catalysts used in TCC units.

Many other process-industry applications involving gravity flow of granular solids could be cited. As a final comment it might be mentioned that, for the design of solids-return piping from cyclone separators to fluidized beds, an understanding of the factors affecting solids flow in vertical pipes will be helpful.

Qualitative Observations. The few experimental studies pertaining to this type of problem are of relatively recent date.[8,14,20,22,23] As far as over-all appraisal of the problem and effects of variables is concerned, Gregory[10] points out the following:

1. The internal pipe diameter should be at least five to seven times as large as the largest particle encountered in the charge.

2. Materials of narrow size ranges will tend to flow more readily, whereas materials with wide size spectra may have sticking tendencies. This is also the case for comparatively small particles, say, $D_p < 0.003$ in.

3. Mild steel may encourage particle sticking, whereas the smoother surfaces of stainless steel and glass are more amenable to unimpeded flow.

4. Flow may be severely affected by surface moisture. Thus a surface moisture content in excess of 1 to 2 per cent is to be avoided.

Gregory states that the factors which influence the ability of a granular solid to flow by gravity are probably related to those which affect the ease with which the material will fluidize. Generally speaking this is probably true, although the tendency to stick and its effect on flow, as pointed out under (2) above, would not appear to support the observation. Hence there will probably be specific instances when the above generalizations may not wholly apply. Moreover, additional factors not mentioned might be of importance. Thus solids density, as well as the character of the material surface, may have an effect. As a final thought, electrostatic effects, so frequently associated with movement of particulate matter, might emerge.

As for flow mechanism, Gregory proposes that there may be either free flow of the charge or a second manifestation, termed "stick-and-slip" flow. By "free flow" is probably meant a steady-state condition whereby the solids pass along the length of the pipe uninterruptedly, presumably at uniform velocity. With stick-and-slip flow, on the other hand, the column is envisaged as moving intermittently, and not necessarily at a constant uniform velocity. For this type of flow solids-delivery rate is described as independent of solids head, whereas in free flow the rate is reported proportional to the square root of solids head. For design it is suggested that operation preferably be with stick-and-slip flow, rather than free flow. In this way no external application of pressure is required to push the solids through the pipe, the force exerted by gravity being all that is demanded. For stick-and-slip flow and delivery into air Gregory proposes[10]

$$W_a = 0.28 D_o{}^{2.5} \qquad (6\text{-}12)$$

where W_a will be in pounds per second if the conduit diameter D_o is expressed in inches. It is to be noted that this formula makes no allowance for system characteristics other than conduit diameter. Thus the constant 0.28 would appear to be specific for a particular class of particles.

Correlations. Wherever gravity flow of solids is part of a solids-handling system and no simultaneous gas or vapor flow through the granular solids is involved, one is normally interested only in the solids-handling capacity of the conduits and orifices. If, on the other hand, simultaneous flow of gases, either countercurrently or concurrently through the descending solids, is an integral part of the system, the prediction of fluid pressure drop is then usually demanded as well.

Gravity Solids Flow without Fluid Flow. In an extensive flow study with 3- and 8-in.-diameter tubes Rausch[22] investigated flow properties of a wide variety of solids, as indicated in Table 6-3. The simple equipment was essentially a hopper with solids-carrying conduit and attached delivery orifices. The arrangement also permitted examination of the effect of the presence of fluids other than air on the rate of solids delivery from the orifice. Orifice diameters considered varied from $\frac{1}{16}$ to 2 in.

TABLE 6-3. SOLIDS CHARACTERISTICS PERTAINING TO THE FLOW STUDY
OF RAUSCH

Particles	D_p, in.	ρ_b, lb per cu ft	Poured angle of repose in air β_a, deg
Alumina spheres.........	0.276	129	34
	0.447	127	38
	0.591	138	43
Glass beads.............	0.0113	91.6	26
	0.205	85.0	32
Lead shot...............	0.050	420	23
	0.150	411	30
	0.250	410	33
Steel balls...............	0.344	313	33
	0.500	301	37
Sea sand...............	0.0050	84.7	35
	0.0071	84.7	36
	0.0100	85.5	36
	0.0198	91	37
Iron powder......... ...	0.0050	138	40
	0.0071	140	40
	0.0100	152	41
	0.0141	148	42
Socony beads.............	0.170	45.5	35
Soy beans...............	0.302	47.7	39
Radish seed.............	0.098	45.5	38

For the entire series of runs the ratio D_o/D_p varied from about 2.5 to 250. Observed effects on solids delivery were as follows:

1. Solids head had practically no effect. From the experience of Gregory[10] this would then indicate that Rausch had stick-and-slip flow.

2. The diameter of the duct carrying the solids had very little effect on solids-delivery rate.

3. Particle size by itself plays a relatively minor part, but not so when it is considered in combination with orifice diameter. With $D_o/D_p < 25$,

the bulk density of solids, while passing through the orifice, appears to be reduced, thus affecting solids-delivery rates. For $D_o/D_p > 25$, this is felt no longer. Obviously this effect is the counterpart of the wall effect in cylindrical packed vessel.

4. The so-called angle of approach in the bottom of a delivery hopper as shown in Fig. 6-11 was of influence. In addition there seemed an effect of surface roughness which was also dependent on the D_o/D_p ratio. When the conduit roughness was of the same order of magnitude as that of the particles, and with D_o/D_p values small, surface effects were reported as being considerable and greatly dependent on the approach angle. With increasing D_o/D_p ratios, these effects decreased, eventually becoming insignificant.

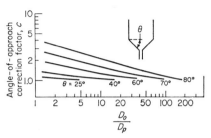

FIG. 6-11. Data of Rausch[22] showing correction factor in gravity flow of solids due to angle of approach.

5. Data pertaining to nonuniform solids are readily analyzed, provided the composite particle diameter is evaluated by $D_p = \Sigma n d_p^2 / \Sigma n d_p$, where n is the number of components and d_p is the diameter of a component. For granules, $d_p = \sqrt{d_1 d_2}$, where d_1 and d_2 are adjacent sieve openings.

6. As would be expected, simultaneous countercurrent flow of air decreases solids-delivery rate greatly.

All data were correlated by the dimensionless equation

$$W_a = cc_0 \frac{(D_o/D_p)^{2.70} g_c^{0.5} \rho_b D_p^{2.5}}{(\tan \beta_a)^{0.5}} \qquad (6\text{-}13)\star$$

where c is a correction factor pertaining to the angle of approach in the hopper bottom and c_0 is a wall-effect correction factor. Expressed as functions of D_o/D_p, these factors are available from Figs. 6-11 and 6-12.

An evaluation of normal bulk density ρ_b may be obtained from the general voidage data of materials given in Chap. 2. The remaining quantity, the angle of repose, is easily determined for any solid; as a guide to possible values, it has been indicated in Table 6-3

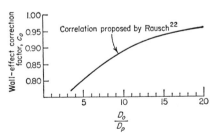

Fig. 6-12. Wall-effect correction factor for gravity flow of solids.[22]

for the various solids used by Rausch. It is interesting to note that, for nonspherical particles, β_a shows little variation with particle diameter, whereas for spherical particles the angle decreases in all instances with decreasing particle diameter. Besides being dependent on particle diameter, β_a is dependent on surface condition. If it is not convenient to measure β_a, the tabulated data may be used to estimate the angle for intermediate particle sizes and similar materials.

Comparisons. Equation (6-13) is readily rearranged to read

$$W_a = cc_0 \frac{g_c^{0.5}\rho_b}{D_p^{0.2}(\tan \beta_a)^{0.5}} D_o^{2.70} = C_s D_o^{2.70} \qquad (6\text{-}13a)$$

where C_s is a constant that is characteristic of the solids involved. Except for exact value of exponent on orifice diameter, Eq. (6-13a) is of the same form as Eq. (6-12) proposed by Gregory.[10]

It may be of interest to evaluate C_s in Eq. (6-13a) for an actual case and compare this with the constants given by Gregory and others. Thus for a typical TCC catalyst of, say, $D_p = 0.15$ in., $\beta_a = 40°$, and $\rho_b = 0.02315$ lb per cu in., it will be assumed that the product $cc_0 = 0.9$. With $g_c = 386.5$ (lb mass) in./(lb force)(sec)(sec) there results then

$$C_s = \frac{0.9 \times 19.66 \times 0.02315}{0.684 \times 0.916} = 0.654$$

This value is considerably higher than 0.28, the constant given by Gregory.

Formulas similar to the Gregory formula have been proposed by others. Thus Newton, Dunham, and Simpson[20] reported on flow of a TCC catalyst of 0.1 in. size through orifices ranging from 1 to 4 in. For these conditions

$$W_a = 0.14L^{0.04}D_o^{2.96} \qquad (6\text{-}14)$$

where W_a is again in pounds per second if D_o is in inches and column height L is in feet. Thus they found that the solids discharge rate is almost independent of column height.

Data similar to those of Newton et al. were correlated by Kelley,[14] who suggests that

$$W_a = 0.16D_o^{2.84} \qquad (6\text{-}15)$$

On the basis of extensive data Franklin and Johanson[8] report that

$$W_a = \frac{0.0166\rho_b D_o^{2.93}}{(6.29 \tan \beta_a + 23.16)(D_p + 1.89) - 44.90} = C_s D_o^{2.93} \qquad (6\text{-}16)$$

Again it is seen that constant C_s is dependent on the already-mentioned solids characteristics. Evaluation of the constant for the already-mentioned catalyst sample yields

$$C_s = \frac{0.0166 \times 40}{(6.29 \times 0.839 + 23.16)(0.15 + 1.89) - 44.90} = 0.051$$

This is not in agreement with 0.654, the constant proposed by Rausch. The exponent on the orifice diameter given by Franklin and Johanson is appreciably higher than that of Rausch and other investigators.

Additional correlations on solids flow through orifices were given by several Japanese workers. Having examined flow of sands, active earth,

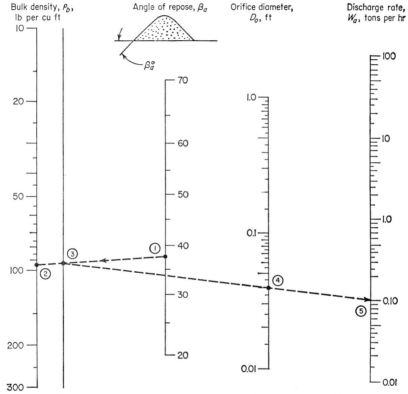

FIG. 6-13. Nomograph of Shirai[23] for flow of powders through orifices. EXAMPLE: Bulk density of sand ρ_b = 95 lb per cu ft, angle of repose β_a = 37°, orifice diameter D_o = 0.04 ft, and discharge rate W_a = 0.10 tons per hour. (*Courtesy of T. Shirai*)

and quartz powder of 30 to 150 mesh through orifices of 0.09 to 0.36 in. diameter, Shirai[23] proposes that

$$W_a = \frac{0.0038\rho_b D_o^{2.5}}{(\tan \beta_a)^{0.5}} \qquad (6\text{-}17)\star$$

For convenient use the formula has been condensed into the nomograph of Fig. 6-13. Of special interest is the exponent 2.5 assigned to the orifice diameter. The exponent has been confirmed by Takahashi,[24] as well as Oyama and Nagano,[21] who report on somewhat related studies.

Kuwai,[17] on the other hand, having investigated solids flow under light aeration, reports that

$$W_a = 0.82 D_o{}^{2.75} \qquad (6\text{-}18)$$

The larger experimental constant emphasizes that aeration will tend to increase solids flow.

Summary

From the considerable variations in the value of the experimental constant it appears that, for flow of solids through ducts and orifices, the effect of all the variables is not yet understood. In particular it appears that an understanding of the effects of particle size and the nature of the surfaces of the duct and the particles is still largely missing. Experimental constants, reported as well as estimated for probable conditions, are given in Table 6-4.

TABLE 6-4. EXPERIMENTAL CONSTANTS AND ORIFICE-DIAMETER EXPONENT IN VARIOUS PROPOSED CORRELATIONS

Reference	C_s	Exponent
Gregory[10]	0.28	2.50
Newton et al.[20]	0.14	2.96
Kelley[14]	0.16	2.84
Franklin and Johanson[8]	0.05	2.93
Rausch[22]	0.65	2.70
Kuwai[17]	0.82	2.75
Shirai[23]	0.18	2.50

Omitting the value of Kuwai, which is high because of the aeration of the solids, the average of the experimental values of the constant becomes 0.24. Orifice-diameter exponents show less variation; they also are indicated for the various investigators in Table 6-4. An average value of 2.74 for all data is indicated.

From the comparison of C_s values it appears that the Rausch equation (6-13) tends to give high values of W_a. For calculation purposes it is therefore suggested that the values obtained by Eq. (6-13) be multiplied by $0.24/0.654 = 0.37$, to account for this high trend.

In its present form Eq. (6-13) applies to flow of solids into air. Rausch has also investigated the effect when the solids will discharge into media other than air. This has led to the relation

$$W_F = W_a \left[\frac{\tan \beta_a (1 - \rho_F/\rho_S)}{\tan \beta_F} \right]^{0.5} \qquad (6\text{-}19)$$

where ρ_F and ρ_s are densities, β_a and β_F are poured angles of repose, and

W is the solids flow rate. Subscripts a, F, and s make reference to air, the other fluid, and the solids, respectively.

Gravity Flow with Fluid Flow. The pressure-drop study through moving beds of solids reported by Happel[11] constitutes virtually the only systematic set of data and correlation pertaining to simultaneous fluid flow and gravity flow of solids. Of course it has been reported,[22] and was known earlier, that simultaneous gas flow in moving beds will either accelerate or impede the rate of flow of the solids, depending on whether gas flow is concurrent or countercurrent. Although the correlation of Happel does not touch on the influence of gas velocity upon solids velocity, it is nevertheless of value in predicting pressure drop for the range of the supporting data.

With gravity flow of solids and a free upper solids boundary desired, there is a limiting upward gas velocity which must not be exceeded. With downward gas flow and gravity flow of solids, no such limitation of gas flow rate exists, except that flow is governed and controlled by extraneous circumstances such as blower capacities and available gas pressures.

Pressure Drop. According to a greatly simplified model, pressure drop though a packed bed may be considered as being composed of a conduit-wall component and a packed-core component. However, since the contribution of the core component to the final pressure drop is much greater than that of the wall component, the latter may in virtually all cases be discounted. Since in fixed beds there is no net movement of packing relative to conduit wall, it is permissible to refer all fluid velocities to the fixed container. This may not be permissible in a moving bed, especially if the particle velocity relative to the conduit wall is appreciable. Hence in moving beds it may become necessary, for certain fluid and solids velocities, to refer velocities to the moving solids rather than use the so-called velocity-of-approach value for correlation purposes.

Another factor that affects pressure drop greatly is the bed voidage. Investigators have indicated that over-all voidage attending gravity flow of solids corresponds closely to the minimum fluid voidages defined and presented in Chap. 2. Furthermore, local variations in voidage, as solids pass down a column, seem insignificant indeed, and true rod-like flow seems to prevail with little or no telescoping occurring. This observation, supported by the fact that in a moving bed composed of a wide size distribution there is virtually no segregation, should help considerably as far as correlation is concerned.

The apparatus of Happel was a standpipe-hopper arrangement. Pressure taps were spaced 6 ft apart and far enough away from solids entrance and exit to preclude entrance effects. Ducts were of 4, 6, and 10 in. diameter. Investigated were a variety of spherical seeds and used and fresh spherical and pelleted catalysts. All particles had a comparatively wide size distribution. Average diameter, calculated by $D_p = 100/\Sigma(X/dp)$, varied from 0.015 to 0.276 in. Fraction voids observed during gravity flow ranged from 33 to 49 per cent.

The data were correlated by relating a modified friction factor to a modified Reynolds number. Thus

$$f_m = \frac{g_c\, \Delta p\, D_p}{2Lu_0{}^2\rho_F(1 - \epsilon)^3} = \psi\left[\frac{D_p u_0 \rho_F}{\mu}(1 - \epsilon)\right] \qquad (6\text{-}20)\star$$

In this equation, velocity u_0 is not the gas velocity relative to the moving solids, but instead represents the superficial velocity in relation to the unpacked tower.

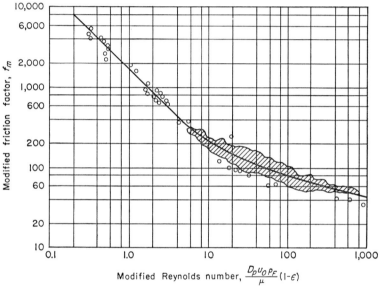

FIG. 6-14. Modified friction factors vs. modified Reynolds number for moving-bed data. (*Data of Happel.*[11] *Courtesy of Industrial and Engineering Chemistry.*)

Equation (6-20) is applicable to gravity flow of solids when under countercurrent or concurrent gas or vapor flow, as long as the solids velocity relative to the wall is not in excess of 20 per cent of the gas or vapor velocity. For moving beds with solids linear velocities exceeding 20 per cent of the superficial gas velocity, it is suggested that the correlation be modified by substituting fluid velocity relative to the moving particles, rather than relative to the conduit wall.

Calculations of pressure drop are readily made by evaluating the modified friction factor from Fig. 6-14 and using it with Eq. (6-20).

Example 6-4. A granular material of 70 lb per cu ft solids density has a size composition as follows:

d_p, in.	Weight per cent X	$\dfrac{X}{d_p}$	$X\,d_p$
Below 0.03819	1.0	26	0.038
0.03819	15.0	393	0.573
0.02795	42.0	1,500	1.174
0.02321	30.0	1,291	0.697
0.01646	11.0	668	0.181
Above 0.01646	1.0	61	0.016
Total........	....	3,939	2.679

While descending a 4-in.-diameter standard steel pipe, the material exhibits an average bulk density of 40 lb per cu ft. The solids flow rate is 120 lb/(min)(sq ft).

The solids are to be contacted countercurrently by air for a 6 ft length of duct. The average temperature is 75°F, the air leaving the system will be essentially at atmospheric pressure. Specify the required inlet pressure for an air mass velocity of 80 lb/(hr)(sq ft).

Solution. As a first orienting step the order of magnitude and approximate ratio of gas and solids velocity will be established. Hence solids velocity

$$u_s = \frac{120}{40 \times 60} = 0.050 \text{ fps}$$

Not knowing the inlet pressure, we shall assume at this point that it is 15.0 psia, giving an inlet air density of 0.076 lb per cu ft. Anticipating that the average air density will then be 0.075 lb per cu ft, the average air velocity will be

$$u_g = \frac{80}{0.075 \times 3,600} = 0.296 \text{ fps}$$

Hence
$$\frac{u_g}{u_s} = \frac{0.296}{0.050} = 5.92$$

and it should be satisfactory to use the unmodified Happel correlation.

Composite particle diameter

$$D_p = \frac{100}{\Sigma(X/d_p)} = 0.0253 \text{ in.}$$

Column voidage

$$\epsilon = 1 - \frac{40}{70} = 0.428$$

Modified Reynolds number,

$$D_p G(1 - \epsilon)/\mu = \frac{0.0253 \times 80 \times 0.572}{12 \times 0.0422} = 2.29$$

From Fig. 6-14 $f_m = 710$, and

$$\Delta p = \frac{2 \times 710 \times 6 \times 0.296 \times 0.296 \times 0.075 \times 0.187 \times 12}{32.2 \times 0.0253 \times 144} = 1.09 \text{ psi}$$

Hence inlet pressure should be $14.7 \times 1.09 = 15.79$ psia. It will be noted that this value is sufficiently close to the originally accepted pressure of 15.0 psia that no further correction is required.

Question: How accurately may the pressure drop be predicted by using Eq. (3-8)?

Answer: In order to use Eq. (3-8), $D_p = \Sigma X d_p = 0.0268$ in. (Note that for this particle-size distribution the two modes of evaluation of D_p give almost identical results.)

$$\text{Re} = \frac{D_p G}{\mu} = \frac{0.0268 \times 80}{12 \times 0.0422} = 4.23$$

According to Fig. 3-3, $f = 23.6$ and $n = 1.0$. Assuming $\phi_s = 0.86$,

$$\Delta p = \frac{2 \times 23.6 \times 6 \times 0.0222 \times 0.0222 \times 12 \times 4.2}{0.0268 \times 32.2 \times 0.075 \times 0.86^2 \times 144} = 1.01$$

Note that this value is only approximately 8 per cent lower than the value predicted by the Happel correlation. A somewhat higher value would result if instead of using the superficial air velocity the air velocity relative to the descending solids were used.

PROBLEMS

6-1. Spherical lead balls of $D_p = 0.75$ in. are passed down a 12-in.-diameter circular shell at a rate of 500 lb per min and are contacted by an upward rising air current. The active length of the shell is 6 ft. The lead spheres enter at 70°F and are to be heated by the air, which enters at a temperature of 650°F. The unit is well insulated, so that heat losses through the shell may be discounted. The air discharges into the atmosphere, and its mass velocity is 80 lb/(hr)(sq ft). While descending, the bed of lead balls displays a voidage of 44 per cent. Estimate the inlet air pressure necessary to maintain the required flow.

6-2. A moving-bed reactor consists of a 10-in.-diameter shell terminating at its lower end in a cone with an apex angle of 60°. The apex is to be fitted with a series of rotating orifices that are intended to be used for solids flow control through the unit. The solids have a bulk density of 42 lb per cu ft, and for the average particle diameter of $D_p = 0.24$ in. an angle of repose of 37° was observed. For these conditions specify the required orifices if the flows through the unit are to be 60, 120, and 300 lb per min.

6-3. Wheat approximately 0.25 by 0.125 in. in dimension and having a bulk density of 50 lb per cu ft is to be conveyed from a bin into a hopper upstairs. On its way the wheat travels 80 ft along the horizontal and passes then through a long-sweep 90° elbow upward for another 20 ft. The long-sweep elbow may be assumed to be equivalent to 20 ft of horizontal pipe. The wheat discharges from the bin by way of a circular 1-in.-diameter orifice and drops into the suction air line where it is picked up.

Estimate the required circular-duct diameters and attending pressure drops if the air velocities are 2, 3, and 4 times the minimum air rate required to move the solids.

Loading will in all cases be assumed to be 25 lb of grain per 1,000 cu ft of air used, and it will be assumed that, for this light load, solids-acceleration effects may be discounted.

6-4. A ground coal of average particle size $D_p = 0.0125$ in. and a solids density of $\rho_S = 80$ lb per cu ft is to be fed into a pilot-plant gasifier. This is to be accomplished by using a fluidized feeder of 24 in. diameter and a smooth ½-in. standard steel pipe as feed line. The feed line will travel only horizontally, and through its 24 ft of length it is desired to transport 100 lb per hr of coal into the reactor. In order to avoid dusting, the fluidized feeder is to be operated at a reduced mass velocity of only 3.0. For the conditions specified find:

1. The air rate required to operate the feeder
2. The required solids-to-air loading ratio
3. The required air rate
4. The inlet air pressure needed for the operation

6-5. A granular solid is to be conveyed vertically upward at a rate of 1,000 lb per hr by a pneumatic duct. The system is to be operated at a solids-to-air ratio of 1:1. Using Eq. (6-6a), estimate the pressure drop through 20 ft of straight flow section, assuming that the solids have been completely accelerated.

In order to use Eq. (6-6a), the equilibrium solids velocity u_p^* must be known. Solve this problem by estimating the equilibrium solids velocity either (1) by correlation (6-5) or (2) independently by a suitable terminal-velocity correlation given in Chap. 5 or, if desired, by the nomograph of Fig. 5-5. It will be noted that correlation (6-5) holds for a velocity range of 66 to 119 fps in horizontal ducts. Therefore, examine this problem for the two instances in which the flow duct is so chosen that the average air velocities are 66 and 119 fps. The air discharges into the atmosphere at 70°F. The solids may be assumed spherical with $D_p = 0.24$ in. and $\rho_S = 100$ lb per cu ft. From the resulting terminal velocities, equilibrium particle velocities, and the calculated pressure drops by Eq. (6-6a), give your opinion of the present status of this problem.

REFERENCES

1. Albright, C. W., J. H. Holden, H. P. Simons, and L. D. Schmidt: *Chem. Eng.*, **56**(6): 108 (1949).
2. Albright, C. W., J. H. Holden, H. P. Simons, and L. D. Schmidt: *Ind. Eng. Chem.*, **43**: 1837 (1951).
3. Barker, K. R., J. J. S. Sebastian, and L. D. Schmidt: *Ind. Eng. Chem.*, **43**: 1204–1209 (1951).
4. Belden, D. H., and L. S. Kassel: *Ind. Eng. Chem.*, **41**: 1174 (1949).
5. Culgan, J. M.: Ph.D. thesis, Georgia Institute of Technology, 1952.
6. Dallavalle, J. M.: *Heating and Ventilating*, **39**(11): 28–32 (1942).
7. Farbar, L.: *Ind. Eng. Chem.*, **41**: 1184 (1949).
8. Franklin, F. C., and L. N. Johanson: *Chem. Eng. Sci.*, **4**(3): 119–129 (1955).
9. Gasterstädt, H.: *Z. Ver. deut. Ingenieurw.*, **68**: 617–624 (1924).
10. Gregory, S. A.: *J. Appl. Chem. (London)*, **2**, Suppl. Issue 1, S1–S7 (1952).
11. Happel, John: *Ind. Eng. Chem.*, **41**: 1161 (1949).
12. Hariu, O. H., and M. C. Molstad: *Ind. Eng. Chem.*, **41**: 1148 (1949).
13. Hinkle, B. L.: Ph.D. thesis, Georgia Institute of Technology, 1953.
14. Kelley, A. E.: *Petrol. Engr.*, **16**(13): 136–142 (1945).
15. Koble, R. A., P. R. Jones, and W. A. Koehler: *Am. Ceram. Soc. Bull.*, **32**: 367 (1953).

16. Korn, A. H.: *Chem. Eng.*, **57**: 108 (1950); **58**: 178 (1951).
17. Kuwai, G.: *Chem. Eng. (Tokyo)*, **17**: 453–459 (1953).
18. Lewis, W. K., E. R. Gilliland, and W. C. Bauer: *Ind. Eng. Chem.*, **41**: 1104–1117 (1949).
19. Longhouse, A. D., D. P. Brown, H. P. Simons, and C. W. Albright: *Agr. Eng.*, **31**(7): 349, 352 (1950).
20. Newton, R. H., G. S. Dunham, and T. P. Simpson: *Trans. AIChE*, **41**: 215 (1945).
21. Oyama, Y., and K. Nagano: *Repts. Sci. Research Inst. (Tokyo)*, **29**: 349–352 (1953).
22. Rausch, J. M.: Ph.D. thesis, Princeton University, 1948.
23. Shirai, T.: *Chem. Eng. (Tokyo)*, **16**: 86–89 (1952).
24. Takahashi, K.: *Bull. Inst. Phys. Chem. Research (Tokyo)*, **12**: 984–994 (1933).
25. Vogt, E. G., and R. R. White: *Ind. Eng. Chem.*, **40**: 1731 (1948).
26. Wen, C. Y.: Ph.D. thesis, West Virginia University, 1956.
27. Wilhelm, R. H., and S. Valentine: *Ind. Eng. Chem.*, **43**: 1199 (1951).
28. Zenz, F. A.: *Ind. Eng. Chem.*, **41**: 2801–2806 (1949).
29. Zenz, F. A.: *Petrol. Refiner*, **36**(6): 133 (1957).

CHAPTER 7

THE SPOUTED BED

Nomenclature

D_i = fluid-inlet diameter, ft
D_p = particle diameter, ft
D_t = spouting-chamber diameter, ft
g_c = gravitational conversion factor, 32.2 (lb mass)(ft)/(lb force)(sec)(sec)
L = bed height before spouting, ft
n = exponent
u_{msp} = minimum fluid velocity for steady-state spouting, fps
ρ_S = solids density, lb per cu ft
ρ_F = fluid density, lb per cu ft

Abstract

This chapter describes the spouted bed and some of its characteristics. Spouting is a new technique for contacting fluids with solids of size and other physical properties that render them difficult to fluidize.

The pressure-drop–flow diagram is discussed, and the apparent similarity between the spouted bed and fluidized beds that have channeling tendencies is stressed. Solids and apparatus requirements for spouting are then taken up and a correlation for the onset of spouting is given. Finally, factors affecting air and solids flow in the spouted bed are presented as far as possible.

DESCRIPTION

"Spouting" is a relatively new technique for contacting fluids with coarse granular solids.[2,3]* From the description so far available it appears that a spouted bed is in a sense a combination of a dilute fluidized phase and a coexistent moving fixed bed of solids. This is readily seen from Fig. 7-1, which is a schematic diagram of a spouted bed. The air enters the apparatus through an opening in the apex of a conical inlet. The air entrance is so abrupt that there is essentially no opportunity for an appreciable lateral distribution over the total apparatus cross section. Hence a central channel is formed, and in it solids are entrained upward. The solids enter the channel mainly in the cone section; however, as will

* Superscript numbers indicate works listed in References at the end of the chapter.

169

be emphasized later, solids also move from higher strata laterally into the channel.

The solids concentration in the central channel increases with height, and at the same time the physical outline of the channel becomes increasingly less distinct. However, for all practical purposes the solids-to-gas ratio in the central channel is of the same order of magnitude as found in a typical dilute-phase fluidized system. At the upper end of the channel the solids spill over radially into an annulus that defines a column of descending solids. In this ring the solids move downward, without essentially varying their relative positions. The prevailing bed voidage and pattern of solids movement are similar to those found and already described in connection with aerated moving-solids beds.

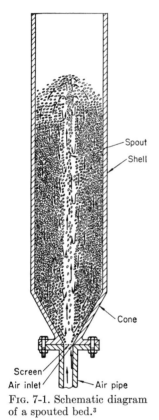

Coexistence of the two phases produces a characteristic solids circulation pattern, by which the material is entrained in the center upward and is caused to descend by gravity through the surrounding dense bed contained in the annular space. The gas distribution over the bed cross section must of necessity be highly nonuniform. In a sense this is similar to conditions found in fluidized beds with strong channeling tendencies. The apparent similarity between spouting and channeling is also recognized from the pressure-drop–flow diagram.

FIG. 7-1. Schematic diagram of a spouted bed.[3]

PRESSURE-DROP–FLOW DIAGRAM

For low gas velocities the system may be a fixed bed. If so it is not different from any fixed bed that precedes the normal fluidization state. This is indicated by the linearity of branch ab of Fig. 7-2. If the air velocity is increased beyond point b, the particles at the base of the cone are lifted and a short internal channel, or spout, is formed. Since the solids concentration in the short spout is lower than in the remainder of the bed, a decrease in pressure drop must accompany an air-mass-velocity increase beyond point b. With further increases in air velocity the height of the spout increases and the pressure drop decreases further to a point c. At this point an appreciable rise in bed level may have occurred, owing to a substantial displacement of solids from the central channel. Hence for a further increase in air mass velocity, say to point d, no further pressure-drop variation may be noted. Up to this point the spout was still completely confined to the inside of the bed; that is to say, the spout had not yet penetrated through the upper-bed boundary. For a further nominal increase in mass velocity to point e the spout now breaks through the bed; the solids concentration in the spout decreases abruptly, especially in the upper region; and as a consequence a further appreciable pressure-drop reduction is noted. At point e the bed is spouting in a

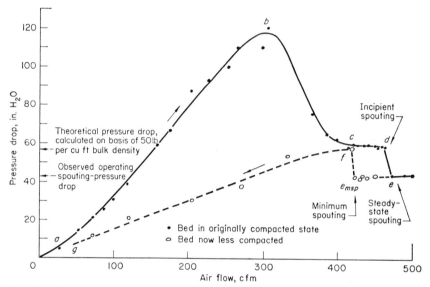

FIG. 7-2. Typical pressure-drop–flow diagram for a spouting bed.[5] Note that stable spouting occurs over flow range e-e_{msp}. Data observed for 24-in.-diameter column carrying 70.5 in. of wheat, 45° cone angle, 4-in. orifice for air. (*Courtesy of G. L. Osberg.*)

steady state. Beyond e the pressure drop remains more or less independent of air mass velocity.

Let us now decrease the air mass velocity. The bed will remain in the spouting condition until point e_{msp} is reached. If at this point the mass velocity is reduced nominally, a sudden increase in pressure drop occurs and the spout submerges into the bed. Obviously then at point e_{msp} the bed is in its minimum spouting condition. The pressure-drop rise to point f is for all practical purposes equal to the pressure-drop decrease de. At point f the spout has virtually entirely collapsed. Branch fg is again characteristic of a fixed bed. The hysteresis loop d-e-e_{msp}-f is due to the fact that a certain energy is required to overcome the normal compaction of the bed. Obviously, then, the fixed-bed line *fg* is below line *ab*, because the bed is now in a more loosely packed condition.

The internal solids rearrangement which is the cause for the hysteresis loop is also sometimes observed in fluidized beds where channeling is prevalent. The apparent similarity between spouting and channeling may also be recognized from the magnitude of the operating pressure drop. It is recalled, as outlined in Chap. 2, that in beds with channeling tendencies the operating pressure drop is lower than the theoretical value calculated from the weight of the bed. The data pertaining to spouting show a similar trend. Thus Fig. 7-2 pertains to spouting of a column of wheat of 70.5 in. original height in a vessel of 24 in. diameter. Assuming a bulk density of 50 lb per cu ft for wheat, the theoretical pressure drop is $(50 \times 70.5 \times 12)/(12 \times 62.3) = 56.3$ in. of water. The indicated operating spouting pressure drop is only 44 in. Hence there is a substantial decrease, just as would result from channeling in otherwise normally fluidizing solids.

SPOUTING REQUIREMENTS

It has already been learned from Chap. 2 that channeling characteristics of solids are difficult to predict. In view of the apparent similarity between spouting and channeling, the question arises whether the prediction of spouting characteristics is equally vague. On the basis of the data so far available it appears that prediction of spouting characteristics, though still incompletely explored, is more promising.

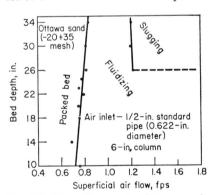

FIG. 7-3. Phase diagram for Ottawa sand, ½-in. standard pipe for air inlet.[3] (*Courtesy of AIChE Journal.*)

The effect of diameter of the gas inlet is readily apparent from a comparison of Figs. 7-3 and 7-4. The figures represent so-called phase diagrams for Ottawa sand of 20–35 mesh size. When the air enters by way of a ½-in. standard pipe, the charge will not spout at all. Thus for a bed depth of, let us say, 20 in., the packed bed becomes fluidized near an air velocity of about 0.8 fps. With the ½-in. standard air inlet now replaced by a ⅜-in. standard pipe and operating with an original bed height of 20 in., the packed bed transforms into a spouting bed. As the air rate is increased, the spout loses shape and fluidization sets in near a velocity of about 1.0 fps. This is shown in Fig. 7-4. For higher original bed heights spouting may not occur at all, and the fluidizing bed, encountered instead, may pass directly into the slugging zone.

This effect of air inlet has of course its counterpart in fluidization. Mention is made of the fluidization-uniformity studies of Takeda,[4] in which the effect of cone angle was investigated, and the work of Grohse,[1] who made similar studies with various gas-distribution grids. The findings are described in detail in Chap. 2.

An effect of bed height on spouting is shown in Fig. 7-5. The data pertain to wheat in columns of 6, 9, and 12 in. diameter. The ratio of column and air-inlet diameters was in all instances equal to 6. For the range considered the minimum air required for steady-state spouting increases linearly with original bed depth. This is entirely different from

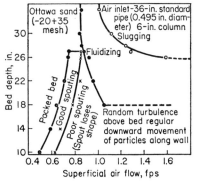

FIG. 7-4. Phase diagram for Ottawa sand, $\frac{3}{8}$-in. standard pipe for air inlet.[3] (*Courtesy of AIChE Journal.*)

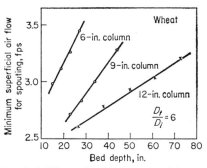

FIG. 7-5. Effect of bed height on minimum air flow required for spouting.[3] (*Courtesy of AIChE Journal.*)

fluidization, for which it has been found that the fluid rate for minimum fluidization is virtually independent of original bed height.

Besides the effects mentioned so far, spouting performance and the minimum air requirement for steady-state operation were found dependent on the gas-inlet diameter and the column diameter, as well as the inlet-cone angle. Qualitatively speaking, larger-diameter air inlets require higher flow rates to induce spouting. This is readily understood if the action of the entering air is compared to that of a jet. Regarding effect of column diameter, the minimum air requirement for spouting is smaller in large columns. This also is expected, since distribution of the entering air is less complete over a large than over a small column cross section. Finally, the smaller the cone angle, the less air will be required for minimum spouting.

No mention has so far been made regarding the extent to which solids properties contribute to spouting. From an examination of the available data[5] it appears that the tendency toward spouting increases as the solids density and the particle diameter increase. However, no definite limiting values for which either spouting or fluidization will result have so far been stipulated. This is probably so because spouting appears to be largely dependent on apparatus construction.

MINIMUM-SPOUTING CORRELATION

Analysis of minimum-spouting data for a relatively wide range of operating conditions led to the following dimensionless correlation:

$$u_{msp} = \frac{D_p}{D_t}\left(\frac{D_i}{D_t}\right)^n \left[\frac{2g_cL(\rho_S - \rho_F)}{\rho_F}\right]^{0.5} \tag{7-1}$$

For a column of $D_t = 6$ in., the exponent n was found equal to $\frac{1}{3}$ and independent of the cone angle as the latter ranged from between 45 to 85°. For a column of 24 in. diameter, however, n was no longer independent of the cone angle. Thus for D_i ranging from $1\frac{7}{8}$ to 4 in., $n = 0.23$ for a cone of 45°, and for a cone of 85° $n = 0.13$.

The correlation is based on spouting experiments in which air as well as water was used as fluid. The full range of variables over which the correlation applies is as follows:

$D_p = 0.023$ to 0.25 in. $\rho_S = 69$ to 464 lb per cu ft
$D_i = 0.0625$ to 4 in. $\rho_F = 0.073$ to 62.4 lb per cu ft
$D_t = 3$ to 24 in. $L = 3.5$ to 106 in.

A comparison of minimum-spouting velocities with minimum-fluidization velocities would be of interest. Thus the data pertaining to a variety of solids contained in the 6-in. tube are shown in Table 7-1, together with minimum-fluidization velocities calculated by Eq. (3-25). As already outlined, minimum-spouting velocities will depend on bed height. Since bed heights varied for the data,[3] the values of u_{msp} have been arithmetically averaged. From the interesting observation that air requirements for minimum spouting and minimum fluidization are in most instances in surprisingly good agreement, it may be inferred that gas distribution in a fluidized bed, even at incipient fluidization, is perhaps not as uniform and homogeneous as is generally accepted.

AIR FLOW IN ANNULUS AND SPOUT

The solids in the annulus were recognized as conforming closely to a loosely packed moving bed. Hence a comparison of pressure drops between such a bed and the bed in the annulus will provide a method for estimating fluid rates through the annulus. From observations in a sectional column, annulus and spout diameters were determined. Thus

TABLE 7-1. MINIMUM AIR REQUIREMENTS FOR SPOUTING AND FLUIDIZATION
IN A 6-IN. COLUMN

No.	Material	D_p, in.	ρs, lb per cu ft	u_{msp}, fps	u_{mf}, fps
1	Peas	0.25	86.6	4.75	5.95
2	Wheat	0.1250	85.9	3.00	3.12
3	Mustard seed	0.0855	75.2	2.00	2.25
4	Rape seed	0.0691	68.9	1.59	1.64
5	Ottawa sand	0.0232	145.0	0.645	0.87
6	Gravel	0.0139	166.6	4.67	5.40
7	Gravel	0.0695	164.0	3.18	2.91
8	Gravel	0.0394	160.0	1.72	1.71
9	Gravel	0.1320	165.3	3.14	5.00
10	Gravel	0.0463	162.0	2.04	1.93
11	Gravel	0.0240	158.0	0.82	0.96
12	Wheat, mustard seed	0.0977	80.8	2.60	2.38
13	Wheat, mustard seed, peas	0.0997	82.7	2.91	2.57

air velocities in the spout could be determined by the difference between
the total air flow and the air flow through the annulus.

The fluid distribution will of course be different for various cross sections above the fluid inlet. Air velocities are shown in Fig. 7-6 in relation to position above the air inlet. The data pertain to a 25-in.-high
wheat bed in a 6-in.-diameter column. The superficial air velocity was

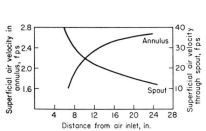

FIG. 7-6. Air velocities through annulus
and spout in relation to position in bed.
Column diameter, 6 in.; wheat bed, 25 in.;
average air velocity, 3.72 fps.

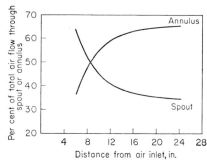

FIG. 7-7. Percentage of total air flow
through annulus and spout in relation to
position in bed. Column diameter, 6 in.;
wheat bed, 25 in.; average air velocity,
3.72 fps.

3.72 fps. It should be noted that this velocity is never realized in the
annulus, the highest attained velocity being about 2.7 fps near the top
of the bed. The velocity through the spout, on the other hand, is about
40 fps near the base and decreases to about 12 to 15 fps near the top.

The percentage flow curves shown in Fig. 7-7 follow the same pattern. The relative variations of the percentage flow curves with bed position are of the same order of magnitude as the variations observed for the air-velocity data. Hence it may be concluded that, for this particular bed, spout and annulus diameters did not vary significantly with bed height.

In addition to being dependent on the lateral position in the bed, the proportion of flow through the annulus increased as (1) the air-inlet diameter decreased, (2) the cone angle decreased, (3) the column diameter increased, and (4) the bed was operated nearer to incipient spouting.

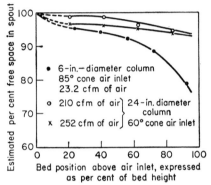

FIG. 7-8. Variation of percentage of free space in spout with position in bed; note that percentage of free space also depends on column diameter and its operation.[5]

SOLIDS FLOW IN ANNULUS AND SPOUT

The movement of the solids in the annulus was observed in a so-called sectional column consisting of a half of a cylinder. The solids and their movement were observed through the flat side of the column. Although this variation in geometry may affect the geometry of annulus and spout to some extent, it was believed that the solids velocity as such was relatively unaffected.

The following observations and conclusions were reached:

1. The order of magnitude of the solids velocity in the annulus is 0.5 to 1.5 ips.

2. For a given bed the solids velocity in the annulus decreases toward the base of the column.

3. The solids velocity in the annulus tends to decrease as the diameter of the air inlet increases. The cone angle, on the other hand, has relatively little effect.

4. The solids velocity is quite sensitive to air velocity, especially if the latter is substantially above the minimum spouting value.

Data pertaining to solids velocity in the spout are still very obscure.

They are obviously linked to solids concentration and air velocity in the spout, factors that are typical of the dilute fluidized phase discussed in Chap. 6. Some characteristic voidage data pertaining to two different spouted wheat beds in 6- and 24-in.-diameter columns are shown in Fig. 7-8. The decrease in voidage with increasing distance from air inlet is of course compatible with the air-velocity data of Fig. 7-6 and the observed decrease with increasing position. This occurs faster in the small-diameter column. Somewhere along the height of the spout the air velocity should be expected to decrease below such a value that saltation occurs. This would then signal the collapse of the spout. The situation is, however, more complex because the path of the spout is not a well-defined duct. The characteristics of the spout are also quite affected by the column diameter.

APPLICATION

The only application reported so far in the literature pertains to the drying of wheat on a pilot scale.[2] Features of the operation are indicated in Fig. 7-9. Preheated air enters the spouting bed, which is contained in a vessel of 12 in. diameter. Wet grain is fed by screw conveyor

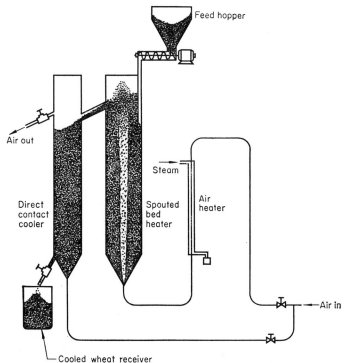

FIG. 7-9. Diagrammatic sketch of pilot wheat drier of the National Research Council of Canada.[5] (*Courtesy of G. L. Osberg.*)

into the upper portion of the annulus of the bed. The solids move downward and up the spout. A solids overflow is also provided at the top, apparently 180° from the feed point. With this arrangement of feed and discharge, a maximum solids-gas contact time will probably result. The solids then flow to a cooler which also embodies the spouted-bed technique.

CONCLUSIONS

The spouted bed offers new possibilities of contacting solids with fluids. Whether a bed will spout or fluidize is, however, not so much a question of the solid material as it is of apparatus construction. Nevertheless, there may be classes of granular solids which will preferentially spout rather than fluidize when contacted with fluids. In this regard particle size seems to be a most determining factor.

The ability to predict the onset of spouting is of course important. The correlation so far proposed does not yet appear to be entirely final, although the effect of virtually all important variables is known, at least in a qualitative sense.

The pressure-drop–flow diagram of a spouting bed defines the onset of spouting. The diagram itself is in many ways similar to the pressure-drop–flow diagram of fluidizing solids with greater or lesser channeling tendencies. The similarity between the spouted bed on the one hand and the channeling fluidized bed on the other is also apparent from the nonhomogeneous fluid distribution over the bed cross section.

The solids movement in a spouted bed is entirely different than in a fluidizing charge. Observations made so far in sectional half columns indicate a downward motion in the outside annulus. In the contained central spout the solids move upward by way of a dilute fluidized phase. Although the solids movement seems largely understood in a qualitative sense, finalized quantitative correlations are still lacking. The same may also be said about fluid flow and prediction of fluid distribution over the column cross section. It may therefore be stated that the spouted-bed technique is still largely unexplored and offers interesting research problems.

REFERENCES

1. Grohse, E. W.: *AIChE Journal*, **1**: 358–365 (1955).
2. Mathur, K. B., and P. E. Gishler: *J. Appl. Chem. (London)*, **5**: 624 (1955).
3. Mathur, K. B., and P. E. Gishler: *AIChE Journal*, **1**: 157–164 (1955).
4. Takeda, K.: *Chem. Eng. (Tokyo)*, **21**(3): 124–129 (1957).
5. Thorley, B., K. B. Mathur, J. Klassen, and P. E. Gishler: "Report on Effect of Design Variables on Flow Characteristics in a Spouted Bed," National Research Council, Ottawa, Canada.

CHAPTER 8

HEAT TRANSFER

Nomenclature

a = constant

A = heat-transfer surface, sq ft

B = shape factor of van Heerden and coworkers, Eq. (8-19)

c, c' = constants

c_F = specific heat of fluid, Btu/(lb)(°F)

c_S = specific heat of solids, Btu/(lb)(°F)

C_m = modified drag coefficient of Bartholomew and Katz, Eq. (8-35)

d = differential

d_p = diameter of a size component in a mixture of particles; $d_p = \sqrt{d_1 d_2}$, where d_1 and d_2 are adjacent sieve openings, in. or ft

D_p = composite particle diameter, in. or ft

D_t = inside diameter of flow chamber or fluidization chamber, in. or ft

D' = tube diameter to be used in Eq. (8-38), ft

e = base of natural logarithms

E = entrance effect

f = function

g_c = conversion factor, 32.2 (lb mass)(ft)/(lb force)(sec)(sec)

G = fluid mass velocity, based on cross section of unpacked tube, lb/(hr)(sq ft)

G_{max} = fluid mass velocity through fluidized column for which a maximum heat-transfer coefficient between the bed and a heat-transfer surface is realized, lb/(hr)(sq ft)

G_{mf} = minimum-fluidization mass velocity, lb/(hr)(sq ft)

G_S = mass velocity of solids entrained in a pneumatic system, lb/(hr)(sq ft)

G' = mass velocity in Eq. (8-38), lb/(hr)(sq ft)

h = heat-transfer film coefficient, Btu/(hr)(sq ft)(°F)

h_{max} = maximum heat-transfer film coefficient, Btu/(hr)(sq ft)(°F)

H = height of heat-transfer surface, ft

j_h = heat-transfer factor, Eq. (8-54)

k = fluid thermal conductivity, Btu/(hr)(sq ft)(°F)/(ft)

k_S = thermal conductivity of the solid, Btu/(hr)(sq ft)(°F)/(ft)

K = constant

L = bed height or tube height, ft

L_f = fluidized bed height, ft

L_{mf} = bed height at minimum fluidization, ft

m' = slope

mf = subscript to indicate that condition pertains to minimum fluidization

n = number of size components in a mixture of particles

n' = slope

Nu = Nusselt number, $h D_p / k$; in Eqs. (8-28) and (8-29) it is $h D_t / k$

$\mathbf{Pr}$ = Prandtl number, $c_F \mu / k$

q = heat transferred, Btu per hr; q_r is the radial heat flux and q_Z is axial heat flux in heat-transfer model of Wicke and Fetting

R = bed-expansion ratio

$\mathbf{Re}$ = Reynolds number, $D_p G / \mu$

S = tube or chamber cross section, sq ft

t_b = temperature of the fluid leaving a fluidized bed, °F

t_G = temperature of the fluid upstream from bed support, °F

t_i = temperature in bed at level $Z = 0$, °F

t_{i0} = temperature of a fluid downstream from bed support, °F

t_S = temperature of the solids surface, °F

t_z = temperature in bed at level $Z = Z$, °F

u_f = linear fluid velocity in a fluidized bed, based on cross section of open tube, fps

u_{mf} = linear fluid velocity at minimum fluidization, fps

u_p = average particle velocity, fps

u_S = solids velocity in Eq. (8-20), not necessarily true individual-particle velocity, fps

U = over-all heat-transfer coefficient, Btu/(hr)(sq ft)(°F)

w = weight rate of fluid flow, lb per hr

W = weight of fluidized bed, lb

X = weight fraction of a size component in a bed

Z = bed-level position, ft

β = interparticle friction factor

γ = kinematic viscosity of fluid, μ / ρ_F, Eq. (8-27)

δ_G = thickness of fluid film, Eq. (8-23)

δ_p = thickness of solids boundary layer, Wicke and Fetting, Eq. (8-3)

Δp = pressure drop, psf

Δt = mean temperature difference obtained from integrated local temperature differences, °F

$\Delta t'$ = local temperature difference, °F

Δt_i = temperature difference at level $Z = 0$, °F

Δt_m = mean over-all temperature difference, °F

Δt_z = temperature difference at level $Z = Z$, °F

Δt_{lm} = logarithmic-mean over-all temperature difference, °F

ϵ = bed voidage

ϵ_{mf} = bed voidage at minimum fluidization

η = fluidization efficiency

θ = time, sec

κ = parameter in Eq. (8-2) of Wicke and Fetting

μ = fluid viscosity, lb/(hr)(ft)

ρ_b = bulk density of bed in nonfluidized state, lb per cu ft

ρ_F = fluid density, lb per cu ft

ρ_{mf} = bulk density of bed at minimum-fluidization point, lb per cu ft

ρ_S = solids density (nonvesicular), lb per cu ft

Abstract

This chapter is divided into three sections. The first section considers heat transfer between dense- and dilute-phase fluidized beds and a boundary heat-transfer surface. The second section discusses heat transfer between pneumatic systems and the exterior; the last section is concerned with heat exchange between the particles and the ambient fluid.

The first section starts with a brief introduction in which order of magnitude, theories, research practices, and abnormalities are discussed. Thereafter it reports in detail the available data and correlations for heat flow between the dense phase and the exterior. This culminates in a generalized data correlation for this type of system. The discussion extends then to dense-phase systems with internal heat-transfer elements. Special consideration is accorded the maximum heat-transfer coefficient observed with fluidized beds. The section terminates with a discussion of the correlations and problems that pertain to heat flow between a dilute phase and its boundaries.

The second section examines the problem of heat flow in pneumatic systems and establishes, as far as possible, the important role which is played by solids concentration in contrast to particle velocity, which was found more important in heat transfer between the dense phase and its boundaries. Correlations and generalizations are given as far as seems justified.

Heat exchange between particles and ambient fluid is discussed in the last section. The available experimental data for this phase do not agree with each other as well as might be desired. The individual contributions and correlations are critically discussed and an effort is made to bring the data together into a generalized correlation. It is especially in this phase of fluidized-bed heat transfer that most of the efforts are still to be expended.

HEAT TRANSFER BETWEEN DENSE-PHASE AND DILUTE-PHASE FLUIDIZED BEDS AND BOUNDARIES.

Order of Magnitude of Wall–Fluidized-bed Coefficients. A comprehension of order of magnitude of data in general is desirable in many ways. It not only enables the engineer to make quick estimates but also directs the basic investigator toward a rational interpretation of phenomena and assists with the conception of probable mechanisms. This is especially true of fluidized-system heat transfer.

Typical heat-transfer data pertaining to an empty tube and fixed and fluidized beds are shown in Fig. 8-1. The fluidized- and fixed-bed data are those reported by Baerg and coworkers.[2]* The fixed-bed data pertain to silica sands, glass beads, catalysts, and iron powder, whereas fluidized-bed data are given only for alumina particles of $D_p = 0.00463$ in. and a coarser sand of $D_p = 0.0126$ in. Although system characteristics, and in particular particle diameter, will to a large extent determine the data level of fluidized-bed coefficients, the values given are quite typical.

The fixed-bed data are in reality prefluidization data. They pertain to particles of sizes that are normally encountered in fluidized beds, and the data are virtually unique in this respect. Other fixed-bed heat-transfer data reported in the literature[7,8,25,27] are for considerably larger particles, and accompanying flow rates are such that modified Reynolds numbers[7] $D_p G/\mu > 10$. For the present fixed-bed data, modified

* Superscript numbers indicate works listed in References at the end of the chapter.

Reynolds numbers extend roughly over the range $0.1 < D_p G/\mu < 10$; hence the data are well within the viscous-flow region in which gas fluidization is normally encountered. Baerg and coworkers[2] covered the particle-size range $0.004 < D_p < 0.035$, and their findings indicate that, for fixed-bed operation in laminar flow, particle diameter has virtually no effect on heat transfer. Data for the empty tube were estimated[35] with the equation

$$\frac{hD_t}{k} = 1.75 \left(\frac{wc_F}{kL}\right)^{\frac{1}{3}} \qquad (8\text{-}1)\star$$

Coefficients were evaluated for air passing through a tube of 1.25-in. diameter immersed in a surrounding heating section of 4 in. length.

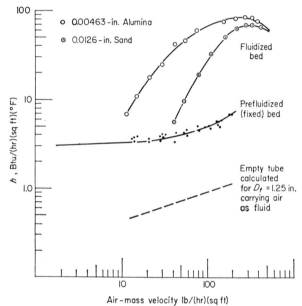

FIG. 8-1. Order of magnitude of wall–fluidized-bed heat-transfer data.

Allowing for absence of fluidizing materials, these conditions are in sufficient agreement with the apparatus conditions of Baerg and coworkers to permit a valid comparison.

For the onset of fluidization the coefficients correspond to those of the viscous-flow-range fixed bed. When the fluid is air, the latter extend over the approximate range $3.5 < h < 7$. With increasing fluid rates, the agitation in the bed becomes more intense and the coefficients increase sharply. They rise to a maximum for which the values are roughly 12 to 15 times as great as in a hypothetical fixed bed. For the major part of the fluidized-bed data the increase in heat-transfer coefficients over the fixed bed is about tenfold. Thus with air as fluid and an average viscous-flow fixed-bed coefficient of about 3 to 5 Btu/(hr)(sq ft)(°F), an approximate fluidized-bed coefficient of about 50 Btu/(hr)(sq ft)(°F) may be anticipated. However for fluids of higher thermal conductivity considerably higher coefficients have been reported. Since fixed-bed coefficients will increase nearly in proportion, this will not seriously alter the relative order of magnitude already indicated.

Also, briefly comparing fixed beds with coefficients in the anticipated empty vessel, the characteristic low slope is not unexpected. It may be taken as an indication that fixed-bed flow is truly laminar and that heat propagation is chiefly by way of conduction through the fluid, with turbulent convection currents probably negligible. With respect to order of magnitude, fixed-bed coefficients are on the average 5 to 8 times as high as empty-tube coefficients. This is in fair agreement with turbulent-flow characteristics, where packed-tube coefficients are in general 6 to 8 times those of the empty tube.[7,8,25]

Now relating empty-tube coefficients to fluidized-bed data it may be stated that, for the point of initial fluidization and the usual particle sizes encountered, coefficients may be from 10 to 15 times as high as in the empty tube. This ratio increases rapidly with rising mass velocity. Thus, near the point of the maximum heat transfer in the fluidized charge, values may be from 75 to 100 times as high as empty-tube coefficients.

Proposed Heat-transfer Mechanism

A fundamental approach to the phenomenon of fluidized-bed heat transfer cannot succeed unless a good conception of the basic mechanism is on hand. As expected, a considerable number of mechanisms have already been proposed. In order to provide a basis for a better understanding of the following correlations, the more important theories regarding fluidized-bed heat-flow mechanism will be briefly discussed.

The earliest qualitative observations indicated that the presence of fluidized solids in a tube caused a substantial increase in bed-wall coefficients. Comparison with fixed-bed data of the type obtained by Baerg and coworkers,[2] and presented in Fig. 8-1, emphasized the sharp increase in coefficients, which can be caused only by the slight incipient motion of the solids past the heat-transfer surface. That this is the reason for the abrupt increase is strikingly shown by some data of Reed and Fenske.[40] Mainly studying the effect of agitation on fluidizability of powders, they also gave some results of heat transfer between an aerated nickel powder and a flat heat-transfer surface. When the plate was vibrated, they found that, for a certain amount of vibration as expressed by the product of frequency and stroke, the heat-transfer coefficient increased abruptly.

The data are shown in Fig. 8-2, and the similarity with the data of Fig. 8-1 need not be stressed further. Similar effects must be involved, and it was only logical to assume that a major resistance to heat flow was due to a fluid film between wall and bed. As far as influence of the solids is concerned, the thickness of the film was believed to be affected by (1) the velocity of the adjacent particles and (2) the bed density as reflected by particle population. These agencies have opposite effects on the film thickness. Since an increase in fluid velocity will lead to (1) generally higher particle velocities and (2) lesser bed densities, it is comparatively simple to explain the characteristic curvature of the fluidized-bed data of Fig. 8-1 and the heat-transfer maximum.

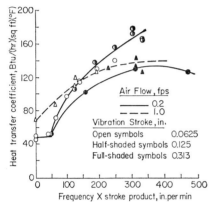

FIG. 8-2. Effect of vibration on heat-transfer coefficients between a bed of powder and a boundary, established by Reed and Fenske.[40] (*Courtesy of Industrial and Engineering Chemistry.*)

The earliest experiments were conducted with sands, glass beads, catalysts, and other materials of relatively low heat capacity. In most instances the experimental techniques were not sufficiently refined to show secondary effects of solids properties. Thus the first proposed film theory[29] assumed that the core of the fluidized bed offered virtually no resistance to heat flow.

More insight into the core resistance and the role of the solids was uncovered by the systematic data of van Heerden and coworkers.[13,14] On the basis of their data they proposed that the heat-transfer properties of a fluidized bed could be compared with the heat-transfer behavior of a well-stirred liquid, with the interstitial gas flow serving principally as a solids-conveying or stirring agent. Thus the particles, owing to their much greater heat capacity as compared to that of the gas, were chiefly responsible for heat dissipation through the bed. In addition to acting as stirring agent, the interstitial gas was believed to act as heat-transferring medium between adjacent particles, as well as the particles and the confining wall. From this last statement it would appear that the model of van Heerden and coworkers[13] does not rely entirely on the heat-carrying capacity of the particles, but accepts the film between main core of the bed and wall. The proposed model, emphasizing the contribution of the solids, probably more nearly corresponds to actual conditions. At any rate, the decided effect of the thermal properties of the solids on heat transfer found by van Heerden[13] and others[9] supports the mechanism. Hence the theory of van Heerden and coworkers has in essence been accepted for the development of a generalized fluidized-bed–exterior-wall heat-transfer coefficient.

As of more recently, a further consideration of the fluid-film–fluidized-core model has been proposed. The model and the correlation of Wicke and Fetting[50] are discussed here because they lead to a correlation of heat-transfer film coefficients in terms of such fundamental quantities as fluid-film thickness and fluidized-solids boundary layer. The Wicke and Fetting model is indicated in Fig. 8-3.

Again, in contact with the wall, we find a fluid film of thickness δ_G. This is followed by a solids boundary layer of thickness δ_p. Beyond this layer there is the fluidized core. In the boundary layer the solids move

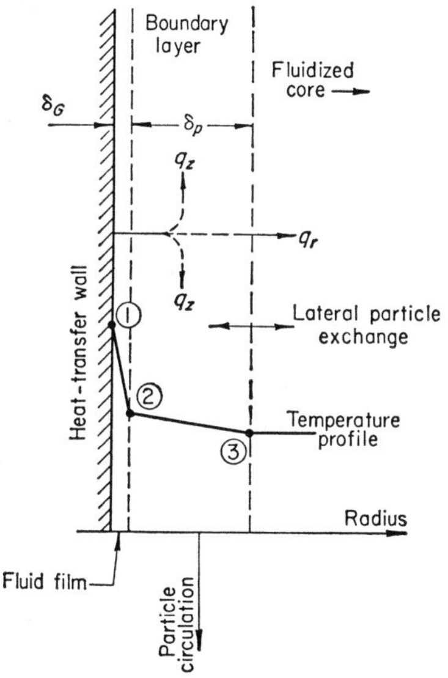

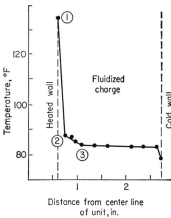

FIG. 8-3. Heat-transfer model of Wicke and Fetting.[50]

FIG. 8-4. Typical radial temperature profile in fluidized bed showing temperature drop through fluid film, boundary layer, and main core of bed. (*Data of Baerg et al.*[2])

essentially parallel to the wall; however, there is also lateral solids flow between the boundary layer and the core.

The temperature profile attending such a model is largely in line with that shown in Fig. 8-4. The drop 1-2 occurs in the film, 2-3 pertains to the boundary layer, and beyond 3 the temperature remains for all practical purposes constant because of the high degree of solids mixing in the fluidized core.

Wicke and Fetting considered that the total heat flux q into the unit divides into two separate components, a radial component q_r and a vertical component q_z. The relative values of these components are height-dependent. A complete presentation of their analysis is beyond the scope of this discussion.   However, expressing these quantities analytically, Wicke and Fetting propose that[50]

$$h = \frac{L_{mf}}{L}\frac{\kappa}{2H}(1 - e^{-2kH/\delta_G\kappa})$$ (8-2)

wherein $\kappa = \rho_S(1 - \epsilon_{mf})c_F u_p \delta_p$ (8-3)

In the expression for κ, u_p is the average particle velocity along the heat-transfer wall.   Only very limited particle-velocity data are so far available.   Particle velocities "en masse," perhaps better termed solids velocities u_S, have been measured, however.   These are related to fluid velocity by $u_S = u_f\eta$, where η is the fluidization efficiency. H in Eq. (8-2) is the height of the heat-transfer area.

Wicke and Fetting obtained new data with silicon carbide, aluminum and lead powders, glass, and SiO_2 particles.   As gases they used air, carbon dioxide, and hydrogen.   Besides providing new data for the entire dense-phase fluidization range, they were interested in the maximum coefficient.   This will be referred to later.   On the basis of their data, as well as those of others,[2,13] they calculated average fluid-film thicknesses. These were generally of the order of magnitude $0.1D_p < \delta_G < 0.5D_p$. The thickness of the particle boundary layer ranged from 1 to 3 mm.

Most recently another and entirely different approach to mechanism has been suggested by Mickley and Fairbanks.[36]   On the basis of their experimental finding that the heat-transfer coefficients obtained with fluidized beds are proportional to the square root of the quiescent-bed thermal conductivity, they conclude that the agencies which control heat transfer may be looked upon as unsteady-state diffusion of heat into mobile portions of the bed termed "packets."   These packets themselves are believed to have a transient existence.   Thus they would tend to disperse and re-form elsewhere.   The packets are pictured as contacting the heater wall and thereby facilitating heat transfer.   A correlation of heat-transfer coefficients along this line will demand the assumption of a so-called stirring factor, necessary for moving the particles, joined together as packets, through the bed.   In regard to the stirring factor, the theory demands that it be related to the heat-transfer coefficient, the thermal conductivity of the quiescent fluid bed, and the bulk density and specific heat of the solids.   Correlations of stirring factors in terms of typical bed properties may eventually be foreseen if adequate data become available.

Thermal and System Components

Coefficients.   For the general case of any surface heat exchanger

$$dq = U \, \Delta t_m \, dA$$ (8-4)

The over-all heat-transfer coefficient U and the mean over-all temperature difference Δt_m are related to q by means of energy and material balances. Separation of the variables and integration yields

$$\int \frac{dq}{U \, \Delta t_m} = \int dA \tag{8-5}$$

In a fluidized system, as in any other exchanger, over-all coefficients are essentially composed of an inside and an outside component. These are usually referred to as film coefficients. Specifically, it is the fluidized-bed film component which is considered here. Depending on the magnitude of the other film coefficient, an experimental unit may yield over-all coefficients which can by themselves be more or less representative of film coefficients. Thus if the other component pertains to condensing steam, which may be of the order of magnitude of 1,000 Btu/(hr)(sq ft)(°F) or more, the observed over-all coefficient may probably be regarded as sufficiently close to film coefficients. However, if the other coefficient should by chance be a liquid-film coefficient, a correction may be required. Instead of correcting the over-all data, one has sometimes the choice of so modifying the experimental technique that film coefficients are immediately obtained. This requires determination of heat-transfer-surface temperatures, thus eliminating the other resistance automatically.

Integration of Eq. (8-5) and substitution of film coefficients h for over-all coefficients U yields

$$h = \frac{q}{A \, \Delta t} \tag{8-6}$$

In Eq. (8-6)

$$q = w c_F (t_z - t_i) \tag{8-7}$$

Also

$$\Delta t = \frac{\int_0^{L_{mf}R} \Delta t' \, dL}{L_{mf}R} \tag{8-8}$$

Assuming that the fluidized charge is contained in a cylindrical vessel,

$$A = D_t \pi L_{mf} R$$

and substitution of Eqs. (8-7) and (8-8) into Eq. (8-6) yields

$$h = \frac{w c_F (t_z - t_i)}{D_t \pi \int_0^{L_{mf}R} \Delta t' \, dL} \tag{8-9}\star$$

Equation (8-9) is a basic form by which fluidized-bed coefficients may be evaluated.

Temperature Differences and Profiles. It is readily shown that the prevailing mean-temperature difference Δt_m in Eq. (8-4) becomes equal to the logarithmic-mean over-all temperature difference Δt_{lm} only if U does not vary with the height of the exchanger. For such a case we would then have

$$\Delta t_m = \Delta t_{lm} = \frac{\Delta t_z - \Delta t_i}{\ln (\Delta t_z / \Delta t_i)} \tag{8-10}$$

As will be apparent from experimental results to be presented later, fluidized-bed film coefficients are *definitely not* independent of apparatus and bed height. For this reason it is not permissible to evaluate an average temperature difference simply by using terminal temperature differences and thereby assume validity of a logarithmic-mean temperature driving force. Obviously then, since the local variations in the coefficient and the resulting integrated effect are the agencies which determine the temperature profile, it becomes a matter of experiment to determine the temperature difference between bed and surroundings. This involves usually a point-to-point temperature-difference evaluation and subsequent graphical integration.

A typical longitudinal temperature profile pertaining to a silica sand, fluidized with air at a mass velocity of 205 lb/(hr)(sq ft), is given in Fig. 8-5. There are two characteristic features of this type of profile:

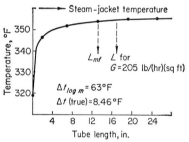

FIG. 8-5. Typical vertical temperature profiles in fluidized bed.[29]

(1) the unusually rapid temperature rise in the bottom of the bed and (2) the remarkable constancy of the temperature a few inches above the bed inlet. The value of the true integrated temperature difference equals 8.46°F. The value of the logarithmic-mean temperature driving force, as evaluated from terminal temperature differences, would be 63°F. A comparison of the two values indicates that a coefficient of an entirely different order of magnitude would have resulted if the logarithmic-mean driving force had been used for evaluation of h, rather than the integrated value. Heat-transfer coefficients in fluidized beds were investigated by Agarwal and Storrow.[1] Their data are very low because they used the logarithmic-mean temperature driving force. Unfortunately there is no way to correct the data and thus use them with the remainder of studies.

A typical radial temperature profile for a bed in an annular space has already been presented in Fig. 8-4. The data, reported by Baerg et al.,[2] emphasize a very steep temperature drop adjacent to the heat-transfer surface, followed by a very flat course leading to the other boundary of the bed. Although the steep drop near the heating wall appears to resemble the steep ascent of the temperature in the bottom of the bed as depicted in Fig. 8-5, the two phenomena have different reasons. Whereas the steepness in Fig. 8-4 is directly related to the high fluid-bed film coefficient, the sudden temperature rise observed in Fig. 8-5 is in part due to an entrance effect. The flat portions of both profiles emphasize, however, the great effect exerted by solids turnover and gas mixing.

Temperature Measurement. Experiments designed to evaluate heat-transfer coefficients between a fluidized bed and its surroundings may require two types of thermal measurements: (1) surface temperatures of heat-transfer areas and (2) representative fluid temperatures in the bed. The first task is by far the easier. The attachment of thermocouple junctions to metal surfaces is standard research procedure. Care should be taken that the thermocouple leads penetrate the bed in such a way that they cause the least interference with the normal operation of the bed.

For measurement of fluidized-bed temperatures, essentially two types of construction have been employed. They are:

1. Bundles of fixed thermocouples extending into various zones of the fluidized bed, both radially and along the vertical axis of the bed.

2. Traveling thermocouples, fastened to a wire which can be manipulated from the outside.

Both methods have advantages and disadvantages. With fixed bundles, temperatures over the entire charge may be recorded virtually simultaneously, but there is reason to believe that the arrangement may perhaps interfere with solids and gas flow patterns and thereby affect the data level. For this reason it is suggested that thermocouple leads be extremely thin.

In general a traveling couple will cause less extraneous disturbance, but because of the often transient conditions in a fluidized charge, data observed with a moving thermocouple may in reality not represent simultaneous conditions.

As a general rule the employment of as fine a thermocouple wire as possible is suggested, in order to preclude or minimize errors caused by conduction to or from the junction by way of the leads. Since temperature differences in fluidized charges are of the order of magnitude of a fraction of a degree, use of a potentiometer possessing an accuracy of a K-2 Leeds and Northrup or the equivalent may be required.

As far as measuring "bed temperatures" is concerned, the question that naturally arises is whether a thermocouple immersed into a fluidized charge will measure the temperature of the solid or of the fluid, or perhaps some temperature average of both.

Very few systematic data on this subject have become available. A fluidizing silica-sand bed was explored[29] simultaneously with two identical couples, except that one couple was shielded by a suitable wire screen to keep off the sand particles and the other couple was bare. The shielded couple could be assumed to record essentially fluid temperatures, whereas the bare couple indicated some average temperature, hereafter called "bed temperature." The bed temperature should be dependent on gas and solids temperatures and possibly the frequency and intensity of bombardment of the junction by the particles. Temperature differences between bed and gas are shown in Fig. 8-6 in relation to column height. Understandably, the difference is greatest at the bed entrance.

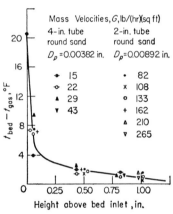

FIG. 8-6. Typical temperature differences between bed and fluid at various levels above fluid inlet.[29]

It decreases so rapidly thereafter that at an inch above the support plate the difference is of the order of magnitude of only a degree Fahrenheit. The downward trend of the curve continues, indicating even smaller differences higher up. Similar results, but of a more comprehensive nature, have been reported by Heertjes and coworkers.[15] From their measurements it may be concluded that bed temperatures referred to in Fig. 8-6 are for all practical purposes temperatures of the solids in the upper strata of the bed. Since for a small distance above the supporting screen solids and gas temperatures are nearly equal, it follows that bare couples may be readily employed for thermal exploration of fluidized beds for the purpose of obtaining heat-transfer coefficients.

Entrance Effects. Exit-fluid temperatures are readily determined by a simple thermocouple which, as may be seen from Fig. 8-6, does not require screening. Measurement of a correct inlet temperature may, on the other hand, be more difficult because of entrance effects. Entrance effects are common phenomena in almost all flow apparatus. They are caused by a sudden modification of the flow pattern induced by local hydraulic characteristics. Thus in conventional heat-exchange equipment, fluids entering a tube bundle from a header undergo a sudden contraction, which for turbulent flow may in most cases be analyzed by means of a simple application of the principle of Bernoulli. So far, the contribution of such a contraction to heat transfer has probably been established only empirically.

Typical entrance effects pertaining to flow of gases into fluidized beds of sand and magnetite particles have been described.[29] The beds were supported on a perforated screen, followed by two glass cloths. A thermocouple junction was sandwiched between the glass cloths and the temperature thus measured was accepted as the correct unit-inlet temperature t_i. For a more or less constant upstream temperature of 80°F, t_i increased sharply with decreasing gas mass velocities.

A systematic study of the entrance effect into fluidized beds of silica gel was reported by Heertjes and coworkers.[15] They defined the entrance effect by

$$E = \frac{t_G - t_{i0}}{t_G - t_b} \qquad (8\text{-}11)\star$$

where t_G = air temperature on upstream side of supporting screen

t_b = temperature of air leaving fluidized column

t_{i0} = temperature of air on downstream side of supporting screen

Examining the action of several screens, Heertjes et al. evaluated E [Eq. (8-11)] and related it to air rate through the screen. Some of their data, together with the earlier sand and magnetite values, are indicated in Fig. 8-7. The data are in agreement as far as trend is concerned; thus with decreasing mass velocities, E increases. The slopes of the various lines are also in fair agreement. Regarding effect of properties of solids carried on the upstream side of the bed support, such an effect is certainly noted, though the data are of a conflicting nature.

It is usually difficult, if not impossible, to preclude entrance effects in flow studies. Frequently one must be satisfied with minimizing their effects and being able to assess the influence they may have on the data that are intended to be measured. Since entrance effects may influence the temperature driving force as well as the sensible heat transferred, a proper accounting of entrance effects may prove a difficult problem.

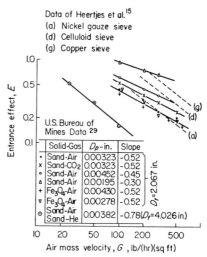

FIG. 8-7. Entrance effects into fluidized beds. (*Data of Heertjes et al.*[15] *and U.S. Bureau of Mines.*[29])

Externally Heated Dense-phase Correlations

Orientation. On the basis of apparatus construction, fluidized-bed heat-transfer correlations are classified into systems that involve (1) external and (2) internal heat-transfer elements. As far as type of bed is concerned, a distinction is made between the dense and the dilute phase. Thus there are the following four basic cases:

1. External surfaces, dense phase
2. Internal surfaces, dense phase
3. External surfaces, dilute phase
4. Internal surfaces, dilute phase

The emphasis of development has so far been on the dense phase, employing external as well as internal heat-transfer elements. As for dilute-phase studies, no systematic differentiation between external and internal heat-transfer equipment has so far been made. A few studies treated the dense as well as the dilute phase, thus they apparently covered the hard-to-define transition state. A survey of fluidized-bed heat-transfer work is given in Table 8-1.

Jolley.[20] This author's fluidized bed consisted of coke particles of $D_p < \frac{1}{16}$ in. The cylindrical fluidization chamber was of 7 in. diameter. While air was passing through, combustion took place. Hence the temperature was in most cases between 800 and 1000°C. In order to estimate the fluidized-bed heat-transfer data level, blocks of copper and aluminum were inserted into the bed for given time intervals. The metal blocks were then rapidly transferred to calorimeters. Heat quantities and surface temperatures could thus be fairly well ascertained, though it seems that, because of heat losses, the coefficients thus found might have a tendency to be low. Tests were also made at a bed temperature of 100 to 120°C to assess radiation contributions at the higher bed temperatures.

Results indicated that at the high temperatures the radiation contribution was not inappreciable; nevertheless, the convective component of the coefficient was still many times as high as would be observed in a static bed or as might be attributed to the carrier gas alone. The high coefficients were believed due to:

1. Local turbulence imparted by the moving particles to the gas
2. Penetration of moving particles through a stagnant film of gas, which normally forms a thermal barrier
3. Transport of heat through the bed by solids convection

Leva, Weintraub, and Grummer.[26,29] In this series of studies tubes of 2.5 and 4 in. diameter were used. Steam heat was supplied through a surrounding jacket and bed temperatures were obtained by bundles of thermocouples which extended along the tube length, through the steam jacket, and into the bed. Each bundle consisted of three couples, and temperatures were measured near the wall, in the center of the tube, and at a position between the wall and center of the bed. Characteristic radial temperature profiles are given in Fig. 8-8. The data pertain to two separate mass velocities and to positions of 2 and 7 in. above the

TABLE 8-1. SUMMARY OF DENSE- AND DILUTE-PHASE FLUIDIZED-BED–HEAT-TRANSFER-SURFACE DATA

Reference	Solids	Voidage range	Absolute density, lb per cu ft	Particle-size range, ft	Type of apparatus and operation	Vessel diam., in.	Height of heat-transfer area, in.	Bed height, in.	Fluids	Flow range, lb/(hr)(sq ft)	Temp, °F
1	Sands, graphite, soft brick	Dense phase	83–166	8–14 mesh to 36–72 mesh	Steam-jacketed column	1.5	14.5	......	Air	150–1,200	......
2	Iron powder, sands, glass beads catalyst	38.8–75	119–434	0.000198– 0.00288	Central electric heat	1.25 in. 5.5	4	10	Air	1.85–605	23.5–65.0
3	Sand, aluminum, calcium carbonate	54–95	160–167	0.000277– 0.000822	Wall electric heat	4.0	30	30	Air	96–935	300–450
4	Glass beads	Dilute phase	......	0.00023– 0.0036	Electric heat from outside	1.959	12	......	Air	95–3,780	......
6	Sand, aluminum, graphite, copper	Dense phase	24.6–27.2	0.00079– 0.0126	Central cooling	2.31	Immersed cooling coil	......	Air	40–100	87–145
9	Aerocat, coke, iron powder	52–69	121–466	0.000363– 0.000560	Wall steam heating	2.06 and 3.07	23 and 26.5	2–13	Air	50–300	200–220
13	Carborundum, iron oxide, coke, lead fly ash, alloy	Dense phase	37.5–694	0.000262– 0.00213	Wall water cooling	3.4	4	16	Air, CH₄, CO₂, town gas, H₂ and N₂ mixtures	44–779	Approx 10–30°C
17	Glass beads	Dense phase	154	0.00010– 0.0011	Internal heating by electric wire	3.0	......	......	Air, CO₂, Freon-12, He, H₂, H₂ and N₂ mixtures	......	......
26, 29	Sand, iron catalyst, silica gel	35–75	80–500	0.000129– 0.00149	Wall steam heat	2.0 and 4.0	25 and 26	12–25	Air, CO₂, He, N₂	1.47–1,095	258–413
30	Coal	Dense phase	......	0.000432– 0.00386	Wall cooling (air)	4.0	24	......	Air	50–1,100	......
31	Glass beads catalyst, coal	41.7–86.2	63.6–180	0.000250– 0.0142	Wall electric heating	4.0	3 sections, 2, 5, and 2 in.	10–30	Air	79–4,350	......
36	Glass beads, microspheres	Dense phase	138–153	0.000022– 0.00027	Small electric heater probe	......	......	Approx 18–20	He, air, CH₄, argon	10–150	......
37	Glass beads	Dilute phase	151–177	0.000133– 0.00149	Internal and external heating	2.875 and 1.00	......	......	Air	2,700	500
38	Silicon carbide, Al₂O₃, silica gel	Dense phase	70–243	0.000287– 0.000817	Center wall	2.0	22	......	Air, He, CO₂	6.4–200	120–414
42	Glass beads	Dense phase	167–179	0.000179– 0.00278	Wall water cooling	4.73	7 sections, each 5 in. high	13.2–24.6	Air	23.7–1,542	......
43, 44	Sand, iron ore	Dense phase	165–330	0.000766– 0.00197	Internal cooling	1.35 in. 22.2	......	47, 68	Air	65–300	Approx 100–400
50	Carborundum sand, aluminum powder, lead powder, glass beads	Dense phase	160–700	0.00020– 0.010	Internal heating by small cylindrical element	3.94	......	......	Air, CO₂, H₂	......	......

193

bed support.   In the vicinity of the support the temperature gradient is still relatively significant, whereas only 5 in. higher the gradient is almost nonexistent.   The entrance gradient is less at the higher than at the lower mass velocity.   This would logically be expected from the higher solids turnover that occurs at elevated gas flow rates.   The solids fluidized were silica sands, iron oxide catalyst (magnetite), and silica gel.   Other pertinent data are apparent from Table 8-1.

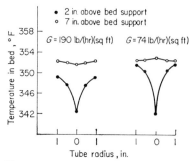

FIG. 8-8. Radial temperature profiles at two bed levels and for two mass velocities; data pertain to air flow through fluidized sand in a 2-in.-diameter tube.[29]

For correlation purposes the modified film theory, discussed earlier, was first proposed.   Briefly stated, the theory postulates that the chief resistance to heat flow into a fluidized bed is in the fluid film.   This film is assumed to be at the peripheral bed boundary.   As the particles move along the film, its thickness is reduced and consequently the thermal resistance is lessened.

For particles of size range $0.00155 < D_p < 0.00430$ in. the data were correlated by the dimensionless equation

$$h = 0.64 \frac{k}{\mu} G\eta \tag{8-12}$$

or by the somewhat more approximate expression

$$h = 0.35 c_F G^{1.15} \tag{8-13}$$

Similar data observed with the same materials for the size range $0.00632 < D_p < 0.0178$ in. were correlated by the dimensional expression

$$h = 3.0 \times 10^6 D_p k \left(\frac{D_p G\eta}{\mu R}\right)^{0.6} \tag{8-14}$$

or alternately by

$$\text{Nu} = 0.5\ \text{Re} \tag{8-15}$$

At low mass velocities the U.S. Bureau of Mines coefficients were observed to be lower than most later-reported data pertaining to this general system.   The reason for the deviation was the unaccounted-for entrance effect.

Levenspiel and Walton.[30,31]   In their early study[30] the authors fluidized coal in a 4-in.-diameter tube.   Sizes ranged from 0.00519 to 0.0463 in. The data were considerably lower than any other data reported for this type of equipment. Sensible-heat quantities were determined from temperature gradients through the outside tube wall and insulation. The method might not have been as accurate as is desirable and could thus have been responsible for the low coefficients. No correlation was proposed, but the study is of interest because the measurements were the first to indicate the characteristic maximum coefficient.

In the later study[31] they reported coefficients for the fluidization of glass beads, catalysts, and coal in a 4-in.-diameter tube. With respect to order of magnitude, the data are still considerably lower than most other data of the general class. The deviation may perhaps be due to heat losses from the unexposed bed section. A correlation on the basis of the modified film theory relates modified Nusselt to the modified Reynolds numbers.

Of several empirical correlations the following seems to be the most useful form:

$$\frac{h}{c_F G} = 0.6 \left(\frac{D_p G}{\mu}\right)^{-0.7} \tag{8-16}$$

Campbell and Rumford.[6] The authors' apparatus was a 2.31-in.-ID copper tube, 24 in. long, that carried an internal helical cooling coil. The fluidizing air, electrically preheated, entered the bottom of the bed through a perforated base. Heat was removed by water passing through the coil. Materials fluidized were sand, aluminum and copper powders, graphite, and catalysts. Particle-size ranges did not vary greatly. However, solids thermal conductivity ranged from about 0.8 to 220 Btu/ (hr)(sq ft)(°F)/ft for the sand and the copper powder, respectively.

Although the main objective was only a qualitative investigation, the effect of the solids thermal conductivity was well demonstrated. For the above range of thermal conductivities and comparable air velocities, the observed increase in heat-transfer coefficients was roughly threefold. This is qualitatively in agreement with packed-bed data, where much larger particles were used in turbulent flow.[7,27] The reported increase in heat-transfer coefficients in the fluidized bed is relatively modest. It indicates that solid conduction in the bed is certainly not the principal agency that promotes the high coefficients encountered.

Dow and Jakob.[9] The equipment used by these authors was steam-heated, and tubes were of 2 and 3 in. diameter. They fluidized aerocat, pitch coke, and iron powders, ranging in size from 69 to 170 microns.

According to the proposed mechanism, a thermal fluid-solid layer is assumed next to the wall. This constitutes essentially the main resistance to heat flow. In the bottom region of the bed is a so-called thermal mixing region. The core of the bed interior is largely at thermal equilibrium, with radial temperature gradients virtually nonexistent. The

Dow and Jakob model is not very different from the model advocating the modified film theory, except that the thermal mixing region in the base is introduced. Existence of this region may be defended on the basis of the comparatively pronounced radial temperature gradients that prevail in the base, as already referred to in Fig. 8-8.

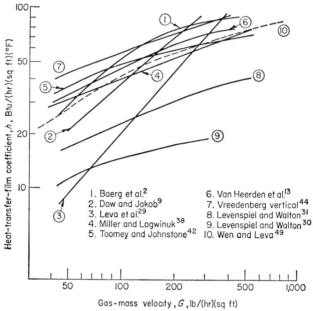

FIG. 8-9. Comparison of dense-phase heat-transfer correlations; data are calculated for a silica sand of $D_p = 0.006$ in. fluidized in air.

From Fig. 8-9 it appears that the data of Dow and Jakob are in good order-of-magnitude agreement with the majority of data of this general type. For the purpose of correlation Dow and Jakob resorted to dimensional analysis. Their proposed equation reads:

$$\frac{hD_t}{k} = 0.55 \left(\frac{D_t}{L_f}\right)^{0.65} \left(\frac{D_t}{D_p}\right)^{0.17} \left[\frac{(1 - \epsilon)\rho_S c_S}{\epsilon \rho_F c_F}\right]^{0.25} \left(\frac{D_t G}{\mu}\right)^{0.80} \quad (8\text{-}17)$$

Mass-velocity Dependence. The Dow and Jakob data extend over a mass-velocity range of about 50 to 300 lb/(hr)(sq ft). From Fig. 8-1 it appears that this range is sufficient to demonstrate that coefficients are not correctly represented by a simple power function of mass velocity. Since Eq. (8-17) specifies that $h \propto G^{0.8}$, it would appear that the application of the equation is limited to the above range. This may also be observed from Fig. 8-10, in which the Dow and Jakob correlation is com-

pared to the data.   The presentation is equivalent to a plot of log h vs.
log G, and the trend toward curvature is quite apparent.   As the correlation is extended beyond the stated limits, predicted coefficients will
have a tendency to be high.

According to the data of van Heerden and coworkers,[13] presented later,
$h \propto G^{0.45}$.   This is a substantially smaller exponent than 0.80, found by
Dow and Jakob.[9]   In quest of an
explanation, Jakob[18] noted that he
and Dow heated the bed, whereas
van Heerden and coworkers worked
with cooling.   Hence he suggested
that the direction of heat flow and
differences of turbulence conditions
associated therewith might have
caused the difference in the exponents.   Interesting as his attempts to
explain the deviation may be, a closer
examination of the two sets of data,
in the light of their range of mass

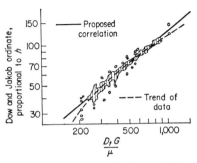

FIG. 8-10. Heat-transfer data of Dow
and Jakob.[9]

velocities, indicates that the van Heerden data refer to a portion of the
heat-transfer curve closer to the maximum than do the Dow and Jakob
data.   For this higher region a smaller exponent of mass velocity is to
be expected.

Tube-diameter–Particle-diameter Effect.   According to Eq. (8-17),
$h \propto (D_t/D_p)^{0.17}$.   This would indicate that in fluidized-bed heat transfer
a wall effect is operative.   Wall effects may be common in fixed beds
where large particles, relative to the tube diameter, are sometimes used.
Because of the larger voidage in the peripheral ring, a somewhat larger
proportion of fluid passes through the ring than through the core of the
tube.   Wall effect is commonly expressed as a function of the diameter
ratio D_t/D_p.   As D_t/D_p increases toward high values, the ratio of ring
to total area decreases rapidly.   For fluidized systems of the type discussed, D_t/D_p values range from about 350 to 1,000, and for these values
the area ratio is virtually negligible.   For this reason it is highly doubtful
that in fluidized beds a wall effect is really operative in the same sense
that it is in fixed beds of larger particles.   Dow and Jakob present data
in support of the above relationship.   However, their threefold variation
of D_t/D_p was mainly brought about by varying particle size from 69 to
170 microns, whereas the tube-diameter variation was inferior in order of
magnitude to the particle-diameter variation.   The situation is by no
means clear; however, rather than interpret the trend as due to wall
effect, it may be that some residual particle-diameter effect is still
involved here.

Toomey and Johnstone.[42] These authors used a fluidization chamber of 4.73 in. diameter, composed of individual vertical sections. Each section was 5 in. high and surrounded by a water jacket. Heat was supplied by a centrally located cylindrical heating element. Glass windows permitted observation of the solids during fluidization. Pressure drops were observed for individual sections, and solids velocities were measured by high-speed photography. Having recognized the importance of particle velocity so far as heat transfer is concerned, the investigators attempted to relate the two concepts. Solids used were spherical glass beads of 55 to 848 microns.

The work primarily yielded data on heat transfer to the outside surroundings, but in some cases thermal data permitted evaluation of simultaneous inside-bed coefficients. The value of these simultaneous inside coefficients will be discussed later. In addition to these general measurements, the effect of bed height on heat transfer was demonstrated. Data were correlated by

$$\frac{hD_p}{k} = 3.75 \left(\frac{D_p u_{mf} \rho_F}{\mu} \log \frac{u_f}{u_{mf}}\right)^{0.47} \tag{8-18}$$

Equation (8-18) is of interest because it correlates a modified Nusselt number with a Reynolds number which refers to the minimum state of fluidization and which has been further modified by the quantity log u_f/u_{mf}. Except for comparatively low values of the reduced velocity, introduction of this term takes into account effect of particle velocity on the heat-transfer coefficient. However, since for the onset of fluidization $u_f/u_{mf} = 1.0$, Eq. (8-18) will predict a zero heat-transfer coefficient for this state. The data underlying Eq. (8-18) pertain to relatively high reduced velocities; hence extension to low reduced velocity is not recommended.

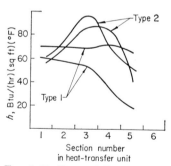

Bed-height Effect. Construction and operation of the unit of Toomey and Johnstone[42] permitted evaluation of bed-height effects. Whereas a column constructed of one continuous section will evaluate only the relationship between coefficients and the bed height as a whole, sectional construction has the advantage that near-differential conditions are approached and local coefficients may thus be observed.

FIG. 8-11. Data of Toomey and Johnstone[42] showing bed height effect on heat-transfer coefficients.

Some local heat-transfer coefficients are shown in Fig. 8-11 in relation to bed height and the appropriate column section. As reported by

Toomey and Johnstone there are apparently two types of data. According to their type 1, the coefficients are slightly higher in the low region of the bed and tend to decrease rather steadily as higher strata are examined. According to type 2, the coefficients pass through a maximum. The dimensionless group $D_p L_f/S$ is proposed as a possible criterion of which type of curve will prevail. Thus for $D_p L_f/S > 0.008$, type 1 will prevail, whereas for values below 0.008 the maxima will appear.

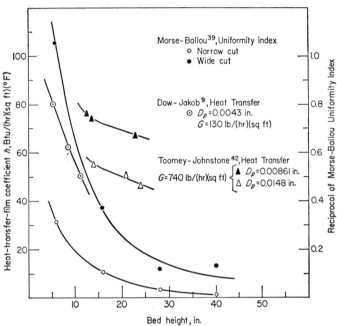

FIG. 8-12. Relation between heat-transfer film coefficient and bed height compared to relation between uniformity coefficient and bed height. The similarity in trends indicates that the deterioration in heat-transfer qualities with bed height is due to a deterioration in fluidization performance caused by increasing bed height.

Unquestionably the characteristics in Fig. 8-11 are associated with fluidization performance. Since the above group contains only apparatus properties and makes no mention of the fluid velocity, its use as a criterion may be somewhat arbitrary.

Local coefficients, as indicated in Fig. 8-11, were graphically integrated to yield over-all coefficients for the entire bed. Returning now to the work of Dow and Jakob,[9] it was reported that $h \propto L_f^{-0.65}$. This appeared adequately supported by their data. For comparable experimental conditions some data of Dow and Jakob were thus compared with the data of Toomey and Johnstone, obtained by the above-mentioned graphical integration. The comparison is made in Fig. 8-12. The most that can be said about the comparison is that trends are the same. The parallel displacement is due to the differences in particle size and mass velocity. The trend in Fig. 8-12 is of course qualitatively in agreement with the effect of bed height on quality of fluidization. This is indicated by the capacitometric measurements of Morse and Ballou,[39] which pertain to quality of fluidization. The observation persists that bed homogeneity deteriorates as bed depth increases. Essentially the same trend is found for the heat-transfer data. In the light of these findings an interpretation of bed depth effects on heat-transfer coefficients through capacitometric studies is therefore indicated.

Effect of Baffles. Reference has already been made to the effect of baffles on expansion characteristics of gas-fluidized beds.[33] Massimilla and coworkers[34] continued their investigation of the effect of these baffles on wall-bed heat-transfer coefficients. The experimental chamber was of 90 mm ID and, similarly to the apparatus of Toomey and Johnstone,[42] consisted of several vertical sections surrounded by cooling-water jackets. Construction was such that coefficients could be obtained for each section. As solid, Massimilla and coworkers used glass beads of 0.7 mm diameter; the fluidizing gas was air.

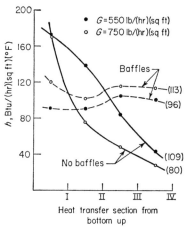

Fig. 8-13. Sectional heat-transfer coefficients for baffled and unbaffled beds. Original bed height, 16 in.; data in parenthesis are integrated average coefficients. (*Data of Massimilla, Bracale, and Cabella.*[34])

Sectional heat-transfer coefficients are shown in Fig. 8-13. The curves for the unbaffled bed are of type 1 as defined by Toomey and Johnstone.[42] For both mass velocities the decrease of the coefficient with bed height is quite appreciable. For the same bed, now baffled, the coefficients are essentially independent of bed height. This leads to the conclusion that baffling tends to render the fluidizing charge more nearly uniform, a result which has already been observed from the expansion behavior of gas-fluidized solids, described in Chap. 4.

An examination of the effect of baffling on the integrated coefficient is also of interest. Integrated coefficients have been plotted vs. mass velocity for the same bed of 16 in. original height. The data, shown in Fig. 8-14, indicate that, for the nonbaffled bed, the familiar maximum heat-transfer coefficient persists. For the baffled bed, on the other hand, the maximum has disappeared. Since the data beyond the maximum coefficient may in part be due to a deterioration of fluidization quality, the better heat-transfer data may be taken as further evidence of an improvement in fluidization performance brought about by the use of certain internal baffles.

For mass velocities below G_{max} the numerical values of the integrated coefficients are somewhat lower in baffled beds than in free fluidization. Beyond G_{max} the reverse is true. This would indicate that, below G_{max}, baffles have the tendency to retard particle velocity along the heat-transfer wall. However, since at high flow rates in nonbaffled beds the velocity along the wall becomes less coordinated, the use of baffles in this region will tend to keep the normal particle-velocity pattern intact.

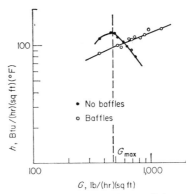

FIG. 8-14. Heat-transfer coefficients in relation to mass velocity for non-baffled and baffled beds.[34]

Van Heerden and Coworkers.[13,14] The most systematic set of fluidized-bed heat-transfer data so far available was obtained by van Heerden and coworkers.[13] The experiments were deliberately planned to indicate effects of major fluid and solid properties. The range of some of the more common variables investigated is given in Table 8-1. The range of other and less frequently considered variables is as follows:

Fluid properties:

Thermal conductivity: 0.00925 to 0.1021 Btu/(hr)(sq ft)(°F)/(ft)
Density: 0.00650 to 0.113 lb per cu ft
Specific heat: 0.127 to 2.71 Btu/(lb)(°F)
Viscosity: 2.25 to 5.4 lb/(hr)(ft)

Solid properties:

Thermal conductivity: 0.29 to 10.4 Btu/(hr)(sq ft)(°F)/(ft)
Density: 37.5 to 694 lb per cu ft
Specific heat: 0.0341 to 0.178 Btu/(lb)(°F)

The apparatus was a brass vessel of 3.34 in. ID. The entering fluids were heated by an electric heating element, and the bed was cooled by a surrounding water jacket. Data correlation, aided by dimensional analysis, yielded

$$\frac{Nu}{Pr^{0.5}} \left(\frac{\rho_{mf}}{\rho_F}\right)^{0.18} \left(\frac{\rho_F c_F}{\rho_{mf} c_S}\right)^{0.36} = 0.58(B\ Re)^{0.45} \qquad (8\text{-}19)$$

The correlation is valid for the range of the modified Reynolds number

$0.1 < BD_pG/\mu < 5.0.$ B is a generalized shape factor.   Values for some materials are given on page 70.

Also proposed was an alternate correlation, wherein heat-transfer coefficients are expressed as a function of the reduced mass velocity G/G_{mf}. The alternate is reproduced in Fig. 8-15.   For a limited range the data are well predicted by the correlation.   Extrapolation to higher- or lower-than-tested reduced mass velocities is not permissible because of the curvature of the data, already elaborated on.   The maximum coefficient seems to be near a value of $G/G_{mf} \approx 50.$

The majority of the experimental data so far discussed were of enough detail and were obtained under sufficiently similar conditions to justify their use for proposing a generalized correlation.

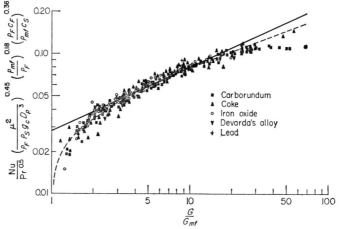

FIG. 8-15. Heat-transfer data correlation of van Heerden and coworkers.[13]

Theoretical Equation.   It has already been pointed out that, for the prefluidization zone, heat-transfer coefficients are approximately equal to those of the fixed bed.   With the first movement of the solids, caused by incipient fluidization, a discontinuity in the heat-transfer curve appears, suggesting that a fundamental change has occurred in the bed.   Returning again to the fixed bed, peripheral heat transfer may be readily understood by assuming a thermal resistance on the inside of the wall.   This thermal resistance is believed to be due to a fluid film through which the heat passes by conduction.   The important difference between a fixed and fluidized charge, as concerns the nature of this film, is that in a fluidized charge the particles move past the film, whereas in the fixed bed the particles do not alter their position in relation to the film.   In a fixed bed the film thickness should therefore be primarily dependent on the properties of the fluid and its velocity.   This is not wholly true for a fluidized bed, where it must also be assumed that in addition to fluid properties the velocity of the particles will influence the film thickness. Hence in order to comprehend the heat-transfer mechanism in a fluidized charge, the effect of particle movement along the film must be accounted for.

A model illustrating a possible heat-transfer mechanism has already been given in Fig. 8-3. In immediate contact with the wall is the supposed fluid film. Its thickness is probably of the order of magnitude of that of fluidized-bed particles. The predominant particle-velocity component along the wall is downward. Next to this layer may be assumed a transition buffer layer. This is in essence the model of Wicke and Fetting,[50] and the thickness of the buffer layer may be several particle diameters. Particle motion in this region is still predominantly downward; however, it is modified by the presence of eddies caused by horizontal-velocity components. Proceeding further toward the center, there follows a central core wherein the particles move predominantly upward, but with strong superimposed horizontal-velocity components.

A model of the type described will go far toward explaining the type of temperature profile given in Fig. 8-4. Heat flow through the film is primarily by conduction where, because of the greatest thermal resistance, the temperature drop is steepest. This corresponds to branch 1-2 of the profile. In the adjoining transition zone the thermal resistance is substantially lessened, as is evidenced by the flattening of branch 2-3 of the temperature profile. Agencies responsible for this lessening of thermal resistance are probably a combination of particle and fluid turbulence. Thus in layer 2-3, heat is chiefly conveyed by particles and fluid from the film to the core. Inside the core the thermal resistance has been further reduced, as reflected by the now nearly flat temperature profile.

Since particle velocity along the wall and particle population must influence the thickness of the fluid film, it is reasonable to attempt correlation of surface heat-transfer coefficients in terms of particle velocities and other mechanical bed properties. This may therefore constitute a first step toward a generalized correlation. On the other hand, a consideration of convective heat flow through the transition buffer layer and the central mixing core would then indicate that such solids properties as solids heat capacity and density must also be involved.

According to an interpretation of gas flow data in fluidized solids, it was postulated that the energy exchange between the fluid and the moving particles may be expressed by[28]

$$u_f S \eta \, \Delta p = \beta u_S W \qquad (8\text{-}20)$$

Since $S \, \Delta p \approx W$,
$$u_f \eta = \beta u_S \qquad (8\text{-}21)$$

wherein the vertical solids velocity along the container wall $u_S = L_{mf} R / \theta$. Hence this velocity of the particles moving in bulk may also be related to fluid and bed height by

$$u_S = \frac{L_{mf}R}{\theta} = \frac{u_f\eta}{\beta} \tag{8-22}$$

where β is the interparticle friction factor.

Assuming that the heat-transfer mechanism through the film is primarily a conduction phenomenon,

$$h \propto (f)\,\frac{1}{\delta_G} \tag{8-23}$$

where the film thickness δ_G is dependent on the particle velocity, the particle population along the wall, and the kinematic viscosity of the fluid. Hence film thickness may itself be expressed as a function of the ratio $\mu R/\rho_F u_S$. Applying this to Eq. (8-23), there follows

$$h \propto (f)K\,\frac{u_S\rho_F}{\mu R} = c'(f)\,\frac{u_f\rho_F\eta}{\beta\mu R} \tag{8-24}$$

Inclusion of the interparticle friction factor into the experimental constant leads to

$$h \propto c\,(f)\frac{G\eta}{\mu R} \tag{8-25}$$

The constant c, to be evaluated from test data, accounts for mechanical and thermal properties of the solid.

Working Equation. The earlier mentioned bed–exterior-wall heat-transfer data[9,13,26,29,42] were analyzed in accord with Eq. (8-25). The usual methods of plotting and cross-plotting yielded

$$\frac{hD_p}{k} = 0.16 \left(\frac{c_S\rho_S D_p^{1.5}g_c^{0.5}}{k}\right)^{0.4} \left(\frac{GD_p\eta}{\mu R}\right)^{0.36} \tag{8-26}\star$$

Equation (8-26) consists of three dimensionless groups. It essentially relates a Nusselt number with the last group, a modified Reynolds number. The central group accounts for the effect of particle properties on heat transfer.

Thermal-conductivity Effect. In fixed-bed heat transfer, $h \propto k^{0.67}$. If heat exchange between a fluidized charge and the surroundings occurs chiefly by conduction through a film, this relation should remain largely intact. The effect of particle motion which, in the vicinity of the film, is believed merely to reduce film thickness, should not interfere with this mechanism. Thus according to Eq. (8-26), $h \propto k^{0.60}$. This is fairly well supported by the data of van Heerden and coworkers,[13] for which fluid thermal conductivities vary more than tenfold. Additional confirmation is provided by measurements of Wicke and Fetting,[50] as well as Jacob and Osberg.[17] Wicke and Fetting transferred heat from a centrally immersed copper cylinder to the bed; Jacob and Osberg used an immersed electric wire as heat source. Apparatus details were therefore quite different from the presently discussed wall-bed system. Since for the purpose of demonstrating the effect of k upon h comparable conditions must prevail, it is especially gratifying that both papers report values of h_{max} for various solids fluidized with gases of widely varying k values. Figure 8-16 reports the Wicke and Fetting data, which pertain to fluidization with air, CO_2, and H_2. Thermal conductivity varied 11.7-fold. For the purpose of presentation and in order to gain the additional point 1-1, the data have been reported in the form of ratios. Average slope of the line is 0.60.

Similarly, the data of Jacob and Osberg, shown in Fig. 8-17, report a twenty-one-fold range in thermal conductivity and extend also over an

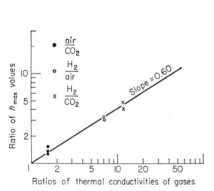

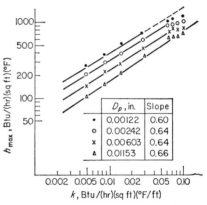

FIG. 8-16. Data of Wicke and Fetting[50] showing effect of gas thermal conductivity on heat-transfer coefficient.

FIG. 8-17. Data of Jacob and Osberg[17] showing effect of gas thermal conductivity on maximum heat-transfer coefficient.

impressive tenfold range in particle diameter. Except for the very high region, average slope of the data is 0.64, also in good agreement with Eq. (8-26).

Effects of solids heat capacity and solids density on heat transfer may be readily demonstrated[49] by suitable experimental data and Eq. (8-26).

Particle-diameter Effect. All experimental data support the observation that wall-bed heat-transfer coefficients increase as, for comparable mass velocities, particle size decreases. Without doubt this is due to the generally more intense state of agitation in the bed and a more intimate contact between the particles and the fluid film on the inside of the vessel.

According to Eq. (8-26), $h \propto D_p^{-0.04}$. Hence it would appear that coefficients are nearly independent of particle size. The controversy will, however, resolve itself if it is recalled that fluidization efficiency increases rapidly, as for a constant mass velocity, D_p decreases. Thus Eq. (8-26) *does* make allowance for effect of D_p on h.

Bed-porosity Effect. Another generally accepted fact is that heat transfer varies inversely with some function of bed porosity. This, too, is to be expected from the modified film theory. As the particle population decreases, the modifying effect of particles and particle motion on the film is lessened.

An increase in average bed porosity is ordinarily caused by an increase in fluid rate. Since the latter will, by itself, frequently increase heat-transfer rates—whereas the resulting dilution of the bed has the opposite

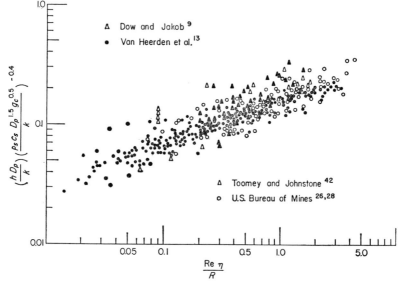

FIG. 8-18. Generalized heat-transfer correlation: dense-phase, wall-bed coefficients.[49]

effect—it is understandable that the influence of bed density is not readily demonstrated.

Application and Limitation.   Figure 8-18 indicates that all data, regardless of origin, are represented about equally well by Eq. (8-26). In consideration of the wide range of experimental conditions, the scatter is therefore not excessive. With the exception of height of bed, heat-transfer surface, and possibly chamber diameter, it appears that the effect of the major variables upon heat-transfer coefficients has been accounted for. Experimental limits pertaining to the correlation as far as particle and tube diameters are concerned are:

Particle diameter: 0.0015 in. $< D_p <$ 0.0335 in.
Tube diameter: 2.0 in. $< D_t <$ 4.73 in.

Other limits pertaining to fluid and solid properties are as obtained from Table 8-1.

Limits of flow range varied from about 20 to 1,500 (lb)/(hr)(sq ft). Considered together with particle size, this limits application of the equation to cases for which $2 < G/G_{mf} < 20$. Bed-expansion-ratio limits were about $1.05 < R < 1.50$. It is to be noted that the equation is not

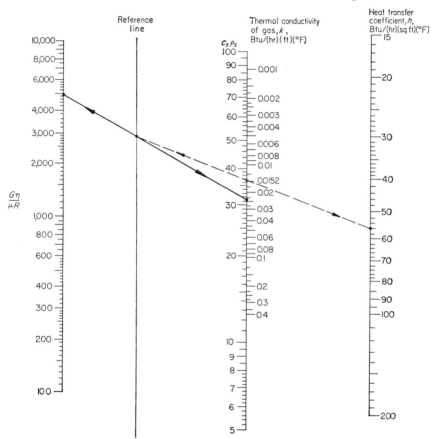

FIG. 8-19. Nomograph for fluidized heat-transfer coefficient.[48]

applicable to the point of incipient fluidization, where for $\eta = 0$, h would have to be zero.

For the purpose of evaluating coefficients it is first required to estimate fluidization efficiency and expansion ratio. For the rapid solution of problems use of Figs. 4-16 and 4-17 and the nomograph of Fig. 8-19 is suggested.[48] Viscosity is to be expressed in centipoises.

Example 8-1. A column of 4 in. ID is charged with glass beads of $D_p = 0.0061$ in. and $\rho_S = 153$ lb per cu ft. While the unit is being heated from the outside by electric resistance winding, the glass beads are fluidized by air, passing through the column with a mass velocity of 159 lb/(hr)(sq ft). The average fluid-solids temperature in the unit is found to be 460°F. The pressure is atmospheric.

The unit is thoroughly insulated toward the outside, so that the heat losses from the heating elements into the ambient air are negligible. The wattage input into the heater therefore gives a fair indication of the heat flux into the column. Under the prevailing conditions, the input is found to be 2700 Btu/(hr)(sq ft). It is desired to evaluate the prevailing wall temperature.

Solution. This is essentially a matter of finding the heat-transfer film coefficient and thereafter calculating the temperature driving force. First we shall have to find the value of G_{mf}:

$$\rho_F = \frac{28.9 \times 492}{359 \times 920} = 0.043 \text{ lb per cu ft}$$

$$\rho_S = 153$$
$$\mu = 0.027 \text{ centipoise}$$

From Fig. 3-15a
$$G_{mf} = 10.0 \text{ lb/(hr)(sq ft)}$$

and
$$\frac{G_f}{G_{mf}} = \frac{159}{10} = 15.9$$

From Figs. 4-16 and 4-17, $\eta = 0.70$ and $R = 1.6$. The average thermal conductivity of the air is $k = 0.024$ Btu/(hr) (sq ft) (°F)/(ft), and c_s will be taken as 0.25 Btu/(lb)(°F). Using Eq. (8-26) the heat-transfer coefficient becomes

$$h = \frac{0.16 \times 0.024}{0.000508} \left[\frac{0.25 \times 153 \times 0.000508^{1.5}(4.18 \times 10^8)^{0.5}}{0.024} \right]^{0.4}$$

$$\left(\frac{159 \times 0.000508 \times 0.7}{0.027 \times 2.42 \times 1.6} \right)^{0.36}$$

$$= 64 \text{ Btu/(hr)(sq ft)(°F)}$$

The prevailing temperature difference is then

$$\Delta t = \frac{2,700}{64} = 42.2°F$$

and the wall temperature will be $460 + 42.2 = 502.2°F$.

An experiment actually conducted by Mickley and Trilling[37] conformed very closely to the stated conditions. They observed a bed temperature of 460°F and a wall temperature of 512°F, and hence a heat-transfer coefficient of 52.5 Btu/(hr)(sq ft)(°F). The observed bed voidage was $\epsilon = 0.582$, which with a possible value of $\epsilon_{mf} = 0.38$ gives a bed-expansion ratio of $R = 0.620/0.418 = 1.48$, acceptably close to the estimated value of 1.6 from the generalized correlation (4-17).

Internally Heated or Cooled Dense Phase

Units with internal heat-transfer elements are extensively used in industry; almost all large-scale fluid catalytic equipment is of this type. Most bench-scale and pilot-plant studies, on the other hand, are made in equipment with exterior heat-transfer surfaces. The latter have severe limitations as far as ratio of heat-transfer surface to reactor volume is concerned, whereas internally heated or cooled reactors may be equipped with virtually any amount of heat-transfer surface. As for cost per unit surface, units with internal heat-transfer elements are more expensive than are units with external surfaces. This is primarily due to the more complex construction of units with internal elements. But because for large capacities externally heated or cooled units are not suitable, cost comparison of the two types of units is really of subordinate importance.

Internal vs. External Heat Exchange. A valid comparison between the two modes of heat exchange may be made only on the basis of experiments which are performed simultaneously with the same solids in the

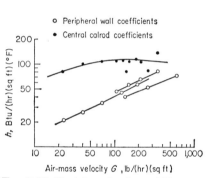

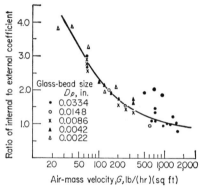

Fig. 8-20. Heat-transfer data of Toomey and Johnstone.[42] Peripheral-wall and central-calrod coefficients originated from the same equipment and indicate that at high fluid mass velocities the data approach each other.

Fig. 8-21. Data of Toomey and Johnstone[42] showing how, for their equipment, the ratio of the internal to the external heat-transfer coefficient depends on the fluidization mass velocity.

same unit. This severe restriction is readily understood if it is recalled that (1) the state and quality of fluidization have an important bearing on the magnitude of the coefficients and (2) that state and quality of fluidization are not readily duplicated if equipment, operation, and solids properties differ by any appreciable amount. Direct comparison is permitted virtually only by the data of Toomey and Johnstone,[42] who reported, for the same equipment, simultaneous bed–exterior wall and bed–interior calrod heat-transfer coefficients. The data extend over an appreciable mass-velocity and particle-size range. Figure 8-20 shows wall and calrod coefficients for a few runs, plotted vs. mass velocity. In the low range the calrod coefficients are considerably in excess of the wall coefficients. At elevated mass velocities the coefficients approach each other. A generalized presentation of these data in the form of ratio of calrod to wall coefficients, related to mass velocity, suggests itself. As far as possible this is given in Fig. 8-21. With the exception of the very largest size $(D_p = 0.0334$ in.), the correlation is quite satisfactory. Particle-size range for the data varies about fifteenfold.

For the low mass velocities of about 25 (lb)/(hr)(sq ft) the ratio of internal to external coefficients is about four. With increasing mass velocity, the ratio decreases; it tends to approach unity for very high mass velocities. Assuming validity of the modified film theory, the path of the curve may be qualitatively predicted from observations of the particle flow pattern. At low mass velocities the solids turnover in the bed is generally small. Thus for this condition wall coefficients are only little in excess of fixed-bed coefficients. Whatever slight solids flow occurs, however, must be felt more intensively over the lesser core cross section. As the gas flow rate increases, the solids flow pattern along the peripheral wall becomes better coordinated, and at the same time the solids flow pattern in the core deteriorates, because of bubble and aggregate formation. Hence heat transfer at the wall improves at the expense of the coefficients in the core of the bed. For a mass velocity of 1,000 to 1,500 lb/(hr)(sq ft) a ratio of unity is indicated. There is, however, no reason why for other systems this ratio could not be less than unity at some other mass velocity or for some other system. Hence the chief value of the data of Fig. 8-21 lies in the fact that the relative heat-transfer values emphasize the nonhomogeneous character of some fluidized beds. If to be used for design, the data must be used with great caution.

TABLE 8-2. CONSTANTS FOR EQ. (8-27) AS REPORTED BY VREEDENBERG FOR VERTICAL ARRANGEMENT

Distance from tube to bed axis, in.	Tube-to-axis distance / Bed radius	a
0.0	0.00	1.05
3.8	0.35	1.85
7.6	0.71	1.65

Vreedenberg.[43–45] VERTICAL POSITION OF COOLING TUBE. The large fluidized bed used was of about 22 in. diameter. A $1\frac{3}{8}$-in.-diameter water line was immersed in various horizontal and vertical positions, and heat-transfer coefficients between bed and tube were reported for the positions. The nonfluidized bed height for the various sands and iron ores was about 67 in., and temperatures for vertical positions were measured in either six or nine places. For the horizontal as well as vertical positions of the cooling tube, the data were correlated by

$$\frac{hD_p}{k} = a \left[\frac{G\gamma}{(G\gamma)_{mf}} \right]^{0.35} \tag{8-27}$$

where γ = kinematic fluid viscosity

D_p = mean volume–surface-area diameter of particles

For the tube in vertical positions the constant a depends on the location in the charge, as shown in Table 8-2.

Zoning of Bed. Assuming that the level of the heat-transfer coefficients depends on solids circulation, Vreedenberg concluded that the bed was composed of various solids circulation zones, telescoped into each other. The interesting observation is that the most active zone in Vreedenberg's bed is found not in the center, but somewhat off center. Proceeding out further the solids circulation rate is believed to decrease again. This flow pattern differs from small-scale solids flow patterns, where the highest solids flow rates appear to occur in the center core.

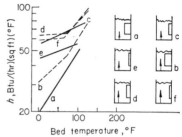

Fig. 8-22. Effect of position of vertical heat-transfer tube in large-diameter fluidized bed; h in relation to bed temperature. (*Data of Vreedenberg.*[44] *Courtesy of Journal of Applied Chemistry, London.*)

The zoning of the bed, as interpreted by Vreedenberg, seems also to depend on the mass velocity. Figure 8-22 reports coefficients for various cooling-tube positions, plotted vs. bed temperature. The data pertain to two values of mass velocities as indicated in Table 8-3. The variation

TABLE 8-3

Tube-to-axis distance / Bed radius	Mass velocity, lb/(hr)(sq ft)	Curve
0.00	67.0	a
	115.0	b
0.35	67.0	c
	115.0	d
0.71	67.0	e
	115.0	f

in coefficient with bed temperature is caused by the kinematic-viscosity change of the air. As the bed temperature is raised, the air viscosity increases, causing a more intense state of fluidization and hence higher heat-transfer rates.

The relative positions of the curves indicate that the geometry of the zones is dependent on mass velocity. Thus an increase in mass velocity will cause an increase in the coefficient for the central and outside zones, whereas in the intermediate zone heat-transfer coefficients are only slightly affected. However, as an over-all result, coefficients increase with increasing mass velocity. This indicates that the bed tends toward greater uniformity as the fluidization velocity is raised.

The Vreedenberg data are enlightening as far as some effects of apparatus construction on fluidized-bed heat transfer are concerned. It is conceivable that the indicated trends are of validity in a general sense. Specifically, however, situations in which the findings of Vreedenberg may not be applicable without considerable deliberation may arise. To cite only one instance: in industrial units, one usually finds bundles of tubes immersed, rather than a single tube, and the question that arises is whether the findings may be extended to such cases. Since immersion of tube bundles may in itself influence fluidization performance, it is evident that additional complicating features are thereby introduced.

HORIZONTAL POSITION OF COOLING TUBE. The earliest-presented data of Vreedenberg[43] pertaining to the cooling tube in horizontal position were also correlated by Eq. (8-27). The value of the constant was then equal to 1.25. Since then, considerable additional data have been made available for the same equipment but for additional sands and cracking catalysts, with volume–surface-area particle diameters ranging from 0.0025 to 0.0125 in. Solids density ranged from 100 to 166 lb per cu ft. The data were correlated by two separate equations. Thus for situations in which $(D_pG/\mu)(\rho_S/\rho_F) < 2{,}050$,

$$\text{Nu} = 0.66 \left[\frac{GD_t\rho_S(1 - \epsilon)}{\rho_F\mu\epsilon} \right]^{0.44} \text{Pr}^{0.3} \qquad (8\text{-}28)$$

and for $(D_pG/\mu)(\rho_S/\rho_F) > 2{,}550$

$$\text{Nu} = 420 \left(\frac{GD_t\rho_S}{\rho_F\mu} \frac{\mu^2}{D_p{}^3\rho_S{}^2g_c} \right)^{0.3} \text{Pr}^{0.3} \qquad (8\text{-}29)$$

For the intermediate range, $2{,}050 < (D_pG/\mu)(\rho_S/\rho_F) < 2{,}550$, Vreedenberg suggests that h be evaluated by both equations and the resulting values be arithmetically averaged. The form of Eq. (8-28) was conceived from an anology of heat transfer to a fluid flowing over the outside of a horizontal tube. The group $\mu^2/D_p{}^3\rho_S{}^2g_c$ in Eq. (8-29), which is really the ratio between the Froude group and the square of the Reynolds number $(D_pG/\mu)(\rho_S/\rho_F)$, is believed to affect the stirring factor, suggested by Mickley and Fairbanks[36] as a correlation parameter.

Miller and Logwinuk.[38] The authors obtained heat-transfer coefficients from fluidized beds in an annular space to a centrally located copper tube. Outside and inside tube dimensions were 2 in. ID and ⅜ in. OD. Heat was supplied by electric resistance winding from the outside and was carried off by water flow through the immersed copper tube. The sensible heat transferred was determined from water rates and terminal temperatures. Temperature differences were obtained from metal-skin and bed temperatures. As solids, silicon carbide, silicon dioxide, aluminum oxide, and silica gel were used with air, CO_2, and He as fluidizing gases. Particle sizes ranged from about 0.0035 to 0.0098 in.

The range of the coefficients extended from about 40 to almost 200 Btu/(hr)(sq ft)(°F). The flow range for this interval extended from about 6 to 200 lb/(hr)(sq ft). This was apparently not high enough to yield a maximum coefficient. Correlating the data empirically, it was proposed that

$$h = 1.5 \frac{G^{0.32} k_S^{0.072} k^{2.4}}{D_p^{0.96} c_F^{1.6} \mu^{0.8}}$$
(8-30)

According to this expression, solids thermal conductivity has only a minor effect on the coefficients. In contrast to heat transfer through exterior walls, it was also believed that solids heat capacity has little or no effect.

The findings of Miller and Logwinuk differ from other work in additional respects. Thus coefficients are reported to vary as the 2.4 power of fluid thermal conductivity, whereas the majority of studies report much lower exponents.

The heat-transfer-coefficient–particle-size dependence appears in better agreement with other investigators. An irregularity was, however, observed with silica gel particles. For this material, coefficients decreased with decreasing particle size. Electrostatic forces and adhesion of particles to the heat-transfer wall were given as possible reasons.

Baerg, Klassen, and Gishler.[2] The most comprehensive heat-transfer measurements so far reported for internally heated beds are those of Baerg and coworkers. Their apparatus consisted of a 5.5-in.-diameter fluidized bed, with a 1.25-in.-diameter electric heater centrally immersed. Approximately 90 per cent of the heat was removed by an outside water jacket. They tested iron powder, several types of sand and silica, glass beads, cracking catalysts, and alumina. Diameters ranged from 0.0024 to 0.035 in., and solids density varied from 119 to 434 lb per cu ft. Additional details are given in Table 8-1. Only air was used, up to mass velocities of about 600 lb/(hr)(sq ft).

A comparison of the data of Baerg et al. with the generalized correlation for wall-bed heat transfer is given in Fig. 8-23. For the major range the data are roughly 25 per cent above the generalized correlation. Possible reasons for this have already been given.

Highest observed coefficients were about 130 Btu/(hr)(sq ft)(°F), hence substantially lower than the values of 200 Btu/(hr)(sq ft)(°F), the highest coefficients reported by Miller and Logwinuk.[38] The reason for the considerably higher data level of Miller and Logwinuk is not definitely known, though it could be that the smaller $\frac{3}{8}$-in. tube diameter of Miller and Logwinuk, as compared to the 1.25-in. tube diameter of Baerg et al., may be largely responsible. At any rate this may be a more probable reason than the observation that the two studies differ as far as direction of heat flow is concerned.

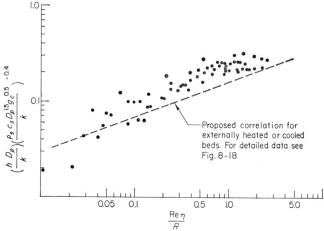

Fig. 8-23. Generalized heat-transfer correlation applied to data of Baerg et al.[2] observed with iron powder, round and foundry sands, jagged silica, Scotchlite beads, and alumina.

The data were correlated empirically by

$$h = h_{\max} - 55e^{-0.012(G-0.71\rho_b)} \tag{8-31}$$

where the maximum coefficient $h_{\max}$ is found to be

$$h_{\max} = 49 \log \frac{0.00037\rho_b}{D_p} \tag{8-32}$$

It is to be noted that Eqs. (8-31) and (8-32) are applicable only when air, at atmospheric pressure and essentially at room temperature, is used as fluid. If in these expressions D_p is in feet, the nonfluidized-bed density ρ_b is in pounds per cubic foot, and G is in pounds per square foot per hour, the heat-transfer coefficient will be in Btu/per hour per square foot per degree Fahrenheit.

Maximum Coefficient. The appearance of maxima or minima in experimental data may be a valuable adjunct as far as interpretation and understanding of the phenomenon are concerned. This is especially true of the maximum fluidized-bed heat-transfer coefficient. The earlier-presented data analysis and generalized wall-bed transfer correlation were based on the modified film theory. This theory was conceived from the characteristic relation between h and G, of which h_{max} is merely a special point.

Baerg et al. examined h_{max} values for the purpose of correlation. All data correlated well, except the Scotchlite-bead coefficients, which yielded maximum coefficients that were roughly 18 per cent higher than the remainder of the data. These higher values were attributed to the greater mobility which the entirely smooth Scotchlite beads showed, as compared with the lesser mobility of the remaining and apparently rougher particles. In subsequent tests the beads were etched with moist hydrogen fluoride gas. Etching had no effect on G_{mf} values, but freedom of particle movement in the bed was somewhat restricted. As a consequence the resulting h_{max} values were substantially lower. This simple, though resourceful, test is significant because it supports the theory that the velocity of the particles is responsible for the high fluidized-bed heat-transfer rates.

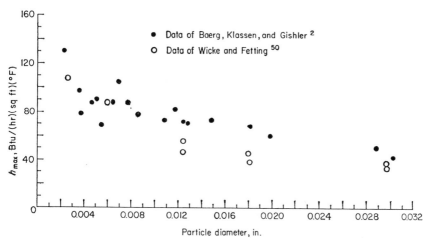

FIG. 8-24. Correlation trend of maximum heat-transfer coefficients with particle diameter.

Particle Diameter. Maximum coefficients increase as particle diameter decreases. This is indicated by the data of Fig. 8-24. The increase may be due to (1) the effect of the particle diameter as such, (2) the accompanying mass velocity, or (3) the solids velocity, as reflected by the value of the reduced mass velocity, relative to particle size. Following the latter lead, G_{max}/G_{mf} values were calculated and plotted vs. particle diameter. The resulting Fig. 8-25 includes also the data of Wicke and Fetting[50] and some measurements of Jacob and Osberg.[17] G_{max}/G_{mf} decreases as D_p increases. Hence it may be concluded that the increase of h_{max} with decrease of D_p, as shown in Fig. 8-24, is chiefly due to an increase in mobility of the particles.

The data of Fig. 8-25 are satisfactorily correlated by

$$G_{max} = 0.0015 \frac{G_{mf}}{D_p^{1.75}} \qquad (8\text{-}33)\star$$

This expression may be used to estimate the fluidization mass velocity for which the heat-transfer coefficient becomes a maximum. The mass velocities are in pounds per hour per square foot and the particle diameter is in inches. It is to be noted that Eq. (8-33) may not be extended to particles for which $D_p > 0.02$ in., because otherwise the ratio G_{max}/G_{mf} would become smaller than unity, a situation which cannot possibly arise. Actually, the correlation should exhibit a curvature convex to the D_p axis as $D_p > 0.015$ in. However, the data are not of sufficient accuracy to establish this definitely.

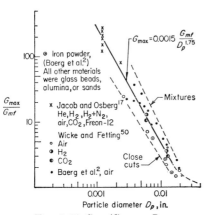

FIG. 8-25. G_{max}/G_{mf} vs. D_p.

For small particles G_{max} may be many times as large as G_{mf}. Hence a plot of h vs. G for small particles would tend to be comparatively flat, whereas for large particles such a curve should rise steeply toward the maximum. This has been verified in Fig. 8-26, pertaining to large-size glass beads.

The line in Fig. 8-25 is also compared with the earlier discussed limiting bed expansion shown in Fig. 4-19. The limiting G_{max} values are located between the limiting expansion data for close cuts and mixtures, which would indicate that G_{max} values in close cuts may just be in the incipient slugging zone, a good reason for expecting a decrease in heat-transfer coefficient if the mass velocity is increased beyond this particular value.

Bed-height Effect. By means of a 3-in.-high electric heater, vertically adjustable in fluidized beds, Brazelton[4] examined the effect of bed height on h_{max}. Typical data pertaining to a bed of 0.0218-in.-diameter glass beads in a tube of 1.96 in. ID and an original static height of 11.8 in. are shown in Fig. 8-26. The individual curves, relating h to G, pertain to four bed positions. The following observations are made:

1. For bed heights up to 6 in. the maximum coefficient is essentially independent of bed height. At a bed level of 12 in. a significantly lower maximum coefficient is observed.

2. As bed height increases, G_{max} has a tendency to increase. Thus for a 3-in. level $G_{max} = 375$, whereas for 12 in. $G_{max} = 475$.

These observations are entirely compatible with the generally observed deterioration of fluidization performance as higher positioned strata of fluidized beds are considered. This has been discussed in detail in Chap. 2.

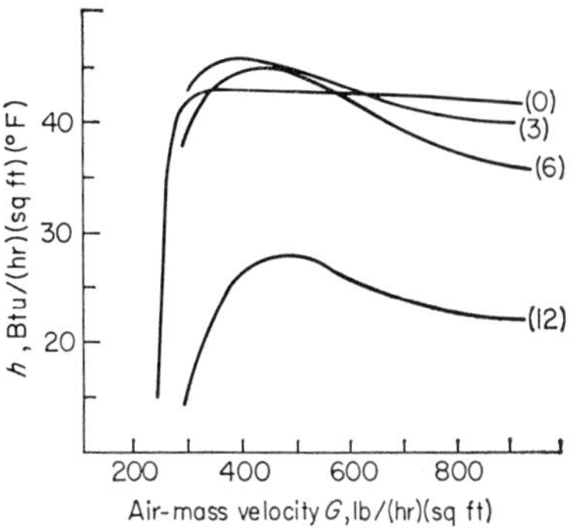

Dilute-phase Heat Transfer

Commercial fluidized reactors are known to operate between extreme ranges of solids concentration. Thus for design and the prediction of coefficients, dense-phase and dilute-phase heat-transfer correlations are of equal importance. For reasons unknown, considerably more emphasis has been given the problem of dense-phase heat transfer. This is especially puzzling because interpretation of dense-phase heat-transfer data appears to be the more complex problem of the two. Whereas the status of the dense phase is sufficiently advanced to permit formulation of some generalized correlations, dilute-phase data are still too fragmentary to permit such treatment.

Fig. 8-26. Data of Brazelton[4] showing local heat-transfer coefficients in relation to bed height. Note that h_{max} is significantly influenced by position in bed. Data in parentheses indicate height in inches of lower edge of 3-in. heater above base of bed.

General Considerations. As has been learned from Chap. 6, the transition from the dense to the dilute phase is not clearly defined in terms of a specific fluid velocity or bed density. For that reason no one particular dense-phase heat-transfer correlation may be extended into the dilute zone. The ideal result would of course be to have one single correlation that covered the entire spectrum of the fluidized state. The dense-phase work so far discussed is valid only up to the maximum coefficient of Fig. 8-1. By implication then, the branch to the right may be designated as the dilute-phase range. As far as trend of data is concerned, the experimentally determined coefficients for the dilute phase are qualitatively in agreement with this branch. Without exception, coefficients for beds of low solids concentration are either independent of mass velocity or decrease as mass velocity increases. The mass-velocity range over which the plateau in Fig. 8-1 extends depends on the mechanical properties of the solids, fluid viscosity, and fluid density. Thus, depending on conditions, the plateau may be more or less pronounced, or in some cases there may hardly be a plateau at all.

Some such conditions are indicated in Fig. 8-27. Solids-fraction as well as heat-transfer coefficients are shown in relation to mass velocity. The solids-fraction curve indicates that for branch a-b the change is relatively gradual, whereas for branch b-c the solids fraction decreases much faster with increasing mass velocity. Some heat-transfer data in Fig. 8-27 first increase with mass velocities, while others are relatively independent of mass velocity in this region. A sharp decline is, however, noted in all curves at the mass velocity for which the solids density changes suddenly to point b.

In the light of the few available bed-density and heat-transfer data, it is interesting to speculate on a possible mechanism by which heat is exchanged between a confining wall and a dilute suspension. Most certainly the modified film theory, which holds that the chief accelerator of heat transfer is the particle velocity past the heat-transfer wall, is not applicable. In the dilute suspension the particle velocities are so high

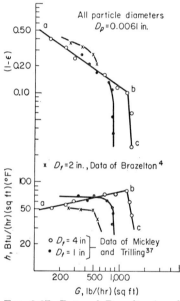

FIG. 8-27. Data of Brazelton[4] and Mickley and Trilling[37] showing response in heat transfer to solids concentration changes in the dilute phase.

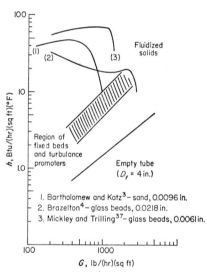

FIG. 8-28. Dilute-phase-fluidization heat-transfer data compared to fixed beds and empty tubes.

that, if they would still primarily affect the film thickness, the coefficients would have to be much higher than they actually are. The fact that dilute-suspension coefficients are lower than dense-phase coefficients indicates that in the dilute phase the solids fraction is the chief factor contributing to improved heat transfer. Thus the role of the solids in dilute suspensions, as far as effect on heat transfer is concerned, may not be unlike that of a thin spiral wire turbulence promoter in contact with the inside tube wall. It will primarily tend to disrupt the continuity of the laminar film and thus affect only little the already highly developed turbulent fluid core. Just as the turbulence promoter will be more effective, the more turns there are per unit length, so will the wall–dilute phase coefficients be higher, the greater the solids concentration becomes in the fluid-solids stream that travels past the fluid film.

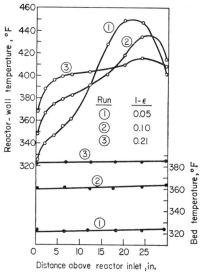

Order of Magnitude. Typical dilute-phase heat-transfer data are given in Fig. 8-28. They are shown in relation to empty- and fixed-bed coefficients. The considerable deviation between the fluidized-solids data is due to particle-diameter effect.

It has already been pointed out in connection with Fig. 8-1 that fixed-bed coefficients in laminar flow are about six times higher than empty-tube data. As shown in Fig. 8-28, dilute-phase fluidized-bed coefficients are, for large particles, not appreciably higher than conventional fixed-bed coefficients. But for small particles the coeffi-

FIG. 8-29. Typical reactor-wall and bed temperature gradients in dilute-phase-fluidization data of Bartholomew and Katz.[3] Note that reactor-wall temperature gradients are greatly affected by solids concentration, whereas bed temperature gradients are virtually unaffected.

cients *are* higher, chiefly because for the small particles the dilute-phase state is reached much earlier and at lower mass velocities, for which the fixed-bed data are lower.

The order of magnitude of the high-velocity-range dilute-phase data and the relation of the data to fixed-bed coefficients support the thought that the solids in the dilute phase act primarily as turbulence promoters. The unimportant role of solids velocity in the dilute phase is also readily understood from the comparison. The dilute phase, wherein solids velocities may attain many feet per second, may show virtually no heat-transfer improvement over fixed beds.

Temperature Gradients. With decreasing solids concentrations, temperature profiles become more pronounced. This is indicated by the data of Bartholomew and Katz,[3] whose unit, to be described in more detail below, was of the externally heated type. Reactor wall temperatures for various heights above the reactor inlet are shown in Fig. 8-29 for runs characterized by a range of solids concentration. Also shown are gradients through the bed itself. The latter are insignificant, even at the lowest value of solids concentration. This is probably due to the fact that, at the high fluid mass velocities required to maintain the low solids concentration, fluid flow was by itself thoroughly turbulent. The bed profiles are not unlike those of Caldas,[5] in which, for fluidization in a liquid phase, $D_p G / \mu > 3,000$.

Appearance of the pronounced wall-temperature profiles with decreasing solids concentration emphasizes the growing thermal resistance in the film. The upper hump irregularity is not caused by heat transfer; rather, it may be due to the oscillating solids level, as suggested by the authors. The intensity and extent of the wall profiles may be used to define roughly the limits between dense and dilute phase. For the 48- to 150-mesh sand tested this limit appears to be near a solids concentration of 10 to 15 per cent. It is to be noted, though, that these data are somewhat higher than the limiting values estimated earlier in Chap. 6.

Correlations

Three major investigations have been reported on dilute-phase heat transfer: Bartholomew and Katz,[3] Brazelton,[4] and Mickley and Trilling.[37]

Externally Heated. The unit of Bartholomew and Katz[3] was of the exterior heat-transfer noncirculatory-solids type, electrically heated. Tube dimensions were 4.0 in. ID and 30 in. height. Thermal measurements were made by wall-imbedded thermocouples. Air was used to fluidize aluminum powder, calcium carbonate, and sand. The range of operating variables is indicated below. All tests were made at atmos-

Variable	Range	Unit
Particle diameter, D_p	0.00333–0.00987	In.
Solids density, ρ_S	160–167	Lb per cu ft
Air mass velocity, G	96.4–935	Lb/(hr)(sq ft)
Voids	54–95	Per cent

pheric pressure. The bed-temperature level varied from 257 to 599°F, and the range of coefficients was reported to be from 9.65 to 66.1 Btu/(hr)(sq ft)(°F).

When equilibrium had been established, wall temperatures were measured and graphically integrated. By comparison with bed temperatures, driving forces were established. Heat flux was calculated from the air-temperature rise. The final correlation reads:

$$\frac{h}{c_F G} = \frac{1.560 + \ln (\text{Re } C_m^{-\frac{2}{3}} - 0.0120)}{-0.227 \text{ Pr}^{\frac{2}{3}} C_m^{0.42}} \qquad (8\text{-}34)$$

where
$$C_m = \frac{D_p{}^3 g_c \rho_F (\rho_S - \rho_F)}{\mu^2} \tag{8-35}$$

The limits of Eq. (8-34) are as indicated above.

In addition to close cuts, the work extended to mixed beds. For mixtures ranging from 48 to 150 mesh

$$D_p = \sum_{n=1}^{n=n} X d_p \tag{8-36}$$

an expression already familiar from earlier chapters.

Some of the studies of Mickley and Trilling[37] were made in equipment of 4.0 in. ID. Externally heated by resistance winding, the unit was similar to that of Bartholomew and Katz, except that provision had been made to operate the unit continuously. Glass beads were fluidized with air. Temperature driving forces were obtained from metal-skin and bed-temperature measurements. Heat flux was calculated from the wattage output of the heater.

The data were tentatively correlated by the empirical form

$$h = 0.0118 \left(\frac{\rho_b G}{D_p{}^3} \right)^{0.263} \tag{8-37}$$

where ρ_b is the average bed density in pounds per cubic foot. Limits of this correlation are indicated in the tabulation below. The runs were

Variable	Range	Unit
Particle diameter, D_p.............	0.00275–0.0178	In.
Solids density, ρ_S................	151–177	Lb per cu ft
Air mass velocity, G..............	135–2650	Lb/(hr)(sq ft)
Voids.......................	56–98	Per cent

made at atmospheric pressure. The bed temperature ranged from 300 to about 460°F. The coefficients ranged from about 20 to about 106 Btu/(hr)(sq ft)(°F).

It will be noted that operating conditions are very close to those of Bartholomew and Katz.[3] Moreover, the range of coefficients observed is also roughly in accord. However, from the entirely different forms of the correlation which have resulted, one is led to conclude that this phase of fluidized-bed heat transfer is not even remotely understood or solved.

In addition to the 4-in.-diameter unit, Mickley and Trilling operated a 1-in. column, 75 in. high. Construction was similar to that of the 4-in. apparatus. Figure 8-27, already introduced, reports bed densities and heat-transfer coefficients for 0.0061-in.-diameter glass beads in both columns. For solids fractions of $(1 - \epsilon) > 0.14$, column diameter has no effect. This is not unexpected, because for this condition the dense phase is rapidly approached and column diameter seems to have little effect on dense-phase fluidized-bed heat transfer.

A distinct column-diameter effect is observed for the dilute branch of the data. The solids-fraction vs. mass-velocity data indicate that the dilute-phase state is attained in the small unit at considerably lower mass velocities than in the large unit. The difference is quite considerable. Thus to yield a fraction of solids of say 0.04 in the small tube, a mass velocity of only 850 (lb)/(hr)(sq ft) is required, as compared to about 1,300 (lb)/(hr)(sq ft) in the large tube. This deviation can at present not be explained. It emphasizes, however, the limited character of the dilute-phase correlations.

Similar limitations are inherent in the correlation of Brazelton, which also requires bed-density data. Coefficients were measured in a 1.96-in.-ID tube of 36 in. height, surrounded by electrical heaters. Glass beads of size range 0.006 to 0.0437 in. were air-fluidized. Temperature driving forces were evaluated from skin temperatures, and heat flux was calculated from the electrical wattage. The data were correlated by the dimensionless equation

$$\frac{h}{c_F G'} = 0.72 \, \mathrm{Re}'^{-0.87}(1 - \epsilon)^{-1.30} \tag{8-38}$$

where $\mathrm{Re}' = \dfrac{D'G'}{\mu}$

D' = equivalent or effective diameter of free area across bed
G' = mass velocity based on void area in bed
D' and G' are thus functions of bed density; they are given below:

ρ_b/ρ_S	D'/D_p	G'/G
0.10	0.70	0.011
0.25	0.24	0.013
0.50	0.080	0.020
0.70	0.036	0.033

In view of the absence of a generalized correlation between bed density and mass velocity, the correlations of Brazelton and of Mickley and Trilling are restricted in their application to specific cases where bed-density data are available.

Internally Heated. Mickley and Trilling[37] also investigated the internally heated bed. The beds of glass beads, air-fluidized, were contained in a steel tube of 2.88 in. ID and 50 in. length. The centrally immersed calrod heater was of 0.49 in. diameter and 34.5 in. length. For bead sizes ranging from 0.0178 to 0.0040 in. the data were correlated by

$$h = 0.0433 \left(\frac{\rho_b{}^2}{D_p{}^3}\right)^{0.238}$$ (8-39)

Here, in contrast to the externally heated bed, gas mass velocity appeared to have no separate effect on heat transfer. It was suggested that the presence of the calrod heater in the center of the bed may have reduced slugging tendencies, thereby eliminating any independent fluid-velocity effect.

In Eq. (8-39) ρ_b is the bed density, in pounds per cubic foot. For the underlying experiments it varied from about 2.5 to 85 lb per cu ft. As far as applicability of the equation is concerned, that will again depend on the availability of bed-density data. For the above size range, coefficients were predicted to within ± 25 per cent. When applied to a set of data obtained with 0.0016-in.-diameter glass beads, the predicted data were considerably higher than those observed. The discrepancy was believed due to agglomeration of the small-diameter beads.

Heat Transfer in Liquid-fluidized Bed

All work so far discussed pertains to gas-fluidized solids. Only one liquid-fluidized study has so far become available. Caldas[5] obtained a revealing set of data by operating a 2-in. steam-jacketed fluidization tube. The glass beads fluidized with water ranged from 0.0086 to 0.0270 in. in diameter. Fraction solids in the beds extended over the range $0.50 > (1 - \epsilon) > 0.08$. Thus the study not only covers the dense phase but also extends well into the dilute phase. For purposes of comparison heat-transfer coefficients were also measured for solids-free water flow.

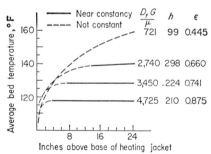

FIG. 8-30. Typical vertical temperature profiles, observed by Caldas[5] in liquid-fluidized beds of $D_p = 0.0197$ in.

Temperature Profiles. Typical longitudinal profiles are shown in Fig. 8-30. At Re = 721 the flow is probably too close to the minimum-fluidization value to cause any significant solids circulation. The temperature profile for this low value is similar to that expected for flow of water alone at this velocity. With increasing turbulence the upper portion of the profile begins to flatten first. As the state of turbulence increases, the flattening progresses to the base of the column.

The profiles pertaining to fluidization under high Reynolds numbers are much flatter than any profiles for water flow alone at the same Reynolds number. From this it may be concluded that in a highly expanded liquid-fluidized column of solids there must be a significant amount of internal top-bottom mixing. The flattening of the profile is due, possibly, to two causes. Owing to the top-bottom mixing, heat equalization results as a consequence of heat transport by the solids themselves. The other possible reason is that, because of the solids top-bottom mixing, substantial liquid quantities are carried up and down in addition to the prevailing macro flow pattern. Effective temperature differences were evaluated by graphical integration of the profiles.

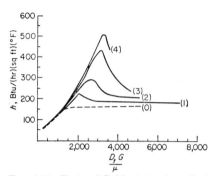

FIG. 8-31. Data of Caldas[5] showing effect of $D_t G/\mu$ on h in liquid-fluidized system composed of solids of various D_p. (0) No solids, (1) $D_p = 0.0270$ in., (2) $D_p = 0.0197$ in., (3) $D_p = 0.0115$ in., (4) $D_p = 0.0086$ in.

Data. Heat-transfer coefficients are shown in relation to Reynolds number in Fig. 8-31. Here too the already familiar maximum coefficient is encountered. Other observations are as follows:

1. For viscous flows ($D_t G/\mu < 2,000$) the fluidized coefficients are of the order of magnitude of solids-free flow.

2. For the viscous flow range particle diameter has virtually no effect on heat transfer.

3. For high flow rates, resulting in low bed densities, the liquid-fluidized coefficients are also of the order of magnitude met in the solids-free system.

4. Coefficients are significantly higher than for solids-free flow only if conditions are such as to produce a maximum or near-maximum coefficient. The maximum coefficients increase very markedly as particle size decreases, a result quite similar to that observed with gas-fluidized systems.

The observations are more or less in accord with the mechanics of liquid-phase particulate fluidization and the role of particle velocity in the modified film theory. For high bed densities particle velocities in particulate fluidization are too low to affect film thickness, and hence no effect is felt on heat transfer. At low bed densities experience with gas-solids systems has indicated that particle-velocity effects are secondary to solids concentration. All this appears also to be substantiated with liquid-solids systems. A significant increase in coefficients occurs only under conditions for which the bed is still relatively dense but is sufficiently dilated to permit a relatively high solids velocity.

Correlation. Maximum coefficients were correlated by

$$h_{\max} = 15.4 D_p^{-0.75} \tag{8-40}\star$$

where particle diameter is to be expressed in inches.

The data to the left of the maximum coefficient, designated to be in the dense phase, were correlated by

$$\frac{h D_p}{k} = 0.055 \frac{D_p G}{\mu} \tag{8-41}\star$$

The dilute-phase data to the right of the maximum were represented by

$$\frac{h}{c_F G}\left(\frac{c_F \mu}{k}\right)^{\frac{2}{3}} = 1.4 \left(\frac{D_t G}{\mu}\right)^{-1.0} \frac{1}{\epsilon} \left(\frac{D_p}{D_t}\right)^{-0.79} \tag{8-42}\star$$

Equation (8-42) correlated the data for the water-fluidized solids with a maximum deviation of ± 20 per cent. It is believed that the correlation will apply satisfactorily to liquid-fluidized systems in general. As indicated in Fig. 8-32, points of division between the dense and dilute phases are a function of D_p and $D_t G/\mu$.

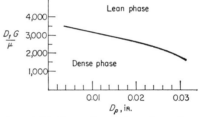

FIG. 8-32. Dense-lean phase boundary in liquid-fluidized solids beds to be used with correlations (8-40) to (8-42) of Caldas.[5]

It will be noted that Eq. (8-42) contains the bed-voidage term. Because the bed is liquid-fluidized, ϵ may be readily estimated for the high range by the relationship of Richardson and Zaki, presented in detail in Chap. 4.

Example 8-2. A catalytic reactor of 6 in. ID is cooled by a centrally immersed cooling tube of 1 in. OD. The particle size of the solids is $D_p = 0.0061$ in.; solids density $\rho_S = 100$ lb per cu ft; the bed height when fluidized is 24 in. It is desired to maintain the temperature in the reactor at 400°F. During the reaction, 1800 Btu per hr have to be carried away through the central cooling element. Estimate the required wall temperature in the cooling element if the charge is fluidized at such a rate that the maximum heat-transfer coefficient is produced. The average viscosity of the reactant-product mixture may be taken as $\mu = 0.025$ centipoise, the average fluid density as $\rho_F = 0.050$ lb per cu ft, and the average thermal conductivity as 0.0280 Btu/(hr)(sq ft)(°F)/(ft).

Solution. We shall first use the correlation of Vreedenberg.[44] Since the unit is to operate at such a mass velocity that the maximum coefficient will result, we find from Fig. 8-25 that it must be operated at $G_{\max}/G_{mf} = 11.0$. With the kinematic viscosity remaining unchanged as the fluid passes through the unit, the heat-transfer coefficient becomes

$$h = 1.05 \frac{0.028 \times 12}{0.0061} 11.0^{0.35} = 133.5 \text{ Btu/(hr)(sq ft)(°F)}$$

The internal surface area of the cooling tube is

$$\frac{1 \times 3.14 \times 2.0}{12} = 0.524 \text{ sq ft}$$

The prevailing temperature difference will then be

$$\Delta t = \frac{1,800}{0.524 \times 133.5} = 25.7°\text{F}$$

and the required wall temperature then becomes

$$400 - 25.7 = 374.3°\text{F}$$

We shall now rework the problem, using the correlation of Baerg and co-workers.[2] It will be recalled that this correlation was originally developed for air. Consequently we shall have to make allowance for the variation in thermal conductivity of the fluid.

We require first the value of G_{mf}. Hence $(\rho_S - \rho_F)\rho_F = 100 \times 0.050 = 5.0$; viscosity $\mu = 0.025$ centipoise, and $D_p = 0.0061$ in. From the nomograph of Fig. 3-15a, $G_{mf} = 7.0$ lb/(hr)(sq ft). The fluidization mass velocity is then $7.0 \times 11 = 77$ lb/(hr)(sq ft).

The maximum heat-transfer coefficient is then estimated from Eq. (8-32). It will be assumed that the bulk density $\rho_b = 55$ lb per cu ft. Hence

$$h_{\max} = 49 \times \log \frac{0.00037 \times 55}{0.000508} = 78.6 \text{ Btu/(hr)(sq ft)(°F)}$$

It will be recalled that this is for air of an average thermal conductivity of $k = 0.0150$ Btu/(hr)(sq ft)(°F)/(ft). Assuming that $h \propto k^{0.60}$, we shall have for our case

$$h_{\max} = 78.6 \left(\frac{0.0280}{0.0150}\right)^{0.6} = 114.2 \text{ Btu/(hr)(sq ft)(°F)}$$

The final heat-transfer coefficient then becomes, according to correlation (8-32),

$$h = 114.2 - 55e^{-0.012(77-0.71\times55)}$$
$$= 79.4 \text{ Btu/(hr)(sq ft)(°F)}$$

The resulting wall temperature would then become 356.7°F.

It will be noted that the heat-transfer coefficient obtained from the Baerg correlation is substantially lower than the Vreedenberg coefficient. This is in part due to the fact that the Vreedenberg correlation (8-27) postulates that $h \propto k$, whereas for estimation purposes with the correlation of Baerg et al. it was assumed that $h \propto k^{0.6}$. Assuming that the coefficient should indeed be directly proportional to the thermal conductivity and applying the assumption to the Baerg correlation would produce a value of $h = 111.7$ Btu/(hr)(sq ft)(°F), still lower than the Vreedenberg value from Eq. (8-27). Conceding that the fluidization performance in the larger unit used by Vreedenberg was superior to the performance in the small-diameter vessel of Baerg et al., it is nevertheless indicated that the Vreedenberg correlation (8-27) overstresses the effect of thermal conductivity. That this is so is also indicated by the subsequent correlations (8-28) and (8-29) of Vreedenberg, where the coefficient is reported to be proportional only to the 0.7 power of the thermal conductivity.

Example 8-3. A 2-in. standard pipe of 72 in. length is surrounded in the lower section by a steam chest, 40 in. high. The upper portion of 2-in. standard pipe extending out of the steam chest is thoroughly insulated. The 2-in. pipe carries in its lower end, flush with the base of the steam chest, a supporting screen for fluidized solids. The unit is charged with a layer of round granular material of $D_p = 0.018$ in. and $\rho s = 100$ lb per cu ft. In the unexpanded state the bed height is exactly 4.0 in. at a voidage of $\epsilon = 0.34$.

Water at 70°F enters the unit from below at a mass velocity of 38,000 lb/(hr)(sq ft). Saturated steam at 220°F is admitted into the well-vented steam chest, with excess steam escaping from the vent to make sure that there is no limit on heat supply and that the steam-side coefficient is high. For these conditions of operation estimate the resulting temperature of the water leaving the unit.

Solution

$$G_{mf} = 688 \times 0.018^{1.82} \frac{[62.3(100 - 62.3)]^{0.94}}{1.0^{0.88}}$$

$$= 678 \text{ lb/(hr)(sq ft)}$$

$$\frac{D_pG_{mf}}{\mu} = \frac{0.018 \times 678}{12 \times 2.42} = 0.42$$

$$\frac{D_pG}{\mu} = \frac{0.018 \times 38,000}{12 \times 2.42} = 23.5$$

Applying the method of Richardson and Zaki for bed expansion, $n = 4.6$ for Re $= 0.42$ and $n = 4.10$ for Re $= 23.5$. Taking an average value of 4.35, there results the expanded-bed voidage $\epsilon = 0.93$. The bed-expansion ratio then becomes $R = 0.66/0.07 = 9.45$, and the expanded-bed height will be $4.0 \times 9.45 = 37.8$ in. The heat-transfer area will then be

$$\frac{37.8 \times 2.067 \times 3.14}{144} = 1.70 \text{ sq ft}$$

Taking the viscosity as that of cold water at 70°F, the empty-tube Reynolds number is now calculated as

$$\frac{D_tG}{\mu} = \frac{2.067 \times 38,000}{12 \times 2.42} = 2,700$$

From Fig. 8-32 it appears that the operation will just about yield the maximum coefficient. Hence we may apply correlation (8-40) and

$$h = 15.4 \times 0.018^{-0.75} = 312 \text{ Btu/(hr)(sq ft)(°F)}$$

On the assumption that the state of turbulence is sufficient to render the temperature in the fluidized bed constant, there follows from a heat balance

$$38,000 \times 0.023 \times 1.0(t_2 - 70) = 1.70 \times 312(220 - t_2),$$
and
$$t_2 = 127°F$$

It will be noted that according to the calculations the solids level is 2.2 in. below the upper end of the steam chest. Hence plain water will proceed for a short distance, being heated in the usual manner. However, this effect is so small that it may be neglected when compared with the much greater heat-transfer rate observed in the bed.

HEAT TRANSFER IN PNEUMATIC-TRANSPORT LINES

The problem of heat exchange between solids in transport and the environment may occasionally arise. In catalytic processes in which portions of a spent catalyst may require continuous regeneration, the problem may even be a common one. Whenever the solids are used in a fluidized bed, it is sometimes desirable to affect the catalyst transfer pneumatically. Under these conditions it is then quite logical to combine the solids-transfer operation with a heat-exchange step.

Commercial solids-transfer lines may vary considerably in diameter. Thus in pilot installations and fluidized-solids feeders, lines a fraction of an inch in diameter may be encountered, whereas in catalytic cracking and similar processes ducts several feet in diameter may be called for. Similarly, the solids concentration may also range between considerable limits. For the dilute end of the concentration spectrum it is difficult to specify definite limits of solids concentration. Thus pneumatic lines are known to carry such low solids loads that they may virtually be considered void of solid matter. On the concentrated end, however, lines carrying in excess of 10 to 15 volume per cent of solids are met relatively seldom. Further details pertinent to pneumatic flow are given in Chap. 6.

Heat-transfer Mechanism. Examining the situation for solids heating, for instance, there is (1) heat flow through a tube wall to a fluid stream and (2) heat flow from the fluid to the solids which are conveyed by the stream. The final solids temperature and thermal equilibrium in a pneumatic-transport line will then depend on the relative rates of the two heat-transfer steps. It is important to visualize the dual nature of this problem properly, because it emphasizes that, for the calculation of the equilibrium solids temperature, both phenomena require consideration.

In pneumatic-transport lines fluid velocities are usually such that turbulent flow conditions prevail. The solids move primarily in the turbulent core. As far as promulgation of a possible heat-transfer mechanism between the environment and a pneumatic-transport line as a whole is concerned, it may therefore be assumed that the first thermal resistance inside the line is again due to a laminar fluid film. In comparison with the dimensions of the solids particles that are commonly conveyed, the fluid-film thickness is now probably of a considerably lesser order of magnitude than the average particle diameter. Hence solids can pass along in the main stream of the fluid, and in so doing effectively bombard the tube wall and thereby reduce the film thickness. Obviously, then, the greater the solids concentration, the more will the influence of the passing solids on the film thickness be felt. Thus solids concentration should influence heat transfer between solids-transport lines and the environment very much in the same way it does in dilute-phase systems. Solids concentration should therefore again be expected to be a major correlation parameter.

A second resistance to heat flow is offered by the turbulent fluid core. Heat passes through the laminar film by conduction, whereas in the turbulent core convection operates. The core resistance is probably the lesser.

Finally, the solids themselves can act as a heat carrier. Their contribution may, however, be considered negligible, owing to the usually low solids concentrations and generally low solids heat capacities.

Experimental Data. Virtually the only published heat-transfer film coefficients pertaining to pneumatic systems are those of Koble et al.,[22,23] and more recently of Farbar and Morley.[11] The unit of Koble et al. was a horizontal $\frac{1}{4}$-in.-OD copper tube of 0.190 in. ID, 6.5 ft long and surrounded by a steam jacket. Air and solids feed ratios in the copper tube could be adjusted. Solids examined were a 40-micron coal and a crushed limestone powder of about 200-micron size. Terminal air-solids temperatures were obtained by thermocouples, inserted at both ends of the $\frac{1}{4}$-in.-diameter copper tube. No further temperature explorations were made at intermediate stations. Film coefficients were based on the inside tube area, and the assumption was made that air and solids temperatures were equal at any point along the heat exchanger. As thermal driving force, terminal temperatures thus obtained were used for calculation of a log-mean temperature difference. Specific results obtained from the test were as follows:

1. For the coal examined $h \propto G_S^{0.39}$, where G_S was the solids mass velocity. The best line through the limestone data indicated that $h \propto G_S^{0.66}$. The difference between the exponents was tentatively attributed to particle diameter.

2. For a constant solids fraction in the suspension, heat-transfer coefficients increased with gas mass velocity. But unfortunately the data do not permit evaluation of the functional relationship, because as gas

mass velocity was increased, the solids feed rate was kept constant. Thus the percentage of solids in the suspension actually decreased as the gas mass velocity increased.

3. Coefficients appear to be inversely proportional to some power of particle size.

Effects of other solids properties, such as true solids density, particle shape, and thermal properties, were not investigated, nor were gas-property effects studied.

Farbar and Morley[11] worked with a vertical tube of 17.5 mm ID, 33 in. long. The unit was surrounded by a vapor jacket to permit addition of heat. As a solid, the alumina catalyst of wide size distribution mentioned in Chap. 6 was used. Heat-transfer coefficients were based on the inside tube area and a logarithmic-mean temperature difference, as obtained from terminal data. All coefficients had been properly corrected for vapor-side resistance.

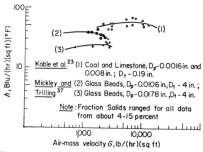

FIG. 8-33. Comparison of heat-transfer coefficients in pneumatic transport and dilute-phase fluidization.

Correlation Trends. From the point of view of solids concentration in the suspension, the Koble et al.[22,23] data are comparable to a portion of the data which Mickley and Trilling[37] have reported for the dilute-fluidization phase. Since solids concentration was recognized as an important variable in both cases, it is of interest to compare the two sets of data. From Fig. 8-33, where the comparison is provided, the following observations result:

1. With respect to order of magnitude, the data are in agreement with each other.

2. The course of the data exhibits a slight upward curvature, due to the effect of solids concentration.

3. The Koble et al. data proceed along a somewhat higher level than the Mickley and Trilling data selected. This is probably due to difference in particle size.

The effect of particle size is clearly recognized from Fig. 8-34, where the coal data of Koble and coworkers are again compared with some glass-bead data of Mickley and Trilling. Heat-transfer coefficients are now plotted vs. solids concentration. The agreement, with respect to both order of magnitude and slope, must be considered excellent, especially in view of the great differences in other solids properties, not to mention the profound apparatus differences. The data of Fig. 8-34 indicate plainly that solids concentration is the chief variable. Apparatus details and mechanical as well as thermal solids properties are probably of subordinate importance in their effect on heat transfer. The Mickley and Trilling data chosen in Fig. 8-34 pertain to their internally heated apparatus. Comparison with the externally heated apparatus data of Mickley and Trilling would lead to essentially the same conclusions.

The Mickley and Trilling data of Fig. 8-34 indicate that $h \propto \rho_b^{0.5}$. The Koble et al. data in Fig. 8-33 exhibit a nearly horizontal path, hence would appear to be independent of the conveying-air mass velocity. It has, however, already been mentioned that this is only apparently so; for, as air mass velocity increased, the solids concentration decreased because of the nonvarying solids feed rate into the heat-transfer tube.

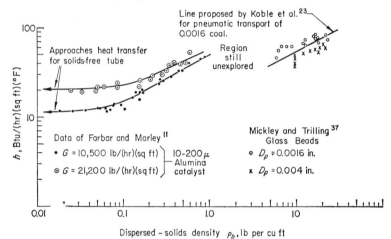

FIG. 8-34. Heat transfer in pneumatic-transport lines in relation to dispersed-solids density in the stream.

With the above relationship between h and ρ_b, the data of Fig. 8-33 could be corrected. This procedure then yielded $h \propto G^{0.33}$. According to Mickley and Trilling, for externally heated units $h \propto G^{0.263}$. With respect to order of magnitude the agreement of the two exponents is quite good, and it may be taken as an indication of the related nature of the problems involved here.

Figure 8-34 also makes reference to the data of Farbar and Morley.[11] As for solids concentration, they were very much lower than the data of Mickley and Trilling, or those reported by Koble and coworkers. The highest solids concentrations were less than a pound per cubic foot; hence there is an appreciable unexplored gap between the two sets of data. The gas mass velocities of Farbar and Morley ranged from 10,500 to 21,200 lb/(hr)(sq ft). This corresponds roughly to a linear velocity range of 40 to 80 fps; hence the data are typical for pneumatic transport. Other data pertaining to the experiments of Farbar and Morley are as follows:

Heat-transfer tube, ID: 0.69 in.
Length of heat-transfer tube: 33 in.
Approximate range of solids-to-air ratio: $0.1 < G_S/G < 10$
Solids density: 152 lb per cu ft
Solids: Oven-dried alumina
Particle-size range: From about 12 to 208 microns

The data of Fig. 8-34 are extremely interesting in that they emphasize clearly the effect of solids concentration. For extremely low concentrations—say, up to a solids bulk density of about 0.1 lb per cu ft—corresponding to a volume solids fraction of appreciably less than 1 per cent, heat-transfer coefficients are almost independent of ρ_b. Moreover, the coefficients are not substantially above those observed for a solids-free tube. However, beyond a volume solids fraction of about 0.1 per cent, the effect of solids concentration is felt markedly. There are several possible explanations for this phenomenon. Perhaps the most probable one is that, below a certain limiting solids concentration, the solids travel primarily inside the turbulent fluid core, with relatively few particles hitting the wall. The solids flow pattern will most likely spread when the solids concentration surpasses this limiting value.

For the branch above $\rho_b \approx 0.1$ Farbar and Morley[11] have suggested

$$\frac{hD_t}{k} = 0.14 \left(\frac{D_t G}{\mu}\right)^{0.6} \left(\frac{G_S}{G}\right)^{0.45} \tag{8-43}$$

where G_S and G are solids and gas mass velocities, respectively. Equation (8-43) is recommended for all instances in which the loading $G_S/G > 2.0$. In the above form the equation applies only to air flow. It is believed that, by inclusion of the Prandtl group, it may be extended to gases in general. Equation (8-43) then becomes

$$\frac{hD_t}{k} = 0.16 \left(\frac{G_S}{G}\right)^{0.45} \left(\frac{D_t G}{\mu}\right)^{0.6} \left(\frac{c_F \mu}{k}\right)^{0.4} \tag{8-44}\star$$

It is to be recalled that the above solids-to-air ratio applies to a solid of $\rho_S = 152$ lb per cu ft. Therefore, since it should really be the volumetric solids fraction that is effective, the solids-to-air ratio in Eq. (8-44) may require correction if solids of greatly different densities are involved.

For instances in which $G_S/G < 2.0$ the Morley and Farbar data may be correlated to give

$$\frac{hD_t}{k} = 0.025 \left(\frac{D_t G}{\mu}\right)^{0.8} \left(\frac{c_F \mu}{k}\right)^{0.4} \tag{8-45}\star$$

The excellent agreement with the Dittus-Boelter equation correlating heat-transfer coefficients for solids-free fluid flow is to be noted. As far as extension of these correlations to larger-diameter pipes is concerned, it should probably be permissible, within reasonable limits of scale-up.

PARTICLE-FLUID HEAT TRANSFER

The problem of particle-fluid heat transfer is widely encountered. Until comparatively recently, all operations involving particle-fluid heat transfer employed fixed and moving beds. A pertinent example is the pebble heater, the contacting unit of which may be of the fixed- or moving-bed type. Another and older example is the blast furnace. The charge descends the furnace shaft and is contacted by a rising stream of hot gases. This is obviously a moving bed of a very complicated type. On their downward journey the particles undergo a chemical change which also markedly alters the physical properties of the entire bed. In the pebble heater no chemical change is involved, and whatever changes in physical properties of the solids may occur are due entirely to temperature variations. In view of the widespread occurrence of the problem of particle-fluid heat transfer, it is somewhat surprising that, even for the relatively easily analyzed case of fixed or moving beds, almost no basic heat-transfer correlations have been developed. In virtually all cases, new installations were built by means of scale-up from pilot units or anticipated performance was arrived at on the basis of earlier similar operations.

In recent years applications of particle-fluid heat transfer in the fluidized state have become more numerous. They may be put into the following three categories:

1. Heat-recovery operations involving no mass transfer and chemical change
2. Physical operations involving simultaneous heat transfer and mass transfer
3. Processes requiring heat transfer to induce and sustain a chemical reaction

The cooling of a granular catalyst by direct contact with a gas may be a case of mere heat recovery. The drying of a gas by a granular adsorbent and the regeneration of a used adsorbent are instances that involve simultaneous heat and mass transfer. Chemical change is involved in many metallurgical operations, notably ore roasting. In the third case, simultaneous heat and mass is usually also involved. Sometimes changes brought about are sufficiently profound to induce secondary effects, such as particle disintegration or the reverse, agglomeration. The fluidization characteristics of the solids phase may therefore be significantly altered, rendering the operation often difficult, if not impossible.

In view of these and other complexities it is understandable that the problem of particle-fluid heat transfer in the fluidized bed is virtually unsolved.

Fundamental Considerations. The particle-fluid heat-transfer coefficient is defined by

$$h = \frac{q}{A \, \Delta t} \qquad (8\text{-}6)$$

where q = heat in transit

A = effective participating surface area between particles and fluid

Δt = mean temperature difference that is operative

Depending on the case in question, q may be sensible heat, as in the case of catalyst heating or cooling; it may be chiefly latent heat as in adsorption or desorption of a vapor on a porous surface; or it could be a heat of reaction, as in ore roasting, for instance. In any of these cases the experimental evaluation of q is usually not insurmountable.

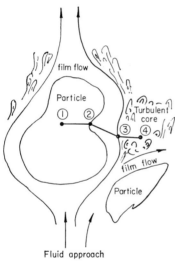

Fig. 8-35. Thermal resistances encountered in particle-fluid fluidized heat transfer.

Evaluation of surface area is more difficult. Let Fig. 8-35 be a typical particle in a fluidizing charge subject to a thermal process. A particle of nonspherical shape is deliberately shown to emphasize that not all portions of the surface area must necessarily be equally effective. In practice this is further accentuated by the fact that a bed is a configuration of particles in which mutual hindrance effects are known to exist.

With the particle placed in a fluid stream it may be thought of as being contained in a thin envelope, consisting of a fluid film. The fluid beyond the film is in a certain state of turbulence. The turbulence may be the result of the over-all velocity of the fluid and its rheological properties; it may be induced in a secondary fashion by the moving particles; or both agencies might be operative. If under the circumstances one may speak of an average film thickness, this will then depend on a number of factors.

The mean temperature difference that is operative in such a system is illustrated by the two temperatures 2 and 3 at either side of the film (Fig. 8-35). From the considerable geometrical irregularities of the system it follows that the variation in local temperature differences in the bed may be appreciable. Considering next temperatures 3 and 4 it may probably be assumed that this drop is nominal for most cases. Hence by recording the bulk temperature 4, as normally indicated by a high-speed suction-type thermocouple (instead of the film temperature 3), no serious error would result.

Measurement of the solids temperature by a thermocouple is much more difficult. This is so for two reasons. To start with, it is probably physically impossible to attach a thermocouple junction to the surface of a fluidizing particle without impairing the mobility of the particle. Next it may be seen from Fig. 8-35 that, since the film around the particles is not of uniform thickness, the surface temperature of the solid surface cannot be uniform. Assuming that a physical attachment of a thermocouple junction were possible, the problems of how to select a truly representative particle and the correct surface region to which to attach the junction would arise. All these considerations assume, of course, that the resistance to heat flow through the body of the particles is small, that is, that temperature 1 essentially equals temperature 2. This will in turn demand either that the particle be of small dimensions or that the solids thermal conductivity be high.

From the preceding considerations it appears, then, that it is evaluation of the solids temperature which is the most difficult step in the experimental evaluation of the particle-fluid heat-transfer coefficient in the fluidized bed. It is probably for this reason more than any other that the few available experimental reports have almost no region of mutual agreement.

Experimental. A brief summary of system details pertaining to the four experimental studies so far reported[16,21,46,47] is given in Table 8-4.

TABLE 8-4. COMPARISON OF PARTICLE-FLUID FLUIDIZED-BED
HEAT-TRANSFER STUDIES

Reference	Solids-gas system	Particle size, in.	Diam of bed, in.	Gas mass velocity range, lb/ (hr)(sq ft)	Order of magnitude of heat-transfer coef, Btu/ (hr)(sq ft)(°F)
Heertjes and McKibbins[16]	Silica gel–air	0.0142– 0.0432	2.36	324–630	7–25
Kettenring, Manderfield, and Smith[21]	Alumina–air Silica gel–air	0.039– 0.0138	2.30	300–800	3–10
Walton, Olson, and Levenspiel[46]	Coal–air	0.0276– 0.0138	4.03	325–920	3–70
Wamsley and Johanson[47]	Glass beads and alumina–air and CO_2	0.035 and 0.0053	2.38	100–600	1.0

The study of Kettenring, Manderfield, and Smith[21] involved the drying of adsorbents; hence heat and mass transfer occurred simultaneously. Transfer coefficients were reported to be significantly lower than in fixed beds operating under similar ranges of mass velocity. As a possible reason for the low values the authors mention that the particles tend to move with the gas in the fluidized condition. Since they employed a dense bed with no net particle movement away from the bed, it was not possible to have particle movement with the gas flow without a simultaneous particle movement against the gas flow, at least in some sections of the bed. There is of course the possibility, as pointed out by Heertjes and McKibbins,[16] that the solids temperature measured by Kettenring, Manderfield, and Smith was too low. For evaluation of the temperature driving force they assumed that the temperature of the solids through the entire bed was that of the bed at its upper interface. Thus an error of only a few degrees in the low part of the bed would have affected the temperature difference severely, and thereby the over-all coefficient. Given the possibility that the temperature difference may have been too high, the data of Kettenring, Manderfield, and Smith may be considered as representing minimum values.

Heat transfer between silica gel particles and air was also studied by Heertjes and McKibbins.[16] Instead of using a bare thermocouple for measuring exit-air temperature, as was done by Kettenring and coworkers, they worked with a screen-protected element. From an earlier temperature exploration,[15] as well as from the findings of Eichhorn and White,[10] it was learned that the temperature of the solid, with the exception of a thin layer near the supporting sieve, is independent of the location in the apparatus. Moreover the opinion was given that in this main region of the bed the solids temperature was essentially equal to the exit-gas temperature. Thus their screened thermocouple precluded occasional bombardment by gel particles from a lower-bed region where the particles were probably of a somewhat lower temperature. Heat-transfer coefficients were obtained as follows:

For a differential height dL of the bed,

$$hA(t_G - t_S)\, dL + c_F GS\, dt_G = 0 \qquad (8\text{-}46)$$

As found experimentally, the solids temperature t_S is essentially constant throughout the bed. Thus the gas temperature t_G varies simply with bed height. Integration between the limits $L = 0$ and $L = L$ will then yield

$$\ln \frac{(t_G - t_S)_0}{(t_G - t_S)_L} = \frac{Ah}{c_F GS} L \qquad (8\text{-}47)$$

Hence a plot of the left-hand part vs. L should give straight lines of slope $Ah/c_F GS$. Assuming that the particles are spherical, the total heat-transfer area A is then calculated from the weight of the bed, and coefficients are readily evaluated from the slopes of the straight lines.

Walton and coworkers[46] were also fully aware of the difficulties associated with solids temperature measurement. Inlet-air temperatures were obtained by a traveling high-speed thermocouple near the bed entrance. For solid temperatures they chose to give two values. One of them was obtained by immersing an unprotected couple in the bottom of the column, and the other value was assumed equal to the equilibrium temperature of gas and solids at the top of the bed. Using the gas temperature with the former they would obtain a maximum coefficient, whereas assumption of the latter temperature as the correct solids temperature would give a minimum coefficient. They reasoned that true values would be somewhere in between.

The study of Wamsley and Johanson[47] utilized the unsteady-state heat flow from hot gas into solids when solids are suddenly placed into the gas stream. Heat-transfer coefficients were calculated from the time-history curves of the solids and the gas. Solids temperatures were essentially based on heat balances. While this method of operation is probably the most promising for an independent evaluation of the heat-transfer coefficient, the assumption of a uniform solids temperature through the bed as well as a uniform gas temperature in various bed regions is not justified. At any rate, their coefficients are abnormally low, which would indicate a serious discrepancy somewhere along the line of data evaluation. As an explanation for the low values, the authors suggest gas bypassing of the solids. They also point out that the data of Kettenring, Manderfield, and Smith might well have been lower than they are. In fact the Kettenring et al. data would be in good agreement with their own if, as solids temperature, the adiabatic saturation temperature of the incoming air were used.[24]

Proposed Correlations. The correlation of Kettenring, Manderfield, and Smith for heat transfer reads as follows:

$$\frac{hD_p}{k} = 0.0135 \left(\frac{D_pG}{\mu}\right)^{1.30} \tag{8-48}$$

Heertjes and McKibbins proposed

$$h = 1.31 \left(\frac{D_pG}{\mu}\right)^{0.76} \tag{8-49}$$

as well as the auxiliary approximate form

$$h = 1.4G^{0.76}D_p^{0.67} \tag{8-50}$$

The Walton, Olson, and Levenspiel correlation is

$$\frac{hD_p}{k} = 0.0028 \left(\frac{D_pG}{\mu}\right)^{1.7} \left(\frac{D_p}{D_t}\right)^{-0.2} \tag{8-51}$$

or an abbreviated dimensional form

$$h = 0.0022G^{1.7}D_p^{0.5} \qquad (8\text{-}52)$$

In the dimensional correlations (8-50) and (8-52) G is in pounds per hour per square foot and D_p in inches.

Particle-diameter and Mass-velocity Effects. According to the above correlations, $h \propto D_p^{n'}$, with n' ranging from $+0.3$ to $+0.67$. The *positive* nature of the slope, reported by Wamsley and Johanson, is of particular interest, especially since, for fluidized bed-wall coefficients, *negative* slopes have been reported universally. The negative slope was found in agreement with the generally accepted mechanism of heat transfer through a thin laminar film inside the tube wall. The present positive slope attending particle-fluid heat transfer still requires explanation. The fact that in beds of large particles slip velocities are higher than in small-particle beds is not wholly satisfactory, because of the mutual hindrance effects in the dense bed. The positive slope must therefore have another reason.

Comparison with the fixed-bed solids heating data of Löf and Hawley[32] appears to offer a clue. The data pertain to unsteady-state heat flow from hot gases to gravel of 4 mesh to 1.5-in. size in a fixed bed. The data were analyzed by the method proposed by Schumann,[41] and coefficients were originally expressed in Btu per hour per cubic foot per degree Fahrenheit. Assuming a voidage of 50 per cent, some of the Löf and Hawley data, recalculated to give the coefficient in the dimension Btu per hour per square foot per degree Fahrenheit, are shown in Fig. 8-36 for constant gas mass velocities in relation to particle size. The slopes are equal to 0.33 and 0.25, hence smaller than the slopes observed from correlations (8-49), (8-50), and (8-52) but still in a fair order-of-magnitude agreement. Since in a fixed bed the concept of slip velocity loses all significance, the positive slope cannot be due to slip velocity.

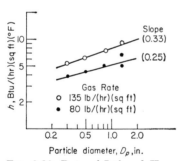

FIG. 8-36. Data of Löf and Hawley[32] showing particle-gas heat-transfer coefficient in relation to particle diameter; bed voidage was assumed to be 50 per cent.

A more logical explanation would be to accept zones of nonhomogeneous packing densities in a packed bed. Thus some regions in the packed bed are less accessible to fluid flow than others. The voids are in reality mutually joined interparticle cellular spaces. These will increase with particle size and at the same time render hitherto blocked regions of the bed accessible to effective fluid penetration. Hence heat-transfer coefficients should, for constant flow rates, be expected to increase with particle size.

Wamsley and Johanson report the unlikely result that particle-fluid heat-transfer coefficients are independent of fluid mass velocity. However, according to the other correlations, $h \propto G^{m'}$, where m' ranges from $+0.76$ to 1.3. Moreover, for the fixed bed, Löf and Hawley[32] as well as Furnas[12] report that $h \propto G^{0.7}$. This is in good agreement with the exponent of Heertjes and McKibbins. The difference between the Furnas exponent and other exponents cannot be resolved at this time.

Nusselt- vs. Reynolds-number Presentation. The correlations so far proposed for fluidized-bed particle-fluid heat transfer differ markedly from each other. Thus a significant advance could be achieved if only a way to indicate which correlation is most probably correct were available. An attempt at such an indication is made by the comparison in Fig. 8-37, where the data are shown along with a generally accepted correlation for heat flow between spheres and ambient fluid.[35] A reliable set of heat-transfer data on a somewhat related system, namely, heat transfer to clouds of falling particles by Johnstone, Pigford, and Chapin,[19] is available. Their data pertain to solids dropping through furnace atmospheres under controlled temperature conditions. The solids temperatures were obtained calorimetrically, and the measurements are such that a high degree of reliance can be placed on the data. It is therefore considered significant that these data correlate reasonably well with the remaining fixed-bed and single-sphere data, observed with particles several hundred-fold larger in diameter.

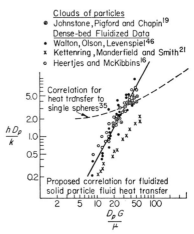

FIG. 8-37. Comparison of dense-phase fluidized-bed particle-fluid heat-transfer data with heat-transfer data for clouds of falling particles.[19]

Of course the falling-cloud data can, at best, be considered as pertaining only to a highly dilute fluidized bed of, say, 99 per cent or higher voids. With the exception of the Wamsley and Johanson data, all other dense-phase particle-fluid data are also plotted. The data of Kettenring and coworkers are low, as expected, but the remaining two sets of data are indeed in very good agreement with the falling-cloud data. This is so despite the great difference in solids concentration. In view of the considerable complexities that prevail, the problem defies a rigorous mathematical analysis; hence a purely qualitative examination of possible effects of solids concentration must suffice. If the earlier-presented film and general-resistance concepts are valid, it would appear that, as a bed becomes more dense, the film thickness will be reduced because of particle collisions. This will tend to *increase* film coefficients.

As the film thickness is thus reduced, the homogeneous gas flow pattern prevailing in the dilute phase would inevitably be replaced by a heterogeneous flow pattern characterized by gas bubbles and bypassing. In addition, bed consolidation would lead to a reduction of effective heat-transfer area. These changes would then tend to *decrease* the coefficients; hence, with these opposing influences at play, it is conceivable that both dilute- and dense-phase particle-fluid heat-transfer data are essentially of the same order of magnitude. At any rate this seems to be indicated by the data of Fig. 8-37, which are tentatively correlated by

$$\frac{hD_p}{k} = 0.0063 \left(\frac{D_p G}{\mu}\right)^{1.8} \tag{8-53}$$

When the data of Wamsley and Johanson[47] were examined in the same manner, they fell several logarithmic cycles below the Kettenring et al.[21] data. Apparently they were in complete disagreement with the general correlation pattern. The Kettenring et al. data, barely in line with respect to order of magnitude, are very low. The trend of the deviation supports the observation that the solids temperatures were indeed higher than Kettenring et al. believed. At low Reynolds numbers there is relatively little mixing in the bed, and hence the assumption that the bottom solids temperatures are then equal to the top temperature would not be as much in error as at high Reynolds numbers. Because more intense solids mixing is induced at higher Reynolds numbers, the temperature error would become accentuated, resulting in lower calculated coefficients. This indeed seems to be indicated by the trend of the data.

Presentation in Terms of Heat-transfer Factors. Fixed-bed particle-fluid heat-transfer data have in the past been extensively correlated by relating the so-called j_h factors to the Reynolds number. By definition,

$$j_h = \frac{h}{c_F G} \left(\frac{c_F \mu}{k}\right)^{2/3} \tag{8-54}\star$$

Figure 8-38 shows the generally accepted fixed-bed correlation line for a range of Reynolds numbers for which fluidized-bed heat-transfer data are also available. Comparison leads to the following observations:

1. Generally speaking there is no agreement; only the highest values of Walton et al.[46] data and Heertjes and McKibbins[16] data approach the correlation line.

2. According to the fixed-bed line, heat-transfer coefficients decrease as, for a constant fluid mass velocity, the particle diameter is increased. This is not indicated by the course of the fluidized data.

Considering first the lack of agreement, it must be emphasized that the fixed beds were composed of much larger particles that ranged from about 0.09 to 0.74 in. Thus a generally better surface-area utilization might have prevailed in these beds, which would possibly have contributed to the high level of the correlation line. Then also, because of the low height of the fixed beds and their large flow cross section, entrance effects could probably not be entirely eliminated or properly accounted for. This might well be a second reason for a high correlation line.

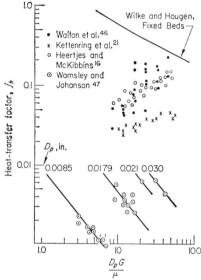

Fig. 8-38. Fixed- and fluidized-bed particle-fluid heat-transfer data shown by means of j_h factors in relation to Reynolds number.

The fact that, according to the fixed-bed line, heat-transfer coefficients decrease as particle diameter increases may be understood from the generally excellent surface-area accessibility that must be assumed to prevail when relatively large particles are used in very shallow beds. This area accessibility remains essentially intact even for the smallest spherical particles employed.

Conclusions

1. The field of fluidized-bed particle-fluid heat transfer is almost unexplored.

2. The major difficulties to be overcome are evaluations of the proper temperature difference and surface area provided. Since direct measurement of solids temperature is probably impossible, it might be worthwhile to consider heating or cooling studies under unsteady conditions,

determine solids temperature calorimetrically, and evaluate heat-transfer coefficients by means of solids-temperature–time data.

3. Except for two relatively unrelated studies, the few available experimental data differ widely. With respect to order of magnitude, it appears that dense-bed particle-fluid heat-transfer data are comparable with heat-transfer data for falling clouds of particles as well as fixed beds. For estimation purposes use of a correlation of Nusselt vs. Reynolds number appears to be most reliable.

4. A conservative set of heat-transfer data may be calculated by using Eq. (8-53) for the Reynolds-number range of about 8 to 60.

PROBLEMS

8-1. Uniform glass beads of 150 to 200 mesh are fluidized in a steel tube of 1.87 in. ID. The tube is surrounded by a steam jacket of 2 ft length. The 325-mesh wire screen which supports the beads is located 4 in. inside the lower end of the steam jacket. $L_{mf} = 16$ in., and the unit is operated with such an air rate that $G/G_{mf} = 5$. For this flow the inlet-air temperature to the tube is found to be 287°F. The steam in the jacket is saturated and its temperature is 360°F. The air from the fluidized bed discharges directly into the atmosphere with an exit temperature of 350°F. The density of the glass beads $\rho_S = 160$ lb per cu ft, and the heat capacity $c_S = 0.24$ Btu/(lb)(°F).

For the conditions specified estimate the heat-transfer-film coefficient, using correlations (8-12), (8-16) to (8-19), and (8-26). Now for the same conditions but $G/G_{mf} = 15$, repeat the calculations and arrive at conclusions regarding the general status of this type of problem.

8-2. A 2-in. standard pipe surrounded by a steam jacket carries 2.21 lb of a round silica sand of $D_p = 0.00323$ in. and $\rho_S = 160$ lb per cu ft. It is fluidized with CO_2 passing through the unit at a mass velocity of 205 lb/(hr)(sq ft). The pressure is atmospheric.

By using bare thermocouples, temperature explorations are made in the bed at levels which are 2, 7, and 13 in. above the bed support. At each lateral level so explored three readings are made at positions $\frac{1}{8}$, $\frac{3}{8}$, and 1 in. from the wall. The data are as follows:

Level, in. above support	Temp, °F, at following distances from wall		
	$\frac{1}{8}$ in.	$\frac{3}{8}$ in.	1 in.
2	349.6	348.3	343.3
7	352	352	351
13	354	354	355

The outside steam jacket is 36 in. high, hence high enough to assure that the expanded bed is submerged at all times. Saturated steam is passed through the jacket and the temperature is measured as 360°F. The CO_2 enters the unit through a double layer of glass cloths. Temperatures are measured as the gas approaches the cloths, between the cloths, and on the downstream side, where the bed actually begins. The temperatures are as follows:

Approach temperature: 80°F
Temperature between glass cloths: 162°F
Temperature downstream at the base of the bed: 306.7°F

For the conditions stated, evaluate (1) the over-all entrance effect and (2) the magnitude of the film coefficient when based on (a) approach temperature, (b) the temperature between the glass cloths, and (c) the temperature at the bottom of the bed. Compare the results with the value obtained from the generalized correlation and arrive at conclusions regarding the importance of entrance effects in tests of this sort. The specific heat of the sand may be assumed to be 0.22 Btu/(lb)(°F).

8-3. A stream of reactants is to be contacted with a granular catalyst in a fluidized unit. There is a considerable evolution of heat, and it is desired to design the system in such a way that the maximum attainable heat-transfer coefficient is to be realized. The anticipated unit is to be of the externally cooled type. Available data are as follows:

Catalyst:

> D_p = 0.0058 in.
> ρ_S = 152 lb per cu ft (nonvesicular)
> ϵ_{mf} = 0.57

Reactant-product mixture:

> ρ_F = 0.055 lb per cu ft
> μ = 0.025 centipoise
> k = 0.038 Btu/(hr)(sq ft)(°F)/(ft)

The available dumped-catalyst volume for the reactor is 0.210 cu ft. The space velocity under actual operating conditions is to be 1,250 volumes of reactant-product mixture per volume of dumped catalyst per hour. The reaction is to be run at 575°F and it is anticipated that 6500 Btu per hr of heat must be removed. Assuming complete temperature homogeneity in the fluidized reactor, calculate the lowest possible wall temperature which will accomplish this task.

8-4. Octane to be used in the extraction of a catalyst is to be preheated before it enters the extractor. Just before entrance the octane must rise 12 ft. For the purpose of preheating, it has been suggested that it rise through a steam-jacketed pipe that carries a bed of the extracted solids. If the steam jacket is to be 10 ft high, calculate the inside fluidized-bed diameter that will raise the octane to the highest possible exit temperature.

Steam is available at 3 psig, saturated. The solids have a density of ρ_S = 97 lb per cu ft. The particle diameter is uniform at 0.024 in. The solids were found to pack in such a fashion that the unexpanded bed has a voidage of ϵ = 0.42. The desired octane flow rate is 75 gal per hr, and the octane is available to the heater at 50°F.

8-5. Hydrogen coming from the reduction of a catalyst bed is being vented out of the reactor by passing horizontally through 10 ft of 1-in. standard pipe. In coming out of the bed the hydrogen entrains catalyst fines which are also carried through the line. The gas enters the vent pipe at 525°F and 24.4 psig pressure. At the point of entrance the linear gas velocity is 40 fps. The entrainment appears to be appreciable and amounts to 3.2 lb of catalyst fines per pound of hydrogen. The particle size of the catalyst is of the order of 30 microns or less, and the specific gravity is 4.85.

The vent pipe is water-jacketed for the entire length of 10 ft. Water is admitted into the jacket at a temperature of 58°F. The rate is such that the temperature rise is nominal and the water-side film coefficient may be taken as 250 Btu/(hr)(sq ft)(°F). For these conditions calculate:

1. The exit temperature of the hydrogen
2. The pressure drop and power requirements of the gas in the vent pipe, assuming that the particles were fully accelerated

The hydrogen, carrying the catalyst fines, is now passed through a proper cyclone separator where the fines are virtually all removed. Assume that the gas leaves the cyclone still at 525°F, that cooling is required in the following vent piping, water-jacketed as before and giving the same water-side film coefficient, and:

1. Find the required vent-pipe length so that the exit temperature of the gas is the same as was found when the gas entrained solids through the shorter pipe.
2. For this condition evaluate pressure drop and power requirements to pass the gas through the vent.

8-6. A fluidized catalytic converter consists of a 2-in. tube (1.87 in. ID) surrounded by a 12-in.-high cooling jacket. The unit carries a spherical catalyst of average particle diameter $D_p = 0.0090$ in. and $\rho_S = 205$ lb per cu ft; it is supported by a 250-mesh screen flush with the lower end of the cooling jacket. The mass velocity of the reactants and products in the reactor is 465 lb/(hr)(sq ft). The average viscosity is 0.018 centipoise, and the average fluid density may be taken as 0.057 lb per cu ft.

For the conditions as specified the temperature in the reactor as recorded by an immersed unscreened thermocouple is found to be almost entirely uniform at 172°F. Cooling water is passed through the jacket at such a rate that its temperature rise is negligible and the wall temperature facing the bed is virtually everywhere 72°F. If the thermal conductivity of the reactants and products through the apparatus is assumed to be 0.024 Btu/(hr)(sq ft)(°F)/(ft), estimate the average surface temperature of the catalyst for a fluidized-bed height of exactly 12 in., $\epsilon_{mf} = 0.42$, and specific heat $c_S = 0.150$ Btu/(lb)(°F).

8-7. A fluidized dense-phase bed is to be used to recover heat from a flue gas by contacting with a granular catalyst. Data pertaining to the catalyst are as follows:

Size distribution:

Mesh	Weight per cent	Mesh	Weight per cent
10–14	5	28–36	39
14–20	12	35–48	8
20–28	36		

Solids density: $\rho_S = 150$ lb per cu ft
Bulk density: $\rho_b = 80$ lb per cu ft
Specific heat: $c_S = 0.25$ Btu/(lb)(°F)
Inlet temperature of the catalyst = 100°F

A total of 200 lb per hr of the catalyst is to be contacted with the gas. The shape of the catalyst particles is nearly spherical, and pressure-drop tests have disclosed $\phi_S = 0.93$.

The gas enters the bed through a multi-orifice support at an inlet temperature of 900°F. The pressure is atmospheric in addition to the pressure drop. The weight rate of flow of gas into the unit is 240 lb per hr. Other data pertaining to the gas are:

Molecular weight: 30.25
Average specific heat: $c_F = 0.26$ Btu/(hr)(°F)

Temperature variation of viscosity:

Temp, °F	Viscosity, centipoises	Temp, °F	Viscosity, centipoises
900	0.034	300	0.023
700	0.030	100	0.018
500	0.027		

For the specified conditions establish the relationship between the exit temperature of the gas and the height-diameter ratio of the fluidized unit if the bed is to contain such quantities of solids that the average residence time of the solids passing through is 15, 30, 60, and 120 min. The cold solids enter at the top, and heated solids are withdrawn from the base.

In order to have almost complete temperature homogeneity in the unit, it is suggested that the column be operated at a reduced mass velocity of at least 4.0.

REFERENCES

1. Agarwal, O. P., and J. Anderson Storrow: *Chem. & Ind.* (*London*), 321–324 (1951).
2. Baerg, A., J. Klassen, and P. E. Gishler: *Can. J. Research*, **F28**: 287–307 (1950).
3. Bartholomew, R. N., and D. L. Katz: *Chem. Eng.-Progr. Symposium Ser.*, **48**(4): 3–10 (1952).
4. Brazelton, W. T.: Ph.D. thesis, Northwestern University, 1951.
5. Caldas, I.: Ph.D. thesis, University of Cincinnati, 1955.
6. Campbell, J. R., and F. Rumford: *J. Soc. Chem. Ind.* (*London*), **69**: 373 (1950).
7. Chu, Y. C., and J. A. Storrow: *Chem. Eng. Sci.*, **1**(5): 230 (1952).
8. Colburn, A. P.: *Ind. Eng. Chem.*, **23**: 910 (1931).
9. Dow, W. M., and Max Jakob: *Chem. Eng. Progr.*, **47**: 637–648 (1951).
10. Eichhorn, Jacob, and R. R. White: *Chem. Eng. Progr. Symposium Ser.*, **48**(4): 11–18 (1952).
11. Farbar, L., and M. J. Morley: *Ind. Eng. Chem.*, **49**: 1143–1150 (1957).
12. Furnas, C. C.: *U.S. Bur. Mines Bull.* 361, 1932.
13. Heerden, C. van, A. P. P. Nobel, and D. W. van Krevelen: *Chem. Eng. Sci.*, **1**(2): 51–66 (1951).
14. Heerden, C. van, A. P. P. Nobel, and D. W. van Krevelen: *Ind. Eng. Chem.*, **45**: 1237–1242 (1953).
15. Heertjes, P. M., H. G. J. de Boer, and A. H. de Haas van Dorsser: *Chem. Eng. Sci.*, **2**(3): 97 (1953).
16. Heertjes, P. M., and S. W. McKibbins: *Chem. Eng. Sci.*, **5**: 161–167 (1956).
17. Jacob, A., and G. L. Osberg: *Can. J. Chem. Eng.*, **35**(1): 5–9 (1957).
18. Jakob, Max: *J. Appl. Phys.*, **23**: 1056 (1952).
19. Johnstone, H. F., R. L. Pigford, and J. H. Chapin: *Trans. AIChE*, **37**: 95 (1941).
20. Jolley, L. J.: *Fuel*, **28**(5): 114–115 (1949).
21. Kettenring, K. N., E. L. Manderfield, and J. M. Smith: *Chem. Eng. Progr.*, **46**: 139 (1950).
22. Koble, R. A.: Ph.D. thesis, West Virginia University, 1952.
23. Koble, R. A., J. N. Ademino, E. P. Bartkus, and T. E. Corrigan: *Chem. Eng.*, **58**(9): 174 (1951).
24. Letters to the Editors: *Chem. Eng. Sci.*, **6**(3): 141–142 (1957).
25. Leva, Max: *Ind. Eng. Chem.*, **39**: 857 (1947).

26. Leva, Max: "General Discussion on Heat Transfer," sec. V, Institution of Mechanical Engineers, London, 1951.
27. Leva, Max, and M. Grummer: *Ind. Eng. Chem.*, **40**: 415 (1948).
28. Leva, Max, and M. Grummer: *Chem. Eng. Progr.*, **48**: 307–313 (1952).
29. Leva, M., M. Weintraub, and M. Grummer: *Chem. Eng. Progr.*, **45**: 563–572 (1949).
30. Levenspiel, O., and J. S. Walton: "Proceedings of the Heat Transfer and Fluid Mechanics Institute," pp. 139–146, American Society of Mechanical Engineers, New York, 1949.
31. Levenspiel, O., and J. S. Walton: *Chem. Eng. Progr. Symposium Ser.* 9, **50**(9): 1–13 (1954).
32. Löf, G. O. G., and R. W. Hawley: *Ind. Eng. Chem.*, **40**: 1061–1070 (1948).
33. Massimilla, L., and S. Bracale: *Ricerca sci.*, **26**: 487–504 (1956).
34. Massimilla, L., S. Bracale, and A. Cabella: personal communication.
35. McAdams, W. H.: "Heat Transmission," 3d ed., McGraw-Hill Book Company, Inc., New York, 1954.
36. Mickley, H. S., and D. F. Fairbanks: *AIChE Journal*, **1**: 374–384 (1955).
37. Mickley, H. S., and C. A. Trilling: *Ind. Eng. Chem.*, **41**: 1135 (1949).
38. Miller, C. O., and A. K. Logwinuk: *Ind. Eng. Chem.*, **43**: 1220 (1951).
39. Morse, R. D., and C. O. Ballou: *Chem. Eng. Progr.*, **47**: 199–204 (1951).
40. Reed, T. M. III, and M. R. Fenske: *Ind. Eng. Chem.*, **47**: 275–282 (1955).
41. Schumann, T. E. W.: *J. Franklin Inst.*, **208**: 405 (1929).
42. Toomey, R. D., and H. F. Johnstone: *Chem. Eng. Progr. Symposium Ser.* 5, **49**: 51–63 (1953).
43. Vreedenberg, H. A.: "General Discussion on Heat Transfer," sec. IV, 32, Institution of Mechanical Engineers, London, 1951.
44. Vreedenberg, H. A.: *J. Appl. Chem. (London)*, **2** (Suppl. Issue 1): S26–S33 (1952).
45. Vreedenberg, H. A.: private communication.
46. Walton, J. S., R. L. Olson, and O. Levenspiel: *Ind. Eng. Chem.*, **44**: 1474–1480 (1952).
47. Wamsley, W. W., and L. N. Johanson: *Chem. Eng. Progr.*, **50**: 347 (1954).
48. Wen, C. Y., and L. T. Fan: *Chem. Eng.*, **64**(7): 254–257 (1957).
49. Wen, C. Y., and Max Leva: *AIChE Journal*, **2**: 482 (1956).
50. Wicke, E., and F. Fetting: *Chem. Ingr. Tech.*, **26**(6): 301–309 (1954).

CHAPTER 9

MASS TRANSFER

Nomenclature

A = cross-sectional area of column, sq ft
A_p = geometric surface area of one packing piece, sq ft
C = concentration
C^* = equilibrium concentration
C_1 = inlet concentration
C_2 = exit concentration
ΔC = concentration difference
$\Delta C_{\log m}$ = log mean concentration difference
D_F = diffusion coefficient, sq ft per hr
D_p = particle diameter, ft
G = fluid mass velocity, lb/(hr)(sq ft)
G_f = fluidization mass velocity, lb/(hr)(sq ft)
G_{mf} = minimum-fluidization mass velocity, lb/(hr)(sq ft)
j_d = mass-transfer factor, defined by Eq. (9-1)
k_F = mass-transfer coefficient, (lb moles)/(hr)(sq ft)(ΔC)
L = bed height, ft
M_m = mean molecular weight of fluid stream
N = number of packing pieces per cubic foot of tower
p_m = mean partial pressure of air in bed, atm [Eq. 9-9)]
Re = $D_p G/\mu$
Sc = abbreviation for Schmidt group, $\mu/\rho_F D_F$
S_{sp} = surface area of the packing contained in one unit volume of the packed tower, sq ft per cu ft
V_p = displacement volume of one packing piece, cu ft
ϵ = void fraction in packed bed
μ = fluid viscosity, lb/(hr)(ft)
ρ_F = fluid density, lb per cu ft

Abstract

The discussion begins with a definition of the mass-transfer factor j_d and dependence of the numerical value on driving force. Thereafter brief consideration is given to the Schmidt number and the effects of particle surface area.

A discussion of fixed-bed mass transfer for both gas- and liquid-operated beds follows next, and the data and individual correlations are presented from the point of view of consistency.

This leads then to fluidized-bed data, first for gas-solid systems and then for liquid-solid systems. Finally a generalized correlation of all liquid-fluidized-bed data and one set of gas-fluidized-bed data is developed.   Its limitations are discussed with reference to future studies.

GENERAL CONSIDERATIONS

In a fundamental paper, Chilton and Colburn[2]* examined the relationship between fluid friction and heat transfer.   Extending the analogy to friction and mass transfer, they defined the mass-transfer factor

$$j_d = \frac{k_F M_m}{G} \left(\frac{\mu}{\rho_F D_F}\right)^{\frac{2}{3}} \tag{9-1}\star$$

The mass-transfer coefficient

$$k_F = \frac{G}{M_m S_{sp} A} \frac{dC/dL}{\Delta C} \tag{9-2}\star$$

Equation (9-2) may be integrated when the variation of the driving force along the fluid path through the unit is known.

In units with complete top-bottom mixing, such as that approached in a well-stirred tank, the driving force

$$\Delta C = C^* - C_2 = \text{const}$$

For isothermal operation of a unit with no top-bottom mixing, a feature also referred to as "piston flow," $\Delta C = C^* - C_1$ for the fluid inlet and $C^* - C_2$ for the fluid exit.   If Eq. (9-2) is integrated for these two extreme conditions, there results for complete mixing

$$k_F = \frac{G}{M_m S_{sp} A L} \frac{C_2 - C_1}{C^* - C_2} \tag{9-2a}$$

and for piston flow

$$k_F = \frac{G}{M_m S_{sp} A L} \ln \frac{C^* - C_1}{C^* - C_2} \tag{9-2b}$$

This may also be written as

$$k_F = \frac{G}{M_m S_{sp} A L} \frac{C_2 - C_1}{\Delta C_{\log m}}$$

where $$\Delta C_{\log m} = \frac{C_2 - C_1}{\ln\left[(C^* - C_1)/(C^* - C_2)\right]}$$

Substitution of (9-2a) or (9-2b) into (9-1) then yields for complete mixing

$$j_d = \frac{Sc^{\frac{2}{3}}}{S_{sp} A L} \frac{C_2 - C_1}{C^* - C_2} \tag{9-3}$$

and for no mixing

$$j_d = \frac{Sc^{\frac{2}{3}}}{S_{sp} A L} \frac{C_2 - C_1}{\Delta C_{\log m}} \tag{9-4}$$

* Superscript numbers indicate works listed in References at the end of the chapter.

Driving Force. Most mass-transfer studies concern themselves merely with the measurement of terminal concentrations; concentrations intermediate between inlet and exit are only infrequently reported. From a consideration of Eqs. (9-3) and (9-4) it follows, however, that the numerical value of the j_d factors will be dependent on how the driving force was evaluated from the terminal data. Obviously it will then be desirable to know whether an operation involves complete mixing, no mixing, or partial mixing. Dividing Eq. (9-3) by Eq. (9-4), for instance, it follows that

$$\frac{j_{d(9-3)}}{j_{d(9-4)}} = \frac{\Delta C_{\log m}}{C^* - C_2}$$

The order of magnitude of the variation may be properly assessed on the basis of some typical concentration data. Thus McCune and Wilhelm[15] report that, for one of their liquid-fluidized-bed mass-transfer runs, $C_2 = 0.000212$, $C_1 = 0$, and $C^* = 0.000539$. Hence for these concentrations and assuming complete mixing

$$j_d \propto \frac{0.000212}{0.000327} = 0.648$$

whereas for the case of no mixing,

$$j_d \propto \frac{0.000212}{0.000424} = 0.500$$

Thus the error in the numerical value of the mass-transfer factor could have been appreciable for this case if the proper fluid-flow mechanism were not known and thus was not accounted for.

In unobstructed-flow systems such as empty pipes, there is virtually no fluid back-mixing. For such a system mass-transfer factors may be evaluated by Eq. (9-4). For packed fixed beds the evidence also points to the nonmixed bed, which will be discussed later. However, in the fluidized bed, because of the motion of the particles, fluid back-mixing should be anticipated to a greater or lesser degree. An understanding of the extent of back-mixing would therefore appear indispensable for development of a rational mass-transfer correlation for the fluidized state. If the effect of the motion of the particles on the mean driving force in a system such as a fluidized bed is neglected, the resulting correlation is not of a general character and cannot be logically extended.

Aside from these considerations of the mechanics of the system, evaluation of driving force also requires reliable equilibrium data. These must usually be obtained for the prevailing solids temperatures in the bed. The difficulties which attend measurement of solids surface temperatures have been pointed out in Chap. 8. To circumvent the real problem, it has frequently been assumed that the solids temperature is equal to the temperature of the ambient fluid. Although this is probably quite correct for liquid-solid systems, where the liquid with its high heat capacity acts as a potential thermostat, the assumption may be substantially in error in many gas-solid mass-transfer operations.

Schmidt-group Exponent. The importance of the Schmidt group in mass transfer is probably best visualized from a brief consideration of mechanism. For fully turbulent flow, and assuming that mass is transferred from a solids surface to a fluid stream, there is next to the surface a thin laminar film through which the transfer of mass occurs by molecular diffusion. The film is followed by a boundary layer of varying thickness wherein eddy diffusion becomes more pronounced. Beyond the boundary layer, mass transfer into the body of the fluid is wholly by eddy diffusion. From these resistance concepts it follows that the importance of the Schmidt group to mass transfer must depend on the extent to which a flow system comprises molecular diffusion on one hand and eddy currents on the other as transfer agencies within itself. The differences in flow systems are thus recognized as being the major reasons for the various exponents that have been ascribed to the Schmidt group in mass-transfer correlations.

Colburn[4,5] suggested originally that mass-transfer coefficients may be inversely proportional to the Schmidt group. Thereafter Chilton and Colburn[2] reported that adoption of the $-\frac{2}{3}$ power would improve many correlations. This exponent was in fact found to hold well for a wide range of conditions. Data pertaining to evaporation from flat surfaces, cylindrical bodies, and wetted wall columns appear notably well covered. Less satisfactory are results in packed towers in which conventional ring and saddle packings are used. The exponent $-\frac{2}{3}$ has been used with good results for describing and predicting mass-transfer data in beds of broken solids.[11]

Effect of Particle Surface Area. Evaluation of the mass-transfer coefficient requires a prior estimate of the specific surface area S_{sp} of the solid. This is defined by

$$S_{sp} = NA_p = \frac{(1 - \epsilon)A_p}{V_p} \tag{9-5}$$

For the evaluation of S_{sp} one must know the shape of the particles and the bed voidage. For more regularly shaped bodies such as spheres and cylinders, evaluation of the surface area according to Eq. (9-5) is convenient; with granules, however, difficulties may appear. The above relation and its inclusion in expressions for the j_d factors imply that all portions of the bed are equally effective so far as offering surface area is concerned. As flow studies in packed and fluidized beds have indicated,

that is by no means always assured.   For that reason Eqs. (9-3) and (9-4)
will give over-all mass-transfer data only for a system as a whole.   Individual local mass-transfer factors may differ widely from the collective
values.

FIXED-BED MASS-TRANSFER DATA

A brief consideration of fixed-bed mass-transfer data prior to a discussion of fluidized systems will be helpful for a better general understanding of the factors that underlie measurements in fluidized beds.   It
will be instructive to discuss gas-solid and liquid-solid systems separately.

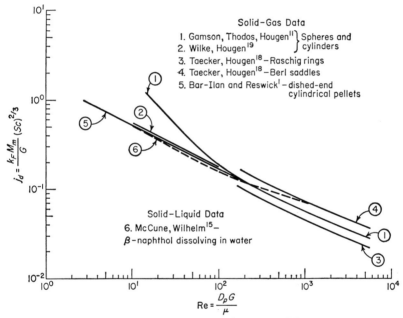

Fig. 9-1. Fixed-bed mass-transfer data, gas-solid systems.

Gas-Solid Systems.   A brief summary of the principal gas-solid mass
transfer appears in Table 9-1.   The proposed correlations relate to j_d factors with functions of $D_p G/\mu$.   A graphical comparison is given in Fig.
9-1.   The data pertain roughly to two kinds of particles.   The spheres,
cylinders, and pellets employed were of relatively small size; the more
complexly shaped ring and saddle bodies were generally larger.   In view
of the considerable differences in shape between the two classes of particles, closer agreement than indicated in Fig. 9-1 is hardly to be expected.
The disagreement between data of Gamson, Thodos, and Hougen[11] and
Wilke and Hougen[19] is more important because the two sets of data pertain to the same materials and apparatus.

For the low range of Reynolds numbers, the data of Gamson et al. appeared too high, and reexamination by Wilke and Hougen confirmed that they were. Reasons given for the discrepancy were inaccuracies in exit partial pressures of water vapor, as well as radiation effects, felt especially strongly at low gas rates. Improved instrumentation installed by Wilke and Hougen lowered the j_d factors sufficiently to bring them in line with a more probable data course. This is definitely indicated by the observed approach to the liquid-solid data by McCune and Wilhelm,[15] shown also for comparison.

As far as experimental technique was concerned, Wilke and Hougen[19] reported that solid-surface temperatures could not be reliably measured

TABLE 9-1. SUMMARY OF GAS-SOLID MASS-TRANSFER STUDIES IN FIXED BEDS

Reference	System	Solids	Expressions for j_d
Gamson et al.[11]	Water-air	Porous spheres and cylinders	$j_d = 16.8 \ Re^{-1}$ Re < 40 $j_d = 0.989 \ Re^{-0.41}$ Re > 350
Wilke and Hougen[19]	Water-air	Porous spheres and cylinders	$j_d = 1.82 \ Re^{-0.51}$ Re < 100
Taeckers and Hougen[18]	Water-air	Porous Raschig rings, Berl saddles, and partition rings	Saddles: $j_d = 0.855(G \ \sqrt{A_p}/\mu)^{-0.34}$ Rings: $j_d = 1.070(G \ \sqrt{A_p}/\mu)^{-0.41}$ The expressions are valid for values of $G \ \sqrt{A_p}/\mu$ ranging from 70 to 3,000
Bar-Ilan and Resnick[1]	Naphthalene-air	Cylindrical pellets, granules	Separate correlation lines obtained for pellets and granules; pellet data were appreciably higher

by direct contact with thermocouples. Hence the solid temperature was believed equal to the wet-bulb temperature of the entering air, as long as the constant-rate drying period prevailed. This assumption is probably correct, at least for the very first layer of the soaked pellets. In view of the fact that the beds were composed of only two to three or four layers of particles, this assumption may be approximately correct for the entire bed. However, for higher beds in which the ascending air current would pick up substantial amounts of water vapor, the assumption would certainly lead to incorrect driving forces.

As driving force, the logarithmic mean obtained from terminal data was used. This is probably satisfactory for low flow rates, provided that no serious entrance effects interfere downstream into the bed. To what extent the data are afflicted by entrance effects can probably not be accurately assessed.

The surface area was calculated on the basis of individual-particle dimensions and the voidage of the bed. Although the beds were very shallow and voidage values could possibly be in error, the values, ranging from 34 to 44 per cent for the spheres and cylinders employed, appear reasonable. A temporary error in surface area may arise if excess surface moisture is being held between particles by capillary forces.

Considering now the mass-transfer data of Taecker and Hougen[18] pertaining to porous Raschig rings and Berl saddles, the substantially higher

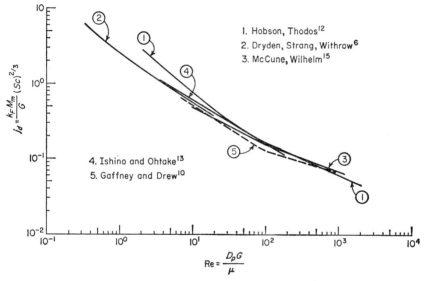

FIG. 9-2. Fixed-bed mass-transfer data, liquid-solid systems. NOTE: Gaffney and Drew data were adjusted from $j_d \propto Sc^{0.58}$ to $j_d \propto Sc^{0.67}$.

j_d factors observed with the saddles are expected, owing to the greater surface-area accessibility of the saddles as compared to the rings. Hence introduction of a shape factor into a correlation could by itself hardly be expected to correlate these data with the earlier work on spheres and cylinders.

Schmidt numbers for the air-water gas-solid systems were essentially constant at Sc = 0.60. Hence the gas-solid data offer no clue by themselves to just how effective the $-\frac{2}{3}$ exponent is. The answer is provided by inclusion of the data of Bar-Ilan and Resnick[1] on the vaporization of naphthalene into air and the liquid-solid data of McCune and Wilhelm.[15] For the naphthalene-air system the Schmidt number was 2.4, and for the system 2-naphthol and water at the prevailing temperatures it was about 1,300. Thus an impressive range of values is provided, and the satisfactory agreement of gas-solid and liquid-solid lines emphasizes that for fixed beds the exponent $-\frac{2}{3}$ appears essentially useful.

Liquid-Solid Systems. Table 9-2 summarizes data pertaining to some liquid-solid mass-transfer studies. A graphical comparison of the correlations, relating j_d factors to D_pG/μ, is given in Fig. 9-2. Except for very low D_pG/μ values, the agreement is quite satisfactory. This is especially significant because $\mu/\rho_F D_F$ ranges from 150 to 1,400 for the data. The satisfactory agreement is in large part due to the following circumstances:

1. In a liquid-solid system, temperature control is virtually assured because, owing to its relatively large heat capacity, the liquid acts as a

TABLE 9-2. SUMMARY OF LIQUID-SOLID MASS-TRANSFER STUDIES IN FIXED BEDS

Reference	System	Solids	Expression for j_d
Hobson and Thodos[12]	Water–isobutyl alcohol Water–methyl-ethyl ketone	Celite spheres	$\log j_d = 0.7683 - 0.9175 \log \text{Re} + 0.0817 (\log \text{Re})^2$
Dryden, Strang, and Withrow[6]	Water–2-naphthol Water–benzoic acid	Cylindrical pellets	Data extend into low Reynolds-number range; for higher range, data are in accord with work of McCune and Wilhelm and Gaffney and Drew
McCune and Wilhelm[15]	Water–2-naphthol	Spherelike pellets and flakes	$j_d = 1.625 \text{ Re}^{-0.507}$ $\quad$ Re < 120 $j_d = 0.687 \text{ Re}^{-0.327}$ $\quad$ Re > 120
Gaffney and Drew[10]	Benzene–salicylic acid n-Butanol–succinic acid Acetone–succinic acid	Spherelike pellets	$j_d' = 1.97 \text{ Re}'^{-0.613}$ $\quad$ Re$' < 200$ $j_d' = 0.290 \text{ Re}'^{-0.254}$ $\quad$ Re$' > 200$ NOTE: $j_d' = \dfrac{k_F M_m}{G} \text{Sc}^{0.58}$ and Re$' = \dfrac{D_p G}{\mu \epsilon}$. (Approximations by Ergun[7])
Ishino and Ohtake[13]	Water–benzoic acid	Cylindrical pellets	$j_d = 2.70(1 - \epsilon)^{0.2} \left(\dfrac{\text{Re}}{1 - \epsilon} \right)^{-0.5}$ Valid for $60 < \text{Re}/(1 - \epsilon) < 60{,}000$

thermostat. With heat-transfer coefficients between the solid and the liquid probably higher than coefficients in gas-solids systems, the temperature of the solid may now definitely be taken as that of the liquid.

2. The action of high columns of solids may be investigated without risking saturated exit streams. Furthermore, since there will be relatively little, if any, fluid mixing along the longitudinal axis, the mean

logarithmic driving force, as obtained from terminal data, will essentially be the correct potential to use.

3. Analytical procedures are usually more reliable, since concentrations in liquid media are, generally speaking, more accurately determined than in gases. Finally, equilibrium data for solid-liquid systems are more readily obtained and, on the whole, are probably more accurate.

Correlation of Ergun. By an extension of the Reynolds analogy to fixed beds, Ergun[7] proposed a correlation of liquid-solid mass-transfer data that is of interest for a number of reasons. Omitting his derivations, which are readily understood from the original paper, there results for the case of complete mixing

$$\beta \frac{\mu}{\rho_F D_F} \frac{C_2 - C_1}{C^* - C_2} = 150 \frac{1 - \epsilon}{\mathrm{Re}} + 1.75 \qquad (9\text{-}6)$$

and for piston flow

$$\beta \frac{\mu}{\rho_F D_F} \ln \frac{C^* - C_1}{C^* - C_2} = 150 \frac{1 - \epsilon}{\mathrm{Re}} + 1.75 \qquad (9\text{-}7)$$

In these equations $\beta = (D_p/L)[\epsilon/(1 - \epsilon)]$, a function of bed geometry. Particle diameter $D_p = 6(1 - \epsilon)/S_{sp}$, where S_{sp} is the surface area of the particles contained in a unit tower volume.

Some of the data that are shown in Fig. 9-2 by relating j_d factors to $D_p G/\mu$ are given in Fig. 9-3 in the form of Eq. (9-7). The solid line is not the best line drawn through the points but instead represents the correlating line of an entirely independent set of pressure-drop data, given in Chap. 3. The agreement, as far as indicated between the correlating line and the data,

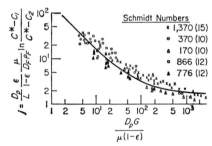

FIG. 9-3. Mass-transfer data in fixed-bed liquid-solid systems; correlation of Ergun.[7] (*Courtesy of Chemical Engineering Progress.*)

lends a certain measure of support to the extension of the Reynolds analogy to fluid resistance and mass transfer in fixed beds, as resorted to by Ergun.

A consideration of the spread of the data reveals a considerable scatter. Specifically the points with the lowest Schmidt number are lowest. Hence a substantial improvement in the scatter would result by including the $\frac{2}{3}$ power of the Schmidt number instead of the first power. Attempts to extend the Ergun correlation to gas-solid systems were not successful. Reasons given were lack of reliable voidage and pressure-drop data.

FLUIDIZED-BED MASS-TRANSFER DATA

Having thus briefly considered the more important fixed-bed gas-solid and liquid-solid mass-transfer data, we shall now give some attention to gas- and liquid-fluidized systems.

Gas-Solid Systems. A summary of all fluidized-bed work reported so far is given in Table 9-3. All systems have in common very small bed heights; they range from a fraction of an inch to at most three inches. This small bed height is of course dictated by the prevailing rapid rates

TABLE 9-3. SUMMARY OF GAS-SOLID AND LIQUID-SOLID FLUIDIZED-BED
MASS-TRANSFER DATA

Reference	System	Schmidt number	Particles and size range	Bed diam, in.	Fluid mass velocity range lb/ (hr)(sq ft)	Reynolds-number range
Resnick and White[17]	Naphthalene–air Naphthalene–CO₂ Naphthalene–H₂	2.39	Naphthalene granules, 14–65 mesh	0.87–1.73	10–1,200	0.6–120
Kettenring, Manderfield and Smith[14]	Water vapor–air	0.60	Silica gel and alumina, 14–48 mesh	2.30	300–750	9–55
Chu, Kalil, and Wetteroth[3]	Naphthalene–air	2.57	Various spherical and cylindrical particles coated with naphthalene, 0.029–0.540 in.	3.75	265–4,200	15–1,300
McCune and Wilhelm[15]	Water–2-naphthol	1,200–1,420	Spherelike naphthalene pellets and flakes, ⅛–¼ inch and 8–18 mesh	4.00	375–11,500	10–1,000
Evans and Gerald[9]	Water–benzoic acid	About 1,050	Benzoic acid granules, 0.025–0.078 in.	1.93	1,150–23,750	1.0–70
Ohtake[16]	Water–benzoic acid	About 1,050	Cylindrical benzoic acid pellets	1.65	7,000–35,000	35–264

of mass transfer and the unwelcome possibility of having an exit gas so close to saturation that an exit-terminal concentration difference may no longer be reliably determined. This would then afflict the mass-transfer coefficients with serious uncertainties.

Aside from having to select a suitable bed height, other considerations of no less difficulty arise. They pertain to the mechanics of administering the gas into a short bed without suffering serious entrance effects. Next, provision must be made for estimating bed voidage and the expansion characteristics of the solid. Frequently this is done in an auxiliary vessel that is probably empty of internal thermocouples and other apparatus elements.   Hence expansion data thus observed may not bear any relationship to the actual expansion behavior of the bed in question.

Then again there arises the problem of measuring temperatures and concentrations of fluid streams.   The measurement of solid temperatures in fluid beds has already been discussed in Chap. 8.   Assuming that reliable terminal data are available, there still remains the problem of evaluating a representative potential.   Since the solids are now in motion, it may probably no longer be assumed that there is no longitudinal mixing in the bed.   In wall-bed heat-transfer studies, high beds could be used and thus temperature paths could be charted more or less reliably; in the short beds that are usually encountered in mass transfer, an evaluation of driving force along the bed axis is virtually impossible.

With the severe experimental problems in gas-solid fluidized mass transfer still largely unsolved, it is not surprising that the data that have so far been reported show little agreement.

Resnick and White.[17]   They measured the rate of vaporization of naphthalene into currents of air, hydrogen, and carbon dioxide.   Gas of an inlet temperature of 77°F entered the fluid bed and left slightly unsaturated.   It continued through saturators, which were weighed before and after gas passage.   From the gas rate through the saturators and the naphthalene pickup, exit-fluid bed concentrations were calculated. As driving force a logarithmic-mean partial pressure was assumed valid. The vaporization process in the fluidized bed was believed to have occurred at 77°F.   The vapor pressure of naphthalene, determined by the authors for a temperature of 77°F,

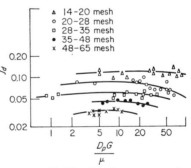

FIG. 9-4. Fluidized-bed mass-transfer data of Resnick and White.[17]

was reported as 0.0829 mm Hg.   This was employed for calculating the driving force.   Schmidt numbers were reported as 2.39, 1.471, and 4.023 for the mixtures of naphthalene in air, carbon dioxide, and hydrogen, respectively.

In Fig. 9-4, j_d factors are related to D_pG/μ for some of the Resnick and White data.   The general data level is far below that of Fig. 9-1, for fixed gas-solid data.   This may be due to the fact that the logarithmic-mean driving force used was incorrect and much too large.   A modest increase in j_d factor with D_pG/μ was reported up to a point considered to be the onset of slugging.   Thereafter j_d factors appeared to decrease with increasing D_pG/μ values.   For the fixed-bed data, Resnick and White proposed that

$$\frac{j_d}{D_p^{1.5}} = 0.19 \left(\frac{D_p G}{\mu}\right)^{-0.27} \tag{9-8}$$

Equation (9-8), valid for $D_p G/\mu < 25$, demands that particle diameter be expressed in millimeters.

Kettenring, Manderfield, and Smith.[14]   These authors reported water-vaporization data from moist silica gel and activated alumina particles. For the purpose of evaluating mass-transfer coefficients, they assumed that the equilibrium pressure of the water vapor on the particle surface equaled the partial pressure of the water vapor in the exit air.   Partial-pressure conditions farther up in the bed were evaluated by a heat balance.   This yielded relationships of partial pressure with respect to bed height, thus permitting evaluation of mass-transfer coefficients by graphical analysis.

The method appears straightforward and should yield the desired data, provided the assumption is correct that the temperature of the leaving gas, as determined by the insertion of bare thermocouples, will in reality measure the gas temperature and not some temperature between that of the gas and the fluidizing solid.

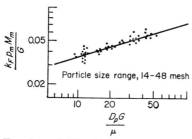

FIG. 9-5. Fluidized-bed mass-transfer data of Kettenring, Manderfield, and Smith.[14]

The mass-transfer data are shown in Fig. 9-5 by relating $k_F p_m M_m/G$ to $D_p G/\mu$.   Since this is roughly equivalent to plotting j_d factors vs. $D_p G/\mu$, comparison with the fixed-bed gas-solid data of Fig. 9-1 suggests itself. This indicates that (1) the data are not of the correct order of magnitude and (2) that the trend with $D_p G/\mu$ is entirely different.   From these observations it appears that severe experimental irregularities may have affected the numerical values of the coefficients.   In view of the over-all stationary nature of the bed relative to the wall of the container, it cannot very well be accepted that the low coefficients are due to the possibility that the solids tend to move with the gas.   The final data correlation proposed reads

$$\frac{k_F p_m M_m}{G} = 0.018 \left(\frac{D_p G}{\mu}\right)^{0.30} \tag{9-9}$$

Chu, Kalil, and Wetteroth.[3]   These authors reported extensive data for the system naphthalene and air.   The column inside diameter was 3.75 in. and thus substantially larger than the diameter used by Resnick and White.   Chu and coworkers were, however, forced to resort to layers equally shallow as those used by Resnick and White, mainly because of saturation difficulties. Their general working procedure was also similar, in that they used follow-up saturations for partial-pressure determinations.

As for particles, Chu et al. coated various materials such as glass beads, rape seed, lead shot, and celite cylinders with naphthalene and subjected the well-defined bodies to the action of air streams. This gave them the advantage of more concrete shapes than are normally provided by naphthalene flakes; thus they could attempt to define bed voidage and particle surface areas.

For the purpose of evaluating vapor pressure they used the relation given in the International Critical Tables, which must have given them a somewhat higher value than that used earlier by Resnick and White. Other data of interest are the reported bed porosities, which for the solid-gas systems under consideration were said to range from as low as 25 to as high as 97 per cent.

Data and Correlation. For the purpose of evaluating the driving force, terminal-concentration data were obtained and the logarithmic mean was assumed. Total particle surface areas were then evaluated, and mass-transfer coefficients were calculated. Using the standard j_d factor as given by Eq. (9-1), mass-transfer factors were evaluated for all the runs.

The j_d factors so conceived are plotted in Fig. 9-6 against D_pG/μ.

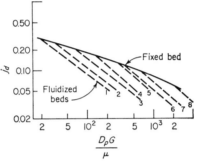

Fig. 9-6. Fluidized gas-solid mass-transfer data of Chu et al.[3] showing characteristic deviation from fixed-bed data. Particle diameter, in.: (1) 0.028, (2) 0.029, (3) 0.077, (4) 0.050, (5) 0.078, (6) 0.215, (7) 0.334, (8) 0.540. (*Courtesy of Chemical Engineering Progress.*)

As is the custom for the purpose of scale condensation, logarithmic coordinates were chosen. Also indicated is a fixed-bed data line, observed by the authors as well. Observations drawn from Fig. 9-6 are as follows:

1. The fixed-bed data are in good agreement with the earlier reported gas-solid data of Gamson et al.[11] and the later liquid-solid data reported by McCune and Wilhelm.[15]

2. The fluidized-particle data are without exception lower than the fixed-bed data.

3. For each material fluidized there exists a characteristic line which has its starting point in the fixed-bed line. The Reynolds number at the point of anchorage is close to that required for minimum fluidization.

4. For increasing Reynolds numbers along any fluidization line the deviation between fixed- and fluidized-bed mass-transfer factors increases steadily.

The characteristics of the data of Fig. 9-6, in agreement with the liquid-solid data of others,[8,13,15] are outlined here in detail because they provide the clue to a general correlation to be given later.

Chu and coworkers found empirically that the data will tend to "fall in line" if the conventional j_d factor is plotted vs. $D_p G / \mu (1 - \epsilon)$. This plot, comprising the fixed-bed data of others as well as the fluidized liquid-solid data of McCune and Wilhelm, is given in Fig. 9-7.

Since it has been the objective of the correlation to align fluidized-bed with fixed-bed mass-transfer factors, it is important to understand that the chief correlating factor was bed voidage. This was reported to vary

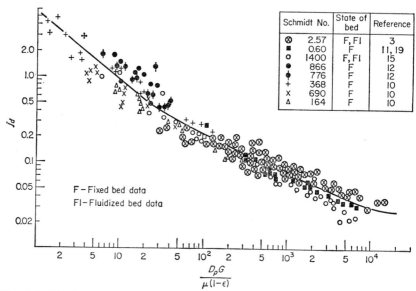

Schmidt No.	State of bed	Reference
⊗ 2.57	F, Fl	3
■ 0.60	F	11, 19
○ 1400	F, Fl	15
● 866	F	12
⦵ 776	F	12
+ 368	F	10
× 690	F	10
△ 164	F	10

F – Fixed bed data
Fl – Fluidized bed data

$$\frac{D_p G}{\mu(1-\epsilon)}$$

Fig. 9-7. Fixed- and fluidized-bed mass-transfer correlation of Chu.[3] (*Courtesy of Chemical Engineering Progress.*)

from as low as 25 to a maximum of 97 per cent. Since prediction of bed voidage in beds of low solids content is notoriously inaccurate, especially when gas-solid systems are involved, a portion of the fluidized-bed data given in Fig. 9-7 must be considered in doubt. The authors recognized the necessity of requiring a suitable voidage correlation so that Fig. 9-7 might be useful. They proposed such a correlation by recommending extension of the earlier presented Kozeny-Carman equation beyond a value of $\epsilon = 0.80$. This is, however, not valid, as is borne out by their own graphical representation of the voidage function obtained. Besides, failure of the Kozeny-Carman equation to apply to systems with a voidage in excess of $\epsilon = 0.80$ has been demonstrated by others and is discussed in Chap. 4. Since at present there is no reliable method by which voidage in gas-solid systems may be predicted when values in excess of, say, 75 per cent are expected, the correlation in Fig. 9-7 appears to be limited in application.

Liquid-Solid Systems. So far only two liquid-solid fluidized mass-transfer studies have been reported, and one set of unpublished data is available. The former are due to McCune and Wilhelm,[15] working with 2-naphthol–water, and Evans and Gerald[9] (as well as Ohtake[16]), who used benzoic acid–water. Table 9-3 gives details of these studies. Operations were in many ways similar. In all instances terminal concentrations were used for calculating logarithmic-mean driving forces, and mass-transfer coefficients and j_d factors were calculated in the usual manner. Some typical data pertaining to these studies are given in

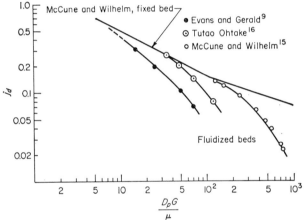

Fig. 9-8. Fluidized liquid-solid mass-transfer data of various investigators showing characteristic deviation from fixed-bed data. NOTE: The fluidized-bed data are anchored to the fixed-bed line at a point that is close to incipient fluidization.

Fig. 9-8. The data and their course are to be compared with Fig. 9-6, which shows similar data observed by Chu and coworkers for the gas-solid system. The observations then made will also apply to the present liquid-solid data. The interesting parallel suggests that there is a fundamental reason for this generally observed characteristic data course.

GENERALIZED CORRELATION OF EXISTING DATA

It has been universally observed that fluidized-bed mass-transfer factors so far reported are always *lower* than fixed-bed data pertaining to the same values of Reynolds number. Moreover the deviation between data in the two kinds of beds increases as, for a given particle size, flow rates are increased. For explaining all this there are the following two possibilities:

1. For a given particle size and flow, fluidized-bed mass-transfer factors are smaller than fixed-bed values because, owing to the expansion of the fluidizing bed, the actual interstitial fluid velocity is smaller than in the fixed bed.

2. Fluidized-bed mass-transfer factors may in reality not be smaller than fixed-bed mass-transfer factors. It may simply appear so because assumption of a logarithmic-mean driving force in a fluidized system is in error.

The merits of the first suggestion are readily tested if in the Reynolds number and the j_d factor G, the superficial fluid mass velocity, is replaced by G/ϵ, the average interstitial mass velocity. Figure 9-9 is a plot on logarithmic coordinates of $j_{d\epsilon}$ vs. $D_pG/\mu\epsilon$. Some of the fluidized-bed data of McCune and Wilhelm have been chosen for this purpose. Figure 9-9 is to be compared with the McCune and Wilhelm data in Fig. 9-8, where for the same run j_d is related to D_pG/μ. The fact that there is

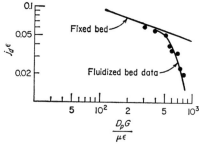

FIG. 9-9. $j_{d\epsilon}$ vs. Re/ϵ for fixed- and fluidized-bed data.[15]   NOTE: Fixed-bed line adjusted to 50 per cent voids.

little, if any, improvement emphasizes that a correlation of fluidized mass-transfer data by this method is not successful. The second possibility will therefore be considered.

The top-bottom mixing in a fluidized bed will tend to reduce the actual driving force below the logarithmic-mean value. If it is assumed that the deviations of Figs. 9-6 and 9-8 are due merely to the decrease in driving force, then the extent by which the driving force should be modified may be ascertained by the ratio of the fluidized- and fixed-bed ordinates for a given Reynolds number. Such driving-force correction factors have been evaluated for all the available data and for as wide a range of Reynolds number as permissible.

The question that next arises is what operating variables are most likely responsible for top-bottom mixing in a fluidized bed. As has already been learned, in addition to specific apparatus effects, the factors that have a bearing on solids mixing are operating mass velocity and particle size, shape, and density. Considering only the latter, it was found that driving-force correction factors could for all particles and systems be satisfactorily related to the quantity $(G_f - G_{mf})/G_f$. This ratio is termed the bed-stirring ratio. Its numerator is the excess of mass velocity over that required for minimum fluidization. Hence if the ratio should lend itself to expressing the extent of top-bottom mixing, it should then be useful for correlating driving-force correction factors.

In order to visualize the significance of the ratio, it is well to recall that G_f is a primary operating variable, whereas G_{mf} is a calculated quantity that depends wholly on such system characteristics as particle size and

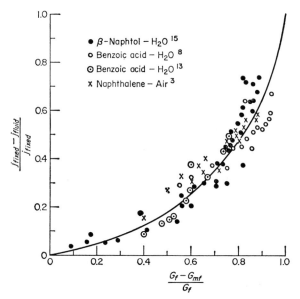

FIG. 9-10. Generalized liquid-solid and gas-solid fluidized-bed mass-transfer data.

shape, solids density, fluid density, and viscosity. Thus it appears that, by using the bed-stirring ratio, all major variables can be accounted for.

Although relating driving-force correction factors to bed-stirring ratios would be entirely satisfactory, it is more convenient from the point of view of correlation to form the ratio $(j_{\text{fixed}} - j_{\text{fluid}})/j_{\text{fixed}}$ and relate *it* to the bed-stirring ratio. The ratio has the obvious advantage that the resulting graph must pass through points 0-0 and 1-1. A presentation along this line is given in Fig. 9-10 for all the liquid-solid fluidized data and the major portion of the gas-solid fluidized data of Chu and coworkers.[3]

Figure 9-10 is directly applicable to evaluation of fluidized-bed j_d factors if the fixed-bed j_d factor is available. For the purpose of estimating the fixed-bed j_d factors it is recommended that the McCune and Wilhelm[15] correlation be used. This is indicated in both Figs. 9-1 and 9-2. For the very low Reynolds-number range the correlations of Wilke and Hougen[19] and Dryden, Strang, and Withrow[6] seem most useful.

Example 9-1.   A column of 1.93 in. ID is charged with benzoic acid spheres of $D_p = 0.0795$ in. and $\rho_S = 79.0$ lb per cu ft.   Water is passed into the base of the column at a mass velocity of $G_f = 23{,}750$ lb/(hr)(sq ft).   The temperature is 74°F and the saturation concentration of the benzoic acid in water at that temperature is 0.00323 lb per lb water.   The Schmidt number of this system under the prevailing conditions is 1,073.

Evaluate (1) the mass-transfer factor and (2) the mass-transfer coefficient.

Solution.   We shall first find the value of G_{mf} from Eq. (3-25).   Hence

$$G_{mf} = 688 \times 0.0795^{1.82}\,\frac{[62.3(79.0 - 62.3)]^{0.94}}{0.93^{0.88}} = 4{,}900$$

$$\frac{D_p G_{mf}}{\mu} = \frac{0.0795 \times 4{,}900}{0.93 \times 2.42 \times 12} = 14.50$$

and from Fig. 3-15 the correction factor will be 0.9.   Hence

$$G_{mf} = 4{,}900 \times 0.9 = 4{,}410 \text{ lb/(hr)(sq ft)}$$

$$\frac{G_f - G_{mf}}{G_f} = \frac{23{,}750 - 4{,}410}{23{,}750} = 0.813$$

and from Fig. 9-10 $\dfrac{j_{\text{fixed}} - j_{\text{fluid}}}{j_{\text{fixed}}} = 0.49$

$$\text{Re} = \frac{D_p G}{\mu} = \frac{0.0795 \times 23{,}750}{0.93 \times 2.42 \times 12} = 70.0$$

From Fig. 9-2 $j_d = 0.19$; hence

$$j_{\text{fluid}} = 0.19 - 0.49 \times 0.19 = 0.0970$$

The mass-transfer coefficient is found next.   By Eq. (9-1)

$$k_F = \frac{0.0970 \times 23{,}750}{18 \times 1{,}073^{0.667}} = 1.22 \text{ lb moles/(hr)(sq ft)}(\Delta C)$$

Evans[8] made a test under the prevailing conditions and found $j_d = 0.0831$ and $k_F = 1.05$ lb moles/(hr)(sq ft)(ΔC).

Example 9-2.   A column of $D_t = 0.333$ ft diameter is charged with 5.877 lb of ball-shaped β-naphthol pellets.   The total packing-surface area as determined from the geometry of the bed is 26.87 sq ft.   Water is passed into the bed from below at a rate of 6,302 lb per hr.   The column is operated at 16.2°C, and at that temperature the solubility of β-naphthol in water is 0.0005174 lb per lb and the value of the Schmidt number is 1,321.   The particle diameter of the pellets may be taken as 0.01575 ft and the solids density as 80 lb per cu ft.   Assume that the solution viscosity is 1.0 centipoise.   For the conditions specified find:

1. The exit concentration when the bed is free to expand in accordance with the given mass velocity

2. The exit concentration when the bed operates under the same mass velocity but its top is restrained by a suitable screen so that the bed is fixed

Solution.   We shall first find the mass velocity for the onset of fluidization. Hence by Eq. (3-25)

$$G_{mf} = 688 \times 0.189^{1.82} \frac{[62.3(80 - 62.3)]^{0.94}}{1.0^{0.88}} = 24,000$$

$$\frac{D_p G}{\mu} = \frac{0.01575 \times 24,000}{1.0 \times 2.42} = 156.5$$

From Fig. (3-15) the correction factor is then found to be 0.48. Hence

$$G_{mf} = 24,000 \times 0.48 = 11,500 \text{ lb/(hr)(sq ft)}$$

Although not required for the solution of the problem, as a matter of interest the voidage of the expanded bed will be found. Thus at maximum expansion

$$G_f = \frac{6,302}{0.0872} = 72,300 \text{ lb/(hr)(sq ft)}$$

$$\frac{D_p G_f}{\mu} = \frac{0.01575 \times 72,300}{1.0 \times 2.42} = 471$$

and at G_{mf}
$$\frac{D_p G_{mf}}{\mu} = \frac{0.01575 \times 11,500}{1.0 \times 2.42} = 74.8$$

We shall therefore use an average value of 272 and evaluate n from Eq. (4-5). Thus

$$n = 4.45 \times 272^{-0.1} = 2.54$$

Assuming an initial voidage of, say, $\epsilon = 0.40$, the layout according to the method of Richardson and Zaki gives a voidage of $\epsilon = 0.83$ at full expansion.

Next j_d values are obtained for the fixed and fluidized beds. From Fig. 9-2,

$$j_{\text{fixed}} = 0.082$$

$$\frac{G_f - G_{mf}}{G_f} = \frac{72,300 - 11,500}{72,300} = 0.840$$

and
$$\frac{j_{\text{fixed}} - j_{\text{fluid}}}{j_{\text{fixed}}} = 0.54$$

hence
$$j_{\text{fluid}} = 0.038$$

Applying Eq. (9-4) to both the freely fluidizing and the restrained bed there follows for the fluidized bed

$$0.038 = \frac{1,321^{0.667}}{26.87} 2.3 \log \frac{0.0005174}{0.0005174 - C_2}$$

This yields $C_2 = 4.4 \times 10^{-6}$. For the restrained bed operating under a mass velocity of 72,300 as a fixed bed the exit concentration $C_2 = 9.4 \times 10^{-6}$ lb of β-naphthol per lb of water.

McCune and Wilhelm[15] actually carried this test out, and their observed data compared with the calculated data as tabulated below. They did not restrain

Parameter	McCune and Wilhelm data	Calculated data
Expanded voidage.................	0.879	0.83
j_d factor.........................	0.0364	0.038
Exit concentration, C_2.............	4.6×10^{-6}	4.4×10^{-6}

their bed and hence they did not report the value of C_2 for the restrained fixed bed operating under the same mass velocity as the freely fluidizing bed. The calculations indicate that the exit concentration is much reduced in the freely expanded fluidizing bed. In part this is due to back-mixing. With respect to order of magnitude, the increase in exit concentration due to restraining the bed is $[(9.4 - 4.4)/4.4]$ 100 = 113.5 per cent.

It is of interest to compare this with some measurements which Evans has made in fluidized as well as restrained fixed beds. Some of his data are given in the tabulation below. The data pertain to the dissolving of benzoic acid in water.

Exper.	Nature of bed	D_p, ft	Wgt of bed, lb	Void-age	G, lb/ (hr)(sq ft)	C_2, lb per lb	Percentage increase due to restrain-ing bed
A¹-9	Fluidized	0.00426	0.0572	0.84	22,996	0.000269	
A¹-13	Fixed	0.00434	0.0610	0.50	22,400	0.000585	117.5

The temperature was in all cases close to 23°C; hence solubility data and Schmidt number are constant for the two experiments. A comparison of the observed increase in C_2 with the value calculated from the McCune and Wilhelm[15] run supports the method of calculation of fixed-bed and fluidized-bed mass-transfer factors and hence the exit concentration.

LIMITATIONS OF GENERALIZED CORRELATION

Probably the most remarkable feature of the generalized correlation is that it incorporates both liquid-solid and gas-solid data. That solids and gas mixing along the longitudinal axis of a fluidized gas-solid system can be quite pronounced is well known; it will be discussed in detail in the next chapter. However, a consideration of liquid-fluidized columns has disclosed that in them the longitudinal mixing is much less important. In fact within the very neighborhood of the point of incipient fluidization there is virtually no deviation from fixed-bed flow patterns. Therefore, the question that arises is how the two types of data can be reconciled into a single correlation that virtually rests on the existence of fluid back-mixing in the bed.

The question may be resolved to some extent by an examination of Figs. 9-6 and 9-8. It will be noted that, from the start, the fluidized data in the gas-solid system deviate very abruptly from the fixed-bed line, whereas in the liquid-solid system the deviation is much more gradual and becomes substantial only at relatively high reduced mass velocities. But this is qualitatively in line with the fluid back-mixing pattern observed in liquid-fluidized columns. It becomes appreciable only at high reduced mass velocities. A closer examination of the gas-solid data in Fig. 9-10 and their relation to the remainder of the data, all liquid-fluidized, indicates a somewhat different trend of the gas-solid data. This is of course due to the different character of the breakaway of the fluidized data from the fixed-bed line. Hence it would appear that the generalized correlation has its limitations in this respect. Thus if applied to gas-solid systems operating at low reduced mass velocities, the correlation will tend to give high values for the gas-fluidized bed.

Limits of applicability of the correlation in Fig. 9-10 as established by the experimental data are as follows:

Particle-diameter range: 0.028 to 0.250 in.
Particle density: Approximately 80 to 700 lb per cu ft
Fluid density: 0.075 to 62.3 lb per cu ft
Fluid viscosity: 0.018 to about 1.0 centipoise

As for operating range, the correlation should certainly hold up to $G_f/G_{mf} \approx 10$ or higher. G_{mf} values are most conveniently obtained from Chap. 3. Of course, no voidage data are required in any step leading to the estimation of the mass-transfer factor.

Regarding extension of the correlation to larger tube diameters than indicated in Table 9-3, caution must be used. Since the tube diameter affects the fluidization performance and the internal fluid and solids flow pattern, it is only logical to expect that mass-transfer factors are influenced by the tube diameter. Hence there is still a field of study virtually unexplored. With regard to other apparatus details—fluid inlet and internal elements such as baffles and heat-transfer surfaces—all of them will influence the internal fluid flow pattern. Hence they should all be expected to influence mass-transfer performance.

SUMMARY AND CONCLUSIONS

Consideration of fluidized-bed mass-transfer data has indicated that deviations observed in some instances may be due to a number of reasons. First to be mentioned are uncertainties in solids temperature at which vapor pressures are to be evaluated. Next there is the difficulty of evaluating the active surface area in the bed. Since in most cases the state of subdivision is so small that, because of the large surfaces, mass-transfer rates are high, very low bed heights are required, in order to yield an unsaturated effluent and permit the establishment of a valid concentration difference. However, with these shallow beds there is danger that the data will be affected by terminal effects. It appears therefore that the difficulties are numerous, and that is particularly true for gas-solid systems.

With liquid-solid systems there are fewer difficulties. First of all, much higher column heights can be used; secondly, concentrations are more readily evaluated in beds for which the total surface area can be calculated with fair precision. Finally, the temperature of the solids is more readily evaluated. In view of all these circumstances it is not surprising that fluidized liquid-solid mass-transfer data are much more reliable.

As far as data levels are concerned, fluidized-bed mass-transfer data are, for the same Reynolds numbers, lower than the corresponding fixed-bed mass-transfer data. All measurements, fixed as well as fluidized bed, were based on a logarithmic-mean concentration difference between solid and fluid through the reactor. Since this is true only for conditions of piston flow and since in many fluidized beds flow deviates notoriously from piston flow and approaches almost complete mixing, the real driving force in the fluidized bed is actually smaller. Using this line of reasoning, a generalized correlation for both fixed and fluidized beds was proposed on the assumption that the variation of driving force in the fluidized bed was related to the quantity $(G_f - G_{mf})/G_f$, termed the bed-stirring ratio. All available liquid-fluidized data and one set of gas-fluidized data could be used to develop the generalized correlation. The range of validity of the generalized correlation is considered. Its extension to larger-diameter units and to units of greater complexity indicates that much fundamental research is still required to uncover the effects of diameter and apparatus construction on internal fluid flow patterns and thereby on mass transfer.

PROBLEMS

9-1. Chu, Kalil, and Wetteroth[3] coated small glass beads with a thin layer of naphthalene and subjected them to a rising current of air to study mass transfer in a fluidized bed.   Typical data observed were as follows:

Air mass velocity: G_f = 2,700 lb/(hr)(sq ft)
Surface temperature of beads: 64.4°F
Pressure: Atmospheric
Particle diameter: D_p = 0.0288 in.
Total available surface area for mass transfer: 1.585 sq ft
Duration of test: 2.5 min
Naphthalene vaporized: 1.04×10^{-3} lb
Partial pressure of naphthalene in exit gas: 2.88×10^{-5} atm

The apparatus used was a column of 3.75 in. ID.   The density of glass beads ρ_S = 158 lb per cu ft, and the variation due to the naphthalene film may be discounted. The vapor pressure of naphthalene is given by

$$\log p_S = -\frac{3,729.3}{T_s} + 11.450$$

where p_s is in millimeters of Hg and T_S is the temperature in degrees Kelvin. For the conditions specified:

1. Evaluate the mass-transfer factor from the experimental data.

2. Calculate the mass-transfer factor from the generalized correlation for (a) the fluidized bed and (b) a restrained fixed bed operating under the same mass velocity as the fluidized bed.

3. Estimate the percentage increase in naphthalene concentration in the effluent when the bed is artificially restrained at the top.

9-2. Bar-Ilan and Resnick[1] investigated mass transfer in fixed beds by vaporizing naphthalene from cylindrical dished-end pellets. They passed air downward through a bed offering 15 sq in. of contacting area. The pellet size was $D_p = 0.163$ in. The average pressure through the reactor was 18.6 psia and the temperature will be assumed as 77°F. Thus for a Reynolds number of $D_p G/\mu = 250$ they observed a $j_d = 0.113$.

Find the percentage change in the effluent concentration when the mass velocity is increased threefold and when the bed is run (1) with downward gas flow and (2) with upward gas flow.

9-3. A supply of β-naphthol pellets has accidentally been contaminated with sodium chloride crystals, and it is proposed to remove the sodium chloride by washing the material with water. In order to lose as little of the β-naphthol in the wash water as possible, it is suggested that the washing operation be carried through in a highly expanded fluidized bed. The entire charge to be washed is 225 lb. An empty packed tower shell is available in the plant, and it is planned to perform the washing operation in that unit. The tower consists of a standard 12-in.-diameter pipe, and its usable height for this purpose is 12 ft. For the data given below estimate the loss in β-naphthol if the washing operation is carried out for 10 min. The entering water is free of β-naphthol, nor does it contain salt. Data are as follows:

Particle size: $D_p = 0.24$ in. (spherical)
$\rho_S = 80$ lb per cu ft
Bulk density: 48 lb per cu ft
$\epsilon_{mf} = 0.40$
Temperature of operation: 59°F
β-naphthol solubility at 59°F: 0.000489 lb per lb water
Diffusivity: 0.882 sq ft per sec
Schmidt number: 1,400

The original salt content in the charge was 2.5 weight per cent. It may be assumed that at the high water rates used the solubility of β-naphthol remains virtually unaffected by the salt.

9-4. Anthracene granules containing 5.0 weight per cent of naphthalene granules are to be exposed to a rising air current to remove some of the naphthalene by vaporization. The solids are of spherical shape, and $D_p = 0.125$ in. for both materials. Densities of anthracene and naphthalene are $\rho_S = 71.4$ and 71.5 lb per cu ft, respectively. The contacting will be done in a fluidized bed at 72°F and under a reduced mass velocity of 5.0, based on the anthracene.

A total of 1 lb of the mixture is thus to be treated in a 2-in.-diameter column and for such a length of time that the naphthalene content will be reduced to 2.5 weight per cent. Estimate the required operating time and the remaining weight of anthracene in the bed if the air enters free of hydrocarbons. For the solids, $\epsilon_{mf} = 0.50$, and vapor pressures in millimeters of mercury are given for anthracene by $\log p_S = -3{,}680/T_S + 8.91$, and for naphthalene by $\log p_S = -3{,}729/T_S + 11.45$. The temperature of the solids T_S is to be expressed in degrees Kelvin.

The diffusivity of anthracene in air may be taken as 0.217 sq ft per hr, and it will be assumed that the presence of either hydrocarbon will not affect the vaporization of the other.

9-5. A charge of naphthalene spheres of $D_p = 0.015$ in. and $\rho_S = 71.5$ lb per cu ft is contaminated by a powder of $D_p = 0.0016$ in. and $\rho_S = 300$ lb per cu ft. The shape of the powder particles is spherical, and the concentration of the powder in the mixture is 19 weight per cent.

It is intended to reduce the concentration of the contaminating powder to 9 weight per cent by fluidizing the mixture for 60 min with the proper air velocity. The material to be processed weighs 3.85 lb, and use of a 4-in.-diameter column is contemplated for the work. The bulk density of the uncontaminated naphthalene spheres is known to be 41.3 lb per cu ft, and that of the foreign solid, 150 lb per cu ft. If the air enters free of naphthalene and at 70°F, and after leaving the bed passes into the atmosphere, estimate the loss of naphthalene.

REFERENCES

1. Bar-Ilan, M., and W. Resnick: *Ind. Eng. Chem.*, **49**: 313–320 (1957).
2. Chilton, T. H., and A. P. Colburn: *Ind. Eng. Chem.*, **26**: 1183 (1934).
3. Chu, J. C., J. Kalil, and W. A. Wetteroth: *Chem. Eng. Progr.*, **49**: 141–149 (1953).
4. Colburn, A. P.: *Ind. Eng. Chem.*, **22**: 967 (1930).
5. Colburn, A. P.: *Trans. AIChE*, **29**: 174 (1933).
6. Dryden, C. E., D. A. Strang, and A. E. Withrow: *Chem. Eng. Progr.*, **49**: 191–196 (1953).
7. Ergun, Sabri: *Chem. Eng. Progr.*, **48**: 227–236 (1952).
8. Evans, G. C.: M.S. thesis, University of Washington, 1951.
9. Evans, G. C., and C. F. Gerald: *Chem. Eng. Progr.*, **49**: 135 (1953).
10. Gaffney, B. J., and T. B. Drew: *Ind. Eng. Chem.*, **42**: 1120 (1950).
11. Gamson, B. W., G. Thodos, and O. A. Hougen: *Trans. AIChE*, **39**: 1 (1943).
12. Hobson, M., and G. Thodos: *Chem. Eng. Progr.*, **45**: 517 (1949).
13. Ishino, T., and T. Ohtake: *Chem. Eng. (Tokyo)*, **15**: 258 (1951).
14. Kettenring, K. N., E. L. Manderfield, and J. M. Smith: *Chem. Eng. Progr.*, **46**: 139–144 (1950).
15. McCune, L. K., and R. H. Wilhelm: *Ind. Eng. Chem.*, **41**: 1124 (1949).
16. Ohtake, T.: In "Review of Fluidization Literature," by T. Shirai, Tokyo Institute of Technology, Tokyo, 1954.
17. Resnick, W., and R. R. White: *Chem. Eng. Progr.*, **45**: 377 (1949).
18. Taecker, R. G., and O. A. Hougen: *Chem. Eng. Progr.*, **45**: 188 (1949).
19. Wilke, C. R., and O. A. Hougen: *Trans. AIChE*, **41**: 445 (1945).

CHAPTER 10

SOLIDS AND FLUID MIXING

Nomenclature

a = experimental constant, Eq. (10-10)

A = cross-section of flow chamber normal to fluid flow, sq ft

C = concentration of tracer at height Z above injection point

C_0 = concentration of tracer when completely mixed; $C = v_{tr}/v_g$, where v_{tr} is the volumetric flow rate of the tracer and v_g that of the main gas

D_L = liquid diffusivity in liquid-fluidized beds, sq ft per hr

D_s = solids-phase "diffusivity" in gas-fluidized beds, sq ft per hr

D_p = particle diameter, ft

D_t = flow-chamber diameter, ft

E_g = eddy diffusivity of gas phase, Eq. (10-8), sq ft per hr

E_s = solids-phase "diffusion" coefficient, Eq. (10-1), lb/(hr)(ft). NOTE: $E_s = D_s\rho_S$, where ρ_S = solids density, lb per cu ft

Fr = Froude number, $u_f{}^2/D_p g_c$

g_c = conversion factor, 32.2 (lb mass)(ft)/(lb force)(sec)(sec)

k = constant, Eq. (10-11)

L = bed height, ft

L_{mf} = bed height at point of minimum fluidization, ft

n = quantity of tracer transferred, Eq. (10-8)

Q = volumetric gas flow rate through a bed, cu ft per hr

r = radius of flow chamber, ft

R = bed-expansion ratio

S = solids-feed mass velocity, lb/(hr)(sq ft) in Eq. (10-1)

t = residence time of solids or gas, either in excess of or less than the average residence time t_0, hr

t_0 = average residence time of solids or gas in the reactor, hr

T = local temperature of water in column, °C

T_0 = resulting water temperature when cold water and hot water used as tracer are completely mixed, °C

u_f = fluid velocity through a bed, fluidizing the charge, ft per hr

u_{mf} = fluid velocity required for minimum fluidization, ft per hr

u_p = average particle velocity, calculated from average residence time and average bed height, ft per hr

V_{cm} = reactor volume required when flow conditions conform to complete mixing

V_{pf} = reactor volume required when flow conditions conform to piston flow, cu ft

x = probability that a particle may have a given residence time t in a fluidized charge

x_1, x_2 = same as x but with reference to various stages in multistage fluidized reactors

Z = position above tracer injection point, ft

β = interparticle friction factor

ϵ = bed voidage
η = fluidization efficiency
θ = time, hr
ρ_S = solids density, lb per cu ft

Abstract

The chapter introduction restates effects created by solids and fluid mixing. The first section considers solids flow patterns, particle and solids velocities, and residence time of solids in through-type fluidized beds. This leads to a consideration of fluid mixing, which is given in two sections. The first deals with gas mixing and the second with liquid mixing. The available experimental data are cited, followed by a presentation of the resulting correlations. A brief final section is devoted to residence time of gases in fluidized reactors and the expected effects on chemical reactions.

Introduction. It was pointed out in Chap. 4 that the main distinguishing difference between fixed and fluidized beds is that in the latter the granular particles are free to move in relation to each other. Because of this solids movement the fluidized bed has the following properties:

1. Wherever heat transfer between the bed as a whole and confining surfaces is involved, particle motion past the heat-transfer surfaces will increase heat-transfer film coefficients appreciably.

2. Owing to the relatively high heat capacity of the solids as compared with the fluidizing gas, the solids mixing inside the fluidized bed tends to equalize temperatures and reduce internal temperature gradients. This applies in both radial and longitudinal temperature gradients.

3. As far as material composition of fluidized beds is concerned, internal mixing will tend to render the charge more homogeneous. This is of course closely related to the temperature equalization (2).

4. Owing to the mixing of the solids in the bed, there may with certain friable materials be excessive solids attrition. Another and possibly more important reason for solids breakup may be generation of internal temperature stresses caused by highly exothermic or endothermic reactions.

5. Solids motion within the bed may lead to excessive equipment erosion. This is particularly true where hard granular substances of very irregular shapes are used in reactors that carry internal baffles and heat-transfer surfaces.

According to all observations, solids mixing is induced by the gross upward passage of the fluid through the bed; it is also required that the bed have an upper unrestricted boundary. Hence solids mixing is a primary induced phenomenon. Because the solids movement takes place in the fluidizing gas, a secondary fluid-mixing phenomenon will be induced through the solids flow pattern. The fluid mixing thus caused may be appreciable, depending on whether the solids are dispersed in the bed more or less as separate granules or tend to move in bulk. In the former case the gas mixing would be relatively small, whereas it would be much more important when whole gas pockets are enclosed in large agglomerates of particles which, moving through the bed as such, drag the gas pockets along. Thus the extent of gas mixing is related to the mode and quality of fluidization.

Solids mixing and the resulting fluid mixing in fluidized beds have so far been only scantily investigated. Nevertheless experiments made with nonbaffled and baffled beds seem to support the above mechanism, whereby gas mixing is greatly influenced by the mode of fluidization.[11]*

Similarly to solids mixing, fluid mixing endows the fluidized bed with properties as follows:

1. Owing to fluid back-mixing, temperature driving forces will be lessened. This has been considered in Chap. 8, which deals with heat transfer.

2. Analogously to heat transfer, driving forces are reduced in mass transfer. This was considered in Chap. 9, dealing with mass transfer.

3. With fluid back-mixing in reactors, there is an unavoidable dilution of reactants with reaction products. Depending on the order of the reaction, this may have an unfavorable effect on yields.

SOLIDS MIXING

Solids Flow Pattern. The normal solids flow pattern in small-diameter beds, when fluidized with a gas, is shown in Fig. 10-1. For gas rates which are substantially above u_{mf} the solids tend to move downward near the wall, somewhat in impulse wavelike fashion. The passage of individual particles is readily observed. Thus a particle will proceed awhile along the wall of the vessel and will then suddenly submerge into the body of the bed. At this point, or somewhat above or below, other particles will emerge from the charge for awhile and travel downward. This goes on until the bottom of the bed is approached. If the bottom section is a cone, the pattern will continue farther than if a flat porous plate of the same diameter as the bed is used as gas inlet. In the latter case there will then be inactive bed portions that may extend upward for as much as a column radius. However, this will depend to a considerable extent on the height of the bed, as will, incidentally, the entire solids flow pattern. Thus in

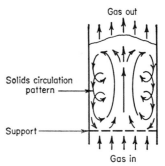

Gas out

Solids circulation pattern

Support

Gas in

FIG. 10-1. Observed solids circulation pattern in gas-fluidized vertical columns.

* Superscript numbers indicate works listed in References at the end of the chapter.

very shallow beds the downward solids flow pattern near the wall is much less clearly defined and the bed as a whole seems to be in a much more turbulent and homogeneous state of agitation.

Considering the flow pattern further in a relatively high bed, the solids tend to move upward in the center. With certain types of solids that do not favor slugging, this internal flow pattern may at times be recognized from the top of the bed, where the solids may spill over in a fountainlike fashion not unlike spouting (Chap. 7). Similarly to spouting, the solids flow pattern in a fluidized charge may be greatly influenced by the air-inlet device. That has been recognized by designers, and for that reason special consideration is usually given to the task of designing support grids and fluid-distribution devices.

The solids flow pattern in liquid-fluidized beds is different from that in gas-fluidized beds. Once the bed has been sufficiently expanded, the particles tend to move as individual elements rather than in bulk. Occasionally, however, particle groups consisting of, say, four to eight individual units may be seen, banded lightly together and rising and falling in the column. However, on the whole this is much less pronounced than the severe cluster formation in aggregative gas-fluidized beds. The terms "particulate" and "aggregative," introduced by Wilhelm and Kwauk to describe these flow patterns, are therefore fitting.[20] Wilhelm and Kwauk have also suggested use of the Froude group $u_f{}^2/D_p g_c$ as a criterion of aggregative or particulate flow behavior. For Fr < 1.0 the system would be considered to be in the particulate state; for Fr > 1.0, the aggregative state.

A comparison of extent of particle movement in gas-fluidized and liquid-fluidized beds operating near incipient fluidization at identical reduced mass velocities indicates much livelier action in the gas-fluidized bed. Many investigators have attempted to define the onset of fluidization by means of intensity of particle movement. Applied to liquid-fluidized beds, this would then yield high values for the onset of fluidization.

If a fluidized vessel is operated in a position that deviates somewhat from the vertical, the solids flow pattern will be adversely affected. Only a few degrees of deviation from the vertical will lead to solids bypassing and short-circuiting. This has been demonstrated by Sackmann[15] in a systematic series of tests with liquid-fluidized columns.

Gas-fluidized systems, when operated at sufficiently high gas velocities, will tend to slug. The solids flow pattern in slugging is entirely different from that attending nonslugging fluidization. Since slugging is an abnormality, particle movement attending slugging will here not be further considered.

Particle Velocities. By means of high-speed photography, Toomey and Johnstone[17] obtained typical particle velocities in dense-phase gas-fluidized beds. The apparatus was of 4.73 in. ID and bed heights of 24 in. and more were investigated. Typical data pertaining to glass beads of 0.0148 in. diameter and a bed height of 23 to 24 in. are given in Fig. 10-2. The measurements were made at a position 15 in. above the bottom of the bed. The air entered the bed through a porous plate.

Particle-velocity data in Fig. 10-2 pertain to three gas velocities. Observations are as follows:

1. The periodic amplitudes shown for all three velocities indicate that the bed has strong slugging tendencies. The data between the amplitudes are apparently true particle velocities. The amplitudes are probably the result of entire slugs rising and falling suddenly.

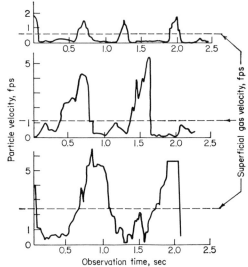

FIG. 10-2. Typical particle velocities observed by Toomey and Johnstone[17] in beds of glass beads of $D_p = 0.0148$ in. and bed heights of 23 to 24 in.; velocities were observed 15 in. above bottom of bed. (*Courtesy of Chemical Engineering Progress.*)

2. Designating the interamplitude velocities as particle velocities, they are consistently lower than the superficial gas velocity. For the particular solid the order of magnitude of the solids velocity ranges from 0.2 to about 2 fps.

3. Particle velocities increase with gas velocity.

Other factors which will influence particle velocity are particle diameter, particle shape, and position above the gas inlet. The latter effect has also been reported by Toomey and Johnstone, and Fig. 10-3, which gives some of their data, indicates that for this particular case the average particle velocity near the wall virtually trebled as higher bed regions were approached.

Velocities of particles moving in bulk were also reported by the Bureau of Mines.[10] The experimental units were of 1.32 and 2.032 in. ID. Silica sands and silica gel particles were used as solids, and a small amount of a dyed portion of the same material was rained on top of a fluidizing column. With the bed height known and gas rates adjusted to desired values, the times required for the dyed materials to reach the base of the column were then noted. This permitted evaluation of penetration velocities of particles down the column. For the solids employed, the velocities ranged from 0.03 to 0.125 fps. Comparison with the data of Toomey and Johnstone[17] just cited indicates no agreement. This may be due to a number of reasons; the most important may possibly be linked to shape. Thus the entirely spherical glass beads of Toomey and Johnstone may tend to move more rapidly than the more irregularly shaped sand and silica gel particles considered here. Another reason for the higher wall velocities observed by Toomey and Johnstone may be associated with their much larger column diameter. Thus as the column diameter increases, the ratio of peripheral surface area to bed volume decreases, which has a direct bearing on frictional resistance between particles

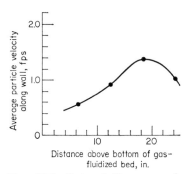

FIG. 10-3. Data of Toomey and Johnstone[17] showing an effect of position on particle velocity near the wall; these data are specific for the case investigated, and different results would probably be observed for other particles, fluidized under different conditions. Data observed for glass beads of $D_p =$ 0.0148 in. fluidized at $G_f = 270$ lb/(hr)(sq ft).

and wall. These explanations, plausible as they may seem, nevertheless appear insufficient to bridge the wide gap between the two sets of data. Hence it would appear that other unknowns are involved.

The velocity data for the silica sands and silica gel have been correlated by

$$u_f\eta = \beta \frac{L_{mf}R}{\theta} \qquad (4\text{-}16)$$

where β is the "interparticle friction factor" believed to depend on the particle-shape and surface characteristics of the granular solid. For round and sharp silica sand β was found to be 2.25 and 2.55, respectively. For the silica gel a value of $\beta = 1.15$ was reported.

Observations resulting from a somewhat similar study have been reported by Brötz.[3] He used differently colored glass beads of the same size and composed an initial bed with 50 per cent of each color. He used an upward flow of water at a velocity sufficient to fluidize the column and cause the glass beads to mix. He observed that, although mixing took place, a comparatively long time was required to approach a high state of homogeneity. Specifically, the nonhomogeneity of the bed was evidenced by the presence of clusters of one color in an environment that was already largely homogeneous. Drawing on an analogy to diffusive mixing in fluids, the data analysis yielded a solid-phase diffusion coefficient, which was found to increase linearly with particle diameter and reduced mass velocity of the system.

Solids Back-mixing. Solids back-mixing has been demonstrated in an interesting manner by Gilliland and Mason.[4,5] The unit used for the purpose consisted of an upper electrically heated section and a lower water-cooled section. Wall temperatures, as well as temperature increases of the cooling water, were measured by thermocouples. Another couple centrally located and movable along the axis of the tube measured the central temperature profile.

Two sets of experiments were made. In both cases the top was heated and the bottom simultaneously cooled; however, in one instance the tube was empty, whereas in the other the tube had been charged with Filtrol. The superficial air velocity was in both instances 1.2 fps. The data, shown in Fig. 10-4, are most revealing and emphasize the profound effect of solids mixing on temperature equalization. With the empty tube there was no temperature gradient in the bottom section,

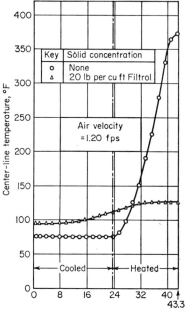

FIG. 10-4. Data of Gilliland and Mason[4] showing effect of solids on vertical temperature profiles in a fluidized tube. (*Courtesy of Industrial and Engineering Chemistry.*)

which indicates that for this situation none of the heat added in the upper zone had reached the lower part of the tube. In the upper zone of the empty tube there was a very steep longitudinal temperature gradient, extending from about 80 to over 350°F. Considering next the tube filled with solids, the upper-zone temperature gradient extended from about 110 to about 127°F, whereas in the lower part of the bed a decided longitudinal gradient of about 15° appeared. The latter can only be the result of back-mixing of hot solids into the cooled section.

Solids-mixing experiments in full-scale catalytic cracking units have been reported by Singer, Todd, and Guinn,[16] who tagged cracking catalysts with radioactive isotopes of scandium-46 and cerium-144 and injected samples at definite stations into nontagged catalysts circulating through a commercial unit. By ascertaining the level of the radioactivity in various parts of the equipment, they could arrive at conclusions regarding solids-mixing efficiencies. The method was found particularly useful for arriving at the total inventory of the catalyst in the system. The data thus calculated checked with values obtained from pressure-drop tests within 2 per cent. The distributions thus determined indicated that, while in the dense beds of reactors and regenerators perfect mixing is approached, there were nevertheless deviations from complete homogeneity, which indicated some catalyst bypassing in certain regions of the system.

As far as quantitative data relating to solids back-mixing are concerned, there are only the measurements of Bart[2] and some later reported data of Massimilla and Bracale.[11] The latter data are really concerned with a comparison of unbaffled and baffled beds.

The column used by Bart was of 1.25 in. diameter. Solids used were cracking catalyst. The system was a circulating type of bed wherein solids were fed continuously into the base and taken out overhead. Tracer solid, cracking catalyst impregnated with sodium chloride, was fed to the system about halfway up the column. The upstream spreading of the tracer could be readily followed. Assuming that a diffusion mechanism prevailed in the bed at the chosen operating conditions, the concentration data were correlated by

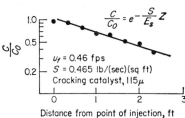

FIG. 10-5. Solids-mixing data of Bart.[2]

$$\frac{C}{C_0} = e^{-SZ/E_s} \qquad (10\text{-}1)$$

where C_0 and C are concentrations of the tracer at the point of injection and at height Z above the injection point. S is the solids-feed mass velocity, and E_s is a solid phase-diffusion coefficient. With Z given in feet and S in pounds per hour per square foot, E_s has the dimension of pounds per hour per foot.

Some data by Bart are given in Fig. 10-5. The slope of the line permits evaluation of E_s. Considerations of data for a range of gas velocities yielded $E_s \propto u_f$.

For the cracking catalyst studied, typical values of E_s in relation to u_f are as follows:

E_s, $lb/(hr)(ft)$	u_f, fps
3,140	0.33
14,500	1.65

Similar data have been observed by Massimilla and Bracale[11] for beds composed of 0.0275-in. glass beads fluidized in a 4-in.-diameter column. Typical data for this system are as follows:

E_s, $lb/(hr)(ft)$	u_f, fps
177	1.41
302	1.65

Comparison with the data of Bart[2] discloses no agreement. Apparently effects of particle characteristics and chamber diameter remain to be investigated.

Residence Time. Wherever solids are being processed chemically or otherwise, some indication of the residence time in the reactor is desirable. Since the solid particles in a fluidizing charge are not all at the same velocity, it is obvious that a true expression of residence time would have to be an integrated value. Because no particle-velocity distribution data are so far available for fluidized beds, only an average residence time can be defined. Let us consider a dense-phase reactor in which solids are added to the lower section through a standpipe and are withdrawn at the top through an overflow arrangement. If under operating conditions the unit contains, say, a ton of material and if solids are fed to and withdrawn from the vessel at a rate of, say, 4 tons per hr, the average residence time of the solids is then $t_0 = \frac{1}{4} \times 60 = 15$ min. On the other hand, if the fluidized-bed height is L and an average particle velocity is equal to u_p, the average contact time would be given by $t_0 = L/u_p$. Assuming that the fluidized-bed height for the above case is 3 ft, the average particle velocity would then be

$$u_p = \frac{3 \times 12}{15 \times 60} = 0.04 \text{ ips}$$

It is to be noted that this velocity is a resultant over-all particle velocity that proceeds in an upward direction between solids terminals. It is not necessarily the true velocity of any particular particle, as may be seen from the order of magnitude of the value and comparison with particle-velocity data given earlier. In reality, individual particles will still move through the charge very much at velocities reported earlier; however, the effective velocity so far as solids removal is concerned will be about 0.04 ips for the above instance.

Because of the complex nature of the solids velocity in such a system, only a portion of the solids that are in the bed and are passing through it will have the residence time of 15 min indicated by the above example. There will be other solids fractions that move more rapidly and still others that will move more slowly through the bed. This problem has been solved analytically by Reboux,[13] who proposes that

$$x = e^{-t/t_0} \qquad (10\text{-}2)$$

where x is the probability that any one particle may have a residence time t, in the charge, either greater or less than the average residence time t_0.

Analyzing the above reactor problem in the light of the probability, the following tabulation results:

t, min	x	t, min	x
0.15	0.991	7.5	0.61
1.5	0.905	15	0.37
3	0.82	75	0.007

Thus it is seen that, although the average residence time is 15 min, 0.9 per cent of the particles introduced will remain in the bed much less than a minute and 0.7 per cent will remain for about 75 min.

Multistage Reactor. The probability consideration just presented is further extended by Reboux[13] to multistage reactors. For the purpose of illustration let us consider a series reactor consisting of two identical beds. Let t_0 be the average contact time in each reactor. If a particle is introduced at time $t = 0$ into the upper bed, the probability that it will still be there after time t is

$$x_1 = e^{-t/t_0} \qquad (10\text{-}3)$$

The probability that it will find itself in the second reactor will be x_2, a quantity to be determined. Between the time interval t and $t + dt$, x_2 increases by dx_2. For the case that the particle enters the second reactor between times t and $t + dt$ the probability will be $x_1\, dt/t_0$. The particle can, however, also leave the second reactor, and the probability for this event is expressed by $x_2\, dt/t_0$. Hence

$$dx_2 = x_1 \frac{dt}{t_0} - x_2 \frac{dt}{t_0} \qquad (10\text{-}4)$$

which upon integration and replacement of x_1 by its value gives

$$x_2 = \frac{t}{t_0} e^{-t/t_0} \qquad (10\text{-}5)$$

Obviously, then, the probability that any one particle will be in either of the two beds in the reactor is given by

$$x = x_1 + x_2 = \left(1 + \frac{t}{t_0}\right) e^{-t/t_0} \qquad (10\text{-}6)$$

This analysis may readily be extended to series reactors of more than two beds.

Equation (10-6) may be applied to the single-bed reactor problem cited in the preceding chapter. For the two-stage reactor there results:

t, min	x	t, min	x
0.15	0.9998	7.5	0.736
1.5	0.9825	15	0.408
3	0.770	75	0.00055

When these probabilities are compared with the single-bed probabilities, it may be seen that, through application of two beds in series collectively employing the same mass of solids as the former single bed, the residence-time variation has been greatly lessened. Whereas in the former single bed as much as about 10 per cent of the charge had a residence time of less than 2.5 min, in the two-stage unit less than 2 per cent of the solids have so brief a residence time.

Action of Baffles. The preceding considerations of residence time in single-bed and multistage series reactors have disclosed that the solids residence-time variation is progressively lessened as the charge is distributed over a greater number of contacting beds. Hence the solids flow pattern through the unit becomes better coordinated and solids back-mixing is impeded.

In a sense, arrangement of baffles in a vessel tends to achieve the same effect. It is already known from Chaps. 4 and 8 that aggregative fluidization may be partly modified into particulate fluidization by the proper choice of baffles. Thus baffles were recognized as being effective for breaking up solids agglomerates, a function that would tend to "straighten out" the solids flow pattern in a reactor. Additional data on the effect which baffles have on the mixing of solids in fluidized beds have been given by Massimilla and Bracale.[11] They used the earlier-described 4-in.-diameter chamber which could be operated either without or with the wire-mesh baffles, spaced about ⅜ in. apart. Solids were glass beads of 0.70 mm diameter. The bulk of the beads were colored red, and a portion intended as tracer was colored green by suitable varnish. The method of operation was to fluidize a bed at a predetermined velocity and add the tracer material as a steady rain. As tracer material was added from the top, equivalent bed portions were removed from the bottom to keep the fluidized-bed height constant. At certain time intervals, bed samples were analyzed for red and green beads at various positions along the bed axis.

During the course of the experiments it was observed that, as long as the operation of the gas-solid system proceeded uniformly and without large bubbles, the mixing of the tracer into the fluidized solids resembled a process of diffusion, which could possibly be analogous to unidirectional heat flow in a solid layer that is not yet at thermal equilibrium. This phenomenon is described by a partial differential equation, analogous to the well-known Fourier equation. Thus the history-position-mixing data when applied to the equation

$$\frac{\partial^2 C}{\partial Z^2} = \frac{1}{D_s} \frac{\partial C}{\partial t} \tag{10-7}$$

yielded D_s, the diffusivity of the solids in the fluidized bed. The diffusivity D_s of Massimilla and Bracale transforms into the solid-phase diffusion coefficient E_s, proposed earlier by Bart,[2] if the former is multiplied by the density of the solid. In the Massimilla and Bracale work, baffled as well as unbaffled beds were analyzed in the manner indicated.

Solid-phase diffusion coefficients obtained for both types of bed and a range of mass velocities are given in Fig. 10-6. The data for the non-baffled bed are appreciably higher than for the baffled bed. Hence the mixing of the solids in the free-fluidizing bed is more rapid than in the baffled system of otherwise the same dimensions. It is to be noted that the comparison is possible only up to a gas velocity of about 1.7 fps. For higher velocities bubble and slug formation interferes with the normal solids diffusion pattern.

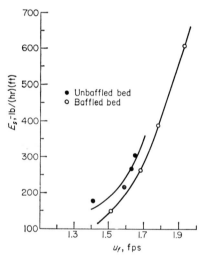

FIG. 10-6. Data of Massimilla and Bracale[11] showing effect of baffling in gas-fluidized bed on solids diffusivity coefficient.

FLUID MIXING

The mechanism of fluid mixing in fluidized beds is far from being satisfactorily understood. Although for the point of incipient fluidization, and slightly beyond, the fluid flow pattern is probably similar to that in fixed beds, the fact is not of very much worth because the fixed-bed flow mechanism is itself still largely enigmatic. Fluid-mixing studies that have so far been reported for the dense-phase fluidized state are of a limited nature so far as equipment size, materials, and operating conditions are concerned. Moreover, all studies were made in nonreaction systems. Because the understanding of the dynamics of the fluidized state is primarily desired in order to learn about the effect of fluidization on reactions, it is quite obvious that, for the proper evaluation of fluid-mixing data so far available, more than the normally required scale-up aspects remain to be considered.

Gas Flow Pattern. Solids flow patterns, as shown in Fig. 10-1, are directly observable. Fluid flow paths, on the other hand, must be tracked by experimental methods. Probably the most suitable method employs a tracer fluid: A bed of solids is fluidized by passing the main gas through the bed at a predetermined velocity and a second fluid is then injected into the bed at a certain rate and location. Upstream and downstream gas-sample analyses will provide a concentration pattern that permits the prevailing fluid flow pattern in the unit to be recognized. Experiments of this sort have been largely the basis of the gas flow pattern indicated in Fig. 10-7. The gas entering the flat distribution plate has a tendency to avoid the outer annular ring. The main gas stream rises, therefore, along the center of the bed, and most of the gas leaves the bed by way of the central core. As the gas approaches the upper bed boundary, a fraction of it is deflected and travels down the column in the outer annular ring. Near the bottom of the bed the flow is reversed, and the gas portion that has passed down the sides of the vessel mixes with gas newly admitted from the porous plate to the charge. Thus a certain recycle pattern is created, quite similar to the solids recycle pattern described in Fig. 10-1. The similarity should, however, not be surprising, since, as already pointed out, the solids flow pattern as the primary phenomenon has induced the secondary phenomenon, namely, the gas

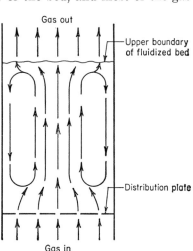

Gas out

Upper boundary of fluidized bed

Distribution plate

Gas in

FIG. 10-7. Greatly simplified gas flow pattern in fluidized systems.

mixing. From this relationship it follows that fundamental studies on gas mixing must be accompanied by systematic solids flow investigations. Solids flow patterns are of course greatly dependent on the type and geometry of the unit.

The flow pattern indicated in Fig. 10-7 is really quite oversimplified. The gas does not, by any means, circulate in such a well-coordinated manner. Instead there will be innumerable eddies within the central core, as well as horizontal components between the outer annulus and the core. Moreover, a part of the gas may rise rapidly in the form of bubbles, getting ahead of the slower-moving interstitial gas component. A considerable amount of bypassing of gas to gas as well as of gas to solid may occur. All these irregularities may take place long before one would designate the bed as slugging. Hence Fig. 10-7 is indicative only of an over-all flow pattern through a reactor with no internal baffles, heat-transfer surfaces, or other built-in devices.

Experimental Data and Correlations. Virtually the only data pertaining to gas mixing were obtained by Gilliland and Mason,[4,5] Askins, Hinds, and Künreuther,[1] and Handlos, Kunstman, and Schissler.[6] The latter two papers give specific data on fluid cracking units, whereas the Gilliland studies are of a fundamental character. The only contributions to the field of liquid mixing in liquid-fluidized systems are contained in the writings of Trawinski[18] and Wicke and Trawinski,[19] and more recently in a paper by Hanratty, Latinen, and Wilhelm.[7]

Gas-Solid Systems. The columns used by Gilliland and Mason[4,5] were of 1 and 3 in. ID. The height ranged from about 3 to 6 ft. The equipment was operated batchwise, and any entrained solids were continuously returned to the base of the column. As solids the investigators used Filtrol, microsphere cracking catalyst, and glass beads. The fluidizing gas was air, and the tracer gas was helium. The latter was injected through a 5-mm glass tube turned upward at a point 2.5 ft from the column top. The gas-sampling tube was stainless steel of 0.075 in. OD. It could be arranged to withdraw gas samples from levels that were 1 in. apart. Air and helium rates were measured by orifices, and gas samples were analyzed for helium by an Edwards gas-density balance. In view of the large density difference between the two gases, this was particularly convenient. It was also reported that, with the combination of helium in air and the solids employed, negligible, if any, adsorption on the solids occurred. In most instances the helium constituted about 10 per cent of the entering gas.

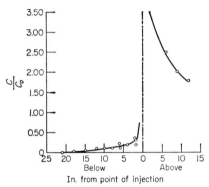

FIG. 10-8. Gas-sampling results at center of column observed by Gilliland and Mason[4] for glass beads and air with helium as a tracer. Air velocity = 1.16 fps. Samples taken centrally. (*Courtesy of Industrial and Engineering Chemistry.*)

For the purpose of analysis the ratio C/C_0 was evaluated for each run. In the above ratio C_0 = (volumetric helium rate)/(volumetric air rate) and hence the composition of the fully mixed gas, whereas C was the local concentration of helium at any particular point in the bed. Therefore, a ratio of $C/C_0 = 1$ at any point in the unit would indicate that, at that location, complete mixing had occurred. At or near the point of helium injection, one would expect to find $C/C_0 \gg 1$, whereas near the top of the bed $C/C_0 \rightarrow 1$ and near the bottom $C/C_0 \rightarrow 0$.

A longitudinal traverse along the center of the tube is given in Fig.
10-8. At the very point of injection, C/C_0 would tend to be infinite.
At a position 5 in. above the injection point, the concentration has already
greatly diminished, and it continues to diminish as the top of the bed is
approached. Considering the bed section below the injection point, there
is a considerable concentration within the first 5 in. of bed. The concentration decreases rapidly, however, and at 20 in. below the injection point
the helium concentration is virtually negligible. The data of Fig. 10-8
pertain to a linear air velocity of 1.16 fps. Similar situations will of
course prevail for other fluidizing velocities. Concentration traverses

were also made and reported for
positions at either side of the center
line. For such locations the pattern is more complicated, but as
with the data of Fig. 10-8, a substantial concentration was found
below the injection point, indicating that in all instances the gas had
been subjected to substantial back-
mixing.

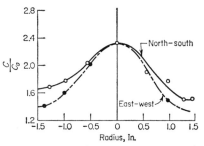

FIG. 10-9. Typical transverse traverses in
two directions. (*Gilliland and Mason.*[4]
*Courtesy of Industrial and Engineering
Chemistry.*)

The question that arises is how
uniform the concentration pattern
is in any one horizontal plane of the
tube. Figure 10-9 is informative
on this point. The figure shows two radial traverses at the same height
above the injection point. The two curves pertain to explorations in
all four quadrants. The following observations are made:

1. The distribution of the helium in the gas rising up the bed is fairly
symmetrical.

2. Helium concentrations near the wall are lower in the east-west
quadrants than in the north-south quadrants. No explanation can be
given for this except, perhaps, that the location of the sampling ports on
one side of the tube may have affected the flow pattern.

3. Over the entire range of the profile $C/C_0 > 1.0$. This is not consistent with the exit-gas analysis for which $C/C_0 \rightarrow 1.0$. An investigation
of the discrepancy indicated that the gas samples taken for analysis were
not truly representative in all cases, because the gas passes through the
bed in the form of bubbles as well as by interstitial motion. Since the
bubbles rise faster than the interstitial gas, the gas bubbles will pick up
relatively less helium from the injection nozzle than the interstitial gas
will. Furthermore, since the sampling tube tends to remove more gas
from between the particles than from the bubbles, the discrepancy is
readily explained. The tendency to form bubbles increases with the

height-to-diameter ratio, and it is therefore reasonable to expect the discrepancy to be worse in relatively high beds. This was actually confirmed.

Half profiles of helium-distribution data pertaining to several levels above and below the injection point are shown in Fig. 10-10. Observations are as follows:

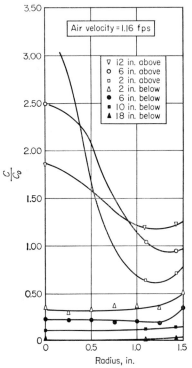

1. For 12 in. above the injection point $C/C_0 > 1.0$. This discrepancy is primarily due to a faulty sampling technique and has just been discussed.

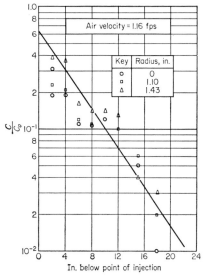

FIG. 10-10. Transverse traverses above and below tracer injection point. (*Gilliland and Mason.*[4] *Courtesy of Industrial and Engineering Chemistry.*)

FIG. 10-11. Correlation of gas back-mixing data of Gilliland and Mason.[4,5] (*Courtesy of Industrial and Engineering Chemistry.*)

2. The traverses pertaining to positions above the injection point show a minimum concentration between the central core and the outside annulus. This is undoubtedly due to the fact that the gas in the central core has a relatively high upward velocity, whereas the gas may actually flow downward between the core and the annulus. The circulation pattern is consistent with that indicated in Fig. 10-7.

3. For traverses below the injection point the concentration distribution is much more uniform than for positions above the injection point. This is to be expected because the solids and gas arriving at the bottom from the top have already undergone a considerable measure of agitation. For levels that are only little below the injection point a somewhat higher helium concentration is still observed nearer the wall than in the center.

This correlates with the minimum observed in the traverse above the injection tube and the down-mixing of the gas observed in this region.

For the purpose of correlation an attempt was made to apply an equation of the type

$$\frac{dn}{d\theta} = E_g \frac{dC}{dZ} \tag{10-8}$$

where n is the quantity transferred per unit area and E_g is an eddy diffusivity. So that Eq. (10-8) may be integrated, it was assumed that once steady-state conditions had been achieved the gas velocity over the bed cross section was uniform and the eddy diffusivity constant all through. This yielded

$$\ln \frac{C}{C_0} = -\frac{u_f}{E_g} Z + b \tag{10-9}$$

or

$$\frac{C}{C_0} = ae^{-(u_f/E_g)Z} \tag{10-10}$$

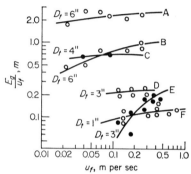

FIG. 10-12. Correlation of Reman[14] between eddy diffusivity of the gas phase and the superficial gas velocity. (A) Air, CO_2, Cr catalyst; (B) air, H_2, Cr catalyst; (C) air, CO_2, Cr catalyst; (D) air, He, Cr catalyst; (E) air, He, glass beads; (F) air, CO_2, Filtrol. (*Courtesy of Chemistry and Industry, London.*)

In accordance with Eq. (10-10), log (C/C_0) of the data was plotted vs. Z—a plot of this type is shown in Fig. 10-11—and the slope yielded E_g. An attempt to correlate E_g with superficial gas velocity was, however, not very successful.[4] The data of Gilliland and Mason have been compared by Reman[14] with unpublished results obtained by Stemerding. The comparison is shown in Fig. 10-12, where E_g/u_f, termed the "mixing length," has been related to the superficial gas velocity u_f. Observations are as follows:

1. There exists a definite effect of vessel diameter. The data indicate clearly that E_g/u_f increases with u_f.

2. E_g/u_f values are higher for systems which are fluidized with the dense gas.

Since for most of the data of Fig. 10-12 the course of the curves is almost horizontal, it follows that E_g is roughly proportional to the superficial gas velocity. The dependence of E_g on the vessel diameter, obvious from Fig. 10-12, has also been reported by Askins, Hinds, and Künreuther.[1]

Liquid-Solid Systems. The study reported by Wicke and Trawinski[19] was conducted in a 9-cm-diameter column, 25 cm high. A diagram of this equipment is given in Fig. 10-13. The water, fluidizing the beds of glass beads, clay, and plastic granules extending over a range of 0.9 to about 12 mm diameter, entered the column through a packed shallow calming section. Tracer injection tubes of 4 or 6 mm could be extended through the distribution section. As tracer a solution of 3N hydrochloric acid was used. The delivery mouth of the injection tube was flush with the glass beads of the calming section, which were held in place by a screen. The exploratory tube proper carried a pair of electric conducts which could be moved horizontally and vertically to sound out the

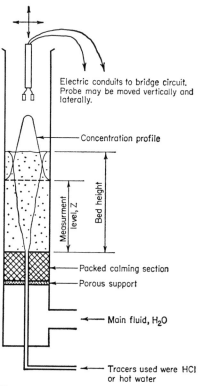

FIG. 10-13. Diagram of experimental unit of Wicke and Trawinski.[19] Column height and diameter were 10 and 3.6 in. (*Courtesy of Chemie-Ingenieur-Technik.*)

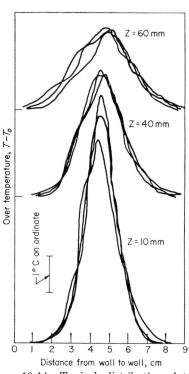

FIG. 10-14. Typical distribution data observed by Wicke and Trawinski[19] for plastic spheres of $D_p = 0.39$ in. with warm water as a tracer. (*Courtesy of Chemie-Ingenieur-Technik.*)

entire bed. Hence the method of operation was simply to permit the hydrochloric acid to mix into the main water stream. Conductivity measurements, both radial and axial, yielded the desired fluid-distribution data. The apparatus could be slightly modified by connecting the injection tube to a source of hot water. The electric contacts were then replaced by a thermocouple, and temperature-distribution data were obtained.

A typical set of data observed with warm-water injection is given in Fig. 10-14. The data pertain to plastic beads of 9.8 mm diameter, packed originally 50 mm high and fluidized with water at a rate of 0.5 liters per sec. Soundings are reported for three separate positions above the tracer inlet. In order to preserve vertical space, the three profiles are somewhat condensed above each other and the respective zero ordinates are indicated in each case. The ordinate is the difference $T - T_0$, where T is the local water temperature of the solution and T_0 is the resulting water temperature when fully mixed. The difference is the equivalent of C/C_0, the concentration ratio employed earlier with gas-distribution studies. A comparison of these traverses with the corresponding gas-mixing traverses as shown in Fig. 10-9 and 10-10 leads to the following observations:

1. Distribution of tracers yields the same type of profiles in both liquid- and gas-fluidized beds.

2. The concentration profiles become steeper as the point of tracer injections is approached.

3. The liquid-solid data do not exhibit the minimum concentration near the tube wall. Hence it may be concluded that in liquid-fluidized beds the liquid does not tend to flow downward near the tube wall. This would also preclude any significant solids downflow, an observation that is readily substantiated by experiment.

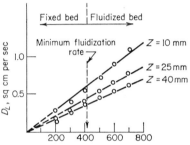

FIG. 10-15. Data of Wicke and Trawinski[19] showing that in liquid-fluidized beds the diffusivity coefficient is linear with the liquid flow rate. Note that there is no discontinuity where the bed begins to fluidize. (*Courtesy of Chemie-Ingenieur-Technik.*)

The data could be successfully correlated by the Gauss distribution function

$$C(r,Z) = k \frac{u_f}{Z} e^{-u_f r^2/4 D_L Z} \qquad (10\text{-}11)$$

where D_L is the liquid diffusivity. Equation (10-11) resulted from an assumption that the distribution of the tracer into the main liquid proceeded according to the differential equation

$$\frac{\partial C}{\partial Z} = \frac{D_L}{u_f} \frac{\partial^2 C}{\partial r^2} \qquad (10\text{-}12)$$

which describes one-dimensional diffusion.

The diffusion coefficient D_L was found to depend on system variables as follows:

1. D_L increases linearly with the superficial gas velocity. This is indicated in Fig. 10-15. It is important to note that the interdependence of

D_L and u_f is not affected by the advent of bed expansion. Hence it may be concluded that the liquid flow pattern in the fluidized bed is essentially the same as in the preceding fixed bed, pertaining to lower flow rates.

2. D_L increases with particle diameter. This is indicated in Fig. 10-16. The average slope of the lines is 0.85. Superficial liquid velocity is merely a parameter.

The above observations yield

$$D_L = 0.33u_fD_p{}^{0.85} \qquad (10\text{-}13)$$

The bases of the units of Eq. (10-13) are feet and hours. Fluidized-bed height and height above tracer injection had little or no effect on D_L,

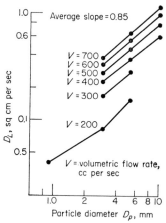

Fig. 10-16. Data of Wicke and Trawinski[19] showing relation between diffusivity coefficient in liquid-fluidized columns and particle diameter. (*Courtesy of Chemie-Ingenieur-Technik.*)

nor was the effect of solid material definitely established. There was good agreement between D_L values obtained from the acid injection and hot-water injection methods.

The study of Hanratty, Latinen, and Wilhelm[7] used a 5.4-cm tube, 25 cm long. It was packed with 3-mm-diameter glass beads. Into the center of the packing-support grid extended a tracer injection tube of ⅛ in. OD and 1/16 in. ID, tapered at one end. The position of the mouth of the injection tube could be adjusted either to be flush with the packing support or to extend as much as 9.2 cm into the packing. As tracer a dilute aqueous solution of methylene blue was used. Provision had been made for removal of liquid probes, and the probes were analyzed electrophotometrically. The main water stream entered the bed through a 12-in.-high calming section packed with small glass beads, similarly to the apparatus of Wicke and Trawinski.[19]

Diffusion measurements were more or less limited to a central portion of the tube in order to exclude the effect of lateral movement of the particles, believed more pronounced at both ends. Radial as well as horizontal traverses along the tube center were made. The Hanratty et al. paper goes extensively into a theoretical discussion of turbulence, and it is pointed out that, in a particulately fluidizing bed operating between extreme voidages ranging from fixed bed to the empty tube, the mixing properties may be defined by the Peclet number, a turbulence intensity, a measure of the lifetime of a turbulent eddy, and a so-called turbulence scale. A plot of the Peclet number $D_p u_f / D_L$ vs. the Reynolds number produced, for a particulately fluidizing bed, a curve that passes through a minimum. This occurs at a fluid mass velocity for which the bed has a voidage of about 70 per cent. This is explained by assuming that the fluid must in its upward course side-step the particles. As the bed expands upward from a fixed-bed voidage, the required fluid path thus increases; hence $D_p u_f / D_L$ decreases with the Reynolds number. Beyond the critical voidage of 70 per cent the turbulence becomes increasingly particle-generated, whereupon D_L is not as dependent on the fluid path as it is on the particle concentration. Hence an increase in the Peclet number with increasing Reynolds number is to be expected beyond the critical voidage.

For cross sections that were substantially above the dye injection point the dye distribution was found to be Gaussian. For lateral positions closer to the origin of the dye the experimental distribution data deviated from the Gauss curve in the extreme radial regions. The distribution data seemed to be of the type reported by Wicke and Trawinski.

Residence Time and Effect on Chemical Reactions. An understanding of fluid residence time in fluidized systems is of fundamental importance in evaluating the effects of fluidization on chemical reactions and physical processes. Some residence-time data are available for gas-fluidized systems,[5] but no such data have so far been reported for liquid-fluidized systems.

Assuming that gas-fluidized systems approach complete internal fluid mixing, Reboux[13] derived an expression for residence time as follows: Let the final concentration of a tracer gas in a bed be equal to C and constant throughout. Flow of the tracer gas is discontinued, but flow of the main gas is continued further; i.e., the system is being purged. The volume of tracer leaving the system in time dt is then $A C u_f \, dt$, where A is the cross section of the flow chamber. The total interstitial gas volume is

$$\epsilon A L$$

The momentary decrease in tracer concentrations due to the tracer leaving the system is then

$$-dC = \frac{ACu_f\,dt}{\epsilon AL} = \frac{Cu_f\,dt}{\epsilon L}$$

Since $\epsilon L/u_f = t_0$, the average residence time,

$$-\frac{dC}{C} = \frac{dt}{t_0}$$

and

$$\frac{C}{C_0} = e^{-t/t_0} \qquad (10\text{-}14)$$

Purge studies of this sort have been reported by Gilliland and Mason.[5] Typical data shown in Fig. 10-17 relate C/C_0 to a quantity $Qt/\epsilon LA$, which equals the number of void volumes of gas passed through the bed. Since the volumetric flow rate $Q = u_f A$, it follows that

$$\frac{Qt}{\epsilon LA} = \frac{t}{t_0} \qquad (10\text{-}15)$$

Hence

$$\frac{C}{C_0} = e^{-Qt/\epsilon LA} \qquad (10\text{-}16)$$

the correlation proposed by Gilliland and Mason.[5]

Figure 10-17 relates the rate of decrease of tracer concentration to the rate of purge gas through the unit. Also shown are data for completely unmixed flow, termed "piston flow," as well as purge data for the case of

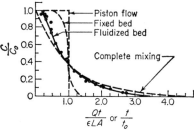

FIG. 10-17. Comparison of fluidized-bed residence times with limiting conditions. (*Data of Gilliland and Mason*[5] *for microspheres.*)

complete mixing. It will be noted that for piston flow the exit-gas concentration remains at a level of $C/C_0 = 1$ until exactly one void volume of gas has been passed through the bed. For the fixed bed the flow is largely of the unmixed type; however, for the gas-fluidized bed the flow pattern is one of almost complete mixing. When the data of Fig. 10-17 are plotted on semilogarithmic coordinates,[5] as shown in Fig. 10-18, an excellent correlation is achieved in accordance with Eqs. (10-14) or (10-16), proposed by Gilliland and Mason[5] and Reboux.[13]

Investigation of effect of height-to-diameter ratio of the bed on residence-time curves disclosed that the curves tend toward piston flow as L/D_t increases. Hence back-mixing is lessened as L/D_t increases. A trend toward piston flow will also develop when, for an equivalent fluidization, the particle size is increased.

The curve for the fluidized-bed data breaks away from $C/C_0 = 1$ at a definite value of $t/t_0 < 1$. This indicates that a portion of the air originally in the bed at the moment that tracer flow was discontinued has reached the outlet of the bed more or less in an undiluted form. For the data of Fig. 10-17 this point occurs at $t/t_0 \approx 0.15$. Hence a portion of the gas passed through the bed at about six times the velocity of the bulk of the gas.

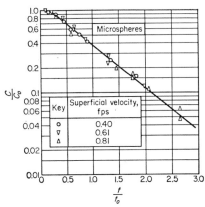

Fig. 10-18. Correlation of residence time. (*Data of Gilliland and Mason.*[5] *Courtesy of Industrial and Engineering Chemistry.*)

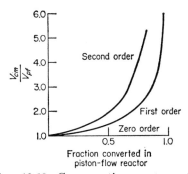

Fig. 10-19. Compensating reactor volumes required because of fluid back-mixing for reactions of zero, first, and second order.[14] (*Courtesy of Chemistry and Industry, London.*)

Residence-time curves of the type discussed have been used by Gilliland and Mason[5] to evaluate the effect of gas back-mixing on reaction rates. When the reaction is of zero order, back-mixing has of course no effect and the fraction of conversion is the same in a completely mixed reactor as it is in completely nonmixed reactor. As the reaction becomes of higher order, the effect of back-mixing and dilution of the reactants by the products of the reaction is increasingly felt. This is indicated in Fig. 10-19, where the ratio V_{cm}/V_{pf} has been plotted vs. fraction converted, for reactions of zero, first, and second order. In the above ratio V_{cm} denotes the volume of a reactor in which the fluid suffers complete mixing, and V_{pf} refers to the volume of a reactor with piston flow. In practice the conditions represented by the curves would be a limiting case for a gas-fluidized bed not quite attained even in very large and well-designed fluid reactors. Nevertheless the curves will give an indication of the additional fluidized-reactor volume required over that of a fixed bed in order to obtain equivalent conversions.

Only a few studies have so far been made with the specific aim of studying reaction courses as they occur in comparable fixed and fluidized beds.[8,9,12] Johnstone, Batchelor, and Shen[8] investigated the oxidation of ammonia in a 4.5-in.-ID tube. The solid was an impregnated cracking catalyst of 120 to 200 mesh. Experiments were made in the same apparatus under both fixed- and fluidized-bed conditions. According to their observations, the investigators distinguished between a conversion rate that pertains to the continuous fluid-solid phase and another rate for the discontinuous bubble phase. For broadening their conclusions and enhancing their findings for the purpose of scale-up, additional experiments with other reactions are suggested. Using essentially the same equipment but letting nitrous oxide decompose catalytically, it was postulated by Johnstone and Shen[9] that the bed was composed of a continuous and a discontinuous phase. In the former the particles are supported by a gas stream which moves through the bed at the same velocity as at minimum fluidization. In the discontinuous phase the gas moves ahead in the form of bubbles or slugs and may actually overtake the gas fraction which travels in the continuous phase. It appeared that under these conditions the reactants must be largely transferred from the bubbles to the continuous phase which participates predominantly in the reaction. Hence a mass-transfer step, aside from reaction, is involved. Regarding fluid velocities, the ratio between incipient two-phase fluidization and the minimum fluidization rate for the entire bed is approximately equal to 1.50 for particles ranging in size from 165 to 200 and 60 to 120 mesh. In a more recent study Mathis and Watson[12] obtained a comparison between fixed- and fluidized-bed catalytic cumene alkylation. The solid was a silica-alumina catalyst. In all instances the fluidized-bed conversions were either equal to or less than conversions that resulted from fixed-bed studies under comparable conditions. Conversions increased as, for the same average fluid rates, L/D increased. Similarly, for the same values of L/D, a reactor-diameter decrease also caused an increase in conversion. It is to be noted that in both instances the tendency is toward more piston flow.

SUMMARY

Solids flow patterns have so far been explored only in equipment of relatively small diameter. With small column diameters, say, up to one or two feet, and several feet of bed height, the solids move principally downward near the wall and upward in the center. This pattern is, however, not strictly coordinated in a vertical direction, and the evidence is that strong horizontal-velocity components exist.

Individual-particle velocities have been determined for a few systems. Particle velocities may vary from a fraction of an inch to one or two feet per second, or more. Of course, the particles do not all move with the same velocity, hence one can only hope to correlate some average particle velocity. A knowledge of such an average particle velocity, if properly combined with direction of particle movement, would be valuable for obtaining representative residence times of solid in through-type fluidized beds. Regarding the study of particle velocities from this point of view, no efforts have so far been reported.

Solids-mixing studies have been made principally in small-diameter equipment. The technique employed a tracer solid, and the results were reported by relating local tracer concentrations to solids feed rate and a solids diffusion coefficient. Solids thus tested were some cracking catalysts, and the resulting diffusion coefficient was found dependent on the fluidization gas velocity. It is probably also dependent on properties of the solid phase such as particle diameter, density, and shape, as well as geometry and design of the flow chamber. However, all these aspects are still entirely unexplored.

Residence time of solids in through-type reactors may vary within wide limits, especially if only one single bed is involved. It was demonstrated that a considerable coordination of flow and a more uniform distribution of individual contact times for particles will result when the single bed is partitioned into a series of smaller beds operated in vertical series. A similar improvement results from the use of baffles.

Fluid mixing has also been explored by the tracer technique. As with solids mixing, the equipment was of small diameters. The results indicated that fluid mixing is greatly dependent on solids mixing and that a study of one entails a study of the other. The interdependence of the two phenomena is also emphasized by the similarity which the resulting correlations display. For both solids and fluid mixing, local concentrations could be presented as an exponential function of solids or fluid velocities and a diffusion coefficient which pertained either to the solids or the gas phase, respectively.

In gas-fluidized systems a considerable amount of back-mixing was observed. This was apparent from examination of reactor strata which were located below the tracer-inlet position. Fluid back-mixing was, however, not observed for low reduced velocities in liquid-fluidized beds. This difference is compatible with the difference in solids flow pattern for the two kinds of systems. Diffusivities for the liquid-fluidized bed, when examined in relation to fluid velocity, disclosed that no sudden change in flow pattern results when a solid-liquid system passes from the fixed bed into the fluidized state. A comparison of concentration profiles in gas- and liquid-fluidized columns indicated that the tracer distribution approached the Gaussian pattern.

The back-mixing of the gas phase has a retarding effect on chemical reactions of order higher than zero. This has been demonstrated for a few reactions. Quantitative relationships are, however, still largely lacking because of the dearth of information on back-mixing and how it is affected by fluid-solids properties and unit geometry.

REFERENCES

1. Askins, J. W., G. P. Hinds, Jr., and F. Künreuther: *Chem. Eng. Progr.*, **47**: 401–404 (1951).
2. Bart, R.: Ph.D. thesis, MIT, Cambridge, 1950.
3. Brötz, W.: *Chem. Ingr. Tech.*, **24**(2): 60–81 (1952).
4. Gilliland, E. R., and E. A. Mason: *Ind. Eng. Chem.*, **41**: 1191 (1949).
5. Gilliland, E. R., and E. A. Mason: *Ind. Eng. Chem.*, **44**: 218 (1952).
6. Handlos, A. E., R. W. Kunstman, and D. D. Schissler: *Ind. Eng. Chem.*, **49**(1): 25–30 (1957).
7. Hanratty, T. J., G. Latinen, and R. H. Wilhelm: *AIChE Journal*, **2**: 372–380 (1956).
8. Johnstone, H. F., J. D. Batchelor, and C. Y. Shen: *AIChE Journal*, **1**: 318–323 (1955).
9. Johnstone, H. F., and C. Y. Shen: *AIChE Journal*, **1**: 349–354 (1955).
10. Leva, Max, and M. Grummer: *Chem. Eng. Progr.*, **48**: 307–313 (1952).
11. Massimilla, L., and S. Bracale: Paper to be published.
12. Mathis, J. F., and C. C. Watson: *AIChE Journal*, **2**: 518–524 (1956).
13. Reboux, P.: "Phénomènes de fluidisation," Association Française de Fluidisation, Paris, 1954.
14. Reman, G. H.: *Chem. & Ind. (London)*, 46–51, Jan. 15, 1955.
15. Sackmann, L. A.: private communication.
16. Singer, E., D. B. Todd, and V. P. Guinn: *Ind. Eng. Chem.*, **49**: 11–19 (1957).
17. Toomey, R. D., and H. F. Johnstone: *Chem. Eng. Progr. Symposium Ser.* 5, **49**: 51–63 (1953).
18. Trawinski, H.: *Chem. Ingr. Tech.*, **17**(18): 416–419 (1951).
19. Wicke, E., and H. Trawinski: *Chem. Ingr. Tech.*, **25**(3): 114–124 (1953).
20. Wilhelm, R. H., and M. Kwauk: *Chem. Eng. Progr.*, **44**: 201–218 (1948).

APPENDIX

Length:
  1 ft = 12 in. = 30.48 cm = 304,800 microns
Area:
  1 sq ft = 144 sq in. = 929.03 sq cm = 0.092903 sq m
Volume:
  1 cu ft = 1,728 cu in. = 7.481 gal = 28.32 liters
Weight:
  1 lb = 16 oz = 7,000 grains = 453.6 g
Density:
  1 lb per cu ft = 0.1336 lb per gal = 0.01602 g per cu cm
Mass velocity:
  1 lb/(hr)(sq ft) = 1.355×10^{-3} kg/(sec)(sq m)
Viscosity:
  1 centipoise = 0.01 g/(sec)(cm) = 0.000672 lb/(sec)(ft) = 2.42 lb/(hr)(ft) = 3.60 kg/(hr)(m)
Pressure:
  1 psi = 27.684 in. H_2O = 6.804×10^{-2} atm = 7.03×10^{-2} kg per sq cm
Energy:
  1 Btu = 778.3 ft-lb = 1.055 joules = 0.2520 kg-cal
Specific heat:
  1 Btu/(lb)(°F) = 1.0 pcu/(lb)(°C) = 416.67 joules/(kg)(°C) = 110.78 gm-cal/(g)(°C)
Thermal conductivity:
  1 Btu/(hr)(sq ft)(°F)/(ft) = 1.730 joules/(sec)(sq m)(°C)/m = 0.004134 gm-cal/(sec)(sq m)(°C)/(m)
Heat-transfer coefficient:
  1 Btu/(hr)(sq ft)(°F) = 5.68 joules/(sec)(sq m)(°C) = 0.0001355 gm-cal/(sec)(sq cm)(°C)

TABLE A-2. THERMAL CONDUCTIVITIES OF GASES AND VAPORS*

$$[k = \text{Btu}/(\text{hr})(\text{sq ft})(\text{deg F per ft})]$$

The extreme temperature values given constitute the experimental range. For extrapolation to other temperatures, it is suggested that the data given be plotted as log k vs. log T or that use be made of the assumption that the ratio $c_p\mu/k$ is practically independent of temperature (or of pressure, within moderate limits).

Substance	Deg F	k	Substance	Deg F	k
Acetone (ref. 10)[a]	32	0.0057	Chloroform (ref. 10)[a]	32	0.0038
	115	0.0074		115	0.0046
	212	0.0099		212	0.0058
	363	0.0147		363	0.0077
Acetylene (ref. 3)[a]	−103	0.0068	Cyclohexane	216	0.0095
	32	0.0108			
	122	0.0140	Dichlorodifluoromethane	32	0.0048
	212	0.0172		122	0.0064
Air (ref. 7)	−328	0.0040		212	0.0080
	−148	0.0091		302	0.0097
	32	0.0140			
	212	0.0184	Ethane (ref. 1, 3)	−94	0.0066
	392	0.0224		−29	0.0086
	572	0.0260		32	0.0106
Ammonia (ref. 7)	−58	0.0097		212	0.0175
	32	0.0126	Ethyl acetate (ref. 10)[a]	115	0.0072
	212	0.0192		212	0.0096
	392	0.0280		363	0.0141
	572	0.0385	Ethyl alcohol (ref. 10)[a]	68	0.0089
	752	0.0509		212	0.0124
Argon (ref. 7)	−148	0.0063	Ethyl chloride (ref. 10)[a]	32	0.0055
	32	0.0095		212	0.0095
	212	0.0123		363	0.0135
	392	0.0148		413	0.0152
	572	0.0171	Ether (ref. 10)[a]	32	0.0077
Benzene (ref. 10)[a]	32	0.0052		115	0.0099
	115	0.0073		212	0.0131
	212	0.0103		363	0.0189
	363	0.0152		413	0.0209
	413	0.0176	Ethylene (ref. 3)[a]	−96	0.0064
Butane (n-) (ref. 9)	32	0.0078		32	0.0101
	212	0.0135		122	0.0131
(iso-) (ref. 9)	32	0.0080		212	0.0161
	212	0.0139			
			Helium (ref. 7)	−328	0.0338
Carbon dioxide (ref. 7)	−58	0.0064		−148	0.0612
	32	0.0084		32	0.0818
	212	0.0128		212	0.0988
	392	0.0177	Heptane (n-) (ref. 10)[a]	212	0.0103
	572	0.0229		392	0.0112
Carbon disulfide (ref. 3)[a]	32	0.0040	Hexane (n-) (ref. 9)	32	0.0072
	45	0.0042		68	0.0080
Carbon monoxide (ref. 7)	−328	0.0037	Hexene (ref. 10)[a]	32	0.0061
	−148	0.0088		212	0.0109
	32	0.0134	Hydrogen (ref. 7)	−328	0.0293
	212	0.0176		−148	0.0652
Carbon tetrachloride (ref. 10)[a]	115	0.0041		32	0.0966
	212	0.0052		212	0.1240
	363	0.0065		392	0.1484
Chlorine (ref. 5)	32	0.0043		572	0.1705

* From W. H. McAdams, "Heat Transmission," 3d ed., McGraw-Hill Book Company, Inc., New York, 1954.

Substance	Deg F	k	Substance	Deg F	k
Hydrogen and carbon dioxide (ref. 4)[a]	32		Neon	32	0.00256
0% H$_2$	....	0.0083	Nitric oxide (ref. 7)	−148	0.0089
20%	....	0.0165		32	0.0138
40%	....	0.0270		122	0.0161
60%	....	0.0410	Nitrogen (ref. 7)	−328	0.0040
80%	....	0.0620		−148	0.0091
100%	....	0.10		32	0.0139
Hydrogen and nitrogen (ref. 4)..	32			212	0.0181
0% H$_2$	....	0.0133		392	0.0220
20%	....	0.0212		572	0.0255
40%	....	0.0313		752	0.0287
60%	....	0.0438	Nitrogen and carbon dioxide		
80%	....	0.0635	(ref. 8)	122	
Hydrogen and nitrous oxide (ref. 4)	32		0% N$_2$	....	0.0105
0% H$_2$	....	0.0092	34.06%	....	0.0121
20%	....	0.0170	52.88%	....	0.0130
40%	....	0.0270	66.50%	....	0.0137
60%	....	0.0410	100%	....	0.0161
80%	....	0.0650	Nitrous oxide (ref. 7)	−148	0.0047
Hydrogen sulfide (ref. 3)[a]	32	0.0076		32	0.0088
				212	0.0138
Mercury (ref. 5)	392	0.0197	Oxygen (ref. 7)	−328	0.0038
Methane (ref. 7)	−328	0.0045		−148	0.0091
	−148	0.0109		32	0.0142
	32	0.0176		122	0.0166
	212	0.0255		212	0.0188
	392	0.0358	Pentane (*n*-) (ref. 10)[a]	32	0.0074
	572	0.0490		68	0.0083
Methyl acetate (ref. 10)[a]	32	0.0059	(iso-) (ref. 10)[a]	32	0.0072
	68	0.0068		212	0.0127
Alcohol (ref. 10)[a]	32	0.0083	Propane (ref. 9)	32	0.0087
	212	0.0128		212	0.0151
Chloride (ref. 10)[a]	32	0.0053			
	115	0.0072	Sulfur dioxide (ref. 2)	32	0.0050
	212	0.0094		212	0.0069
	363	0.0130			
	413	0.0148	Water vapor, zero pressure (ref.	212	0.0136
Methylene chloride (ref. 10)[a]	32	0.0039	7)[b]	392	0.0182
	115	0.0049		572	0.0230
	212	0.0063		752	0.0279
	413	0.0095		932	0.0328

[a] Data from Eucken[3] and Moser[10] are measurements relative to air. Data in this table from these sources are based on the thermal conductivity of air at 32°F of 0.0140 Btu/(hr)(sq ft)(deg F per ft).

[b] For saturated water vapor (ref. 6):

lb/sq in. abs	250	500	1000	1500	1750	2000
Deg F	401	467	545	596	617	636
k	0.0212	0.0250	0.0316	0.0380	0.0412	0.0445

(*Table references on next page*)

References:

1. T. H. Chilton and R. P. Genereaux, personal communication, 1946.
2. B. G. Dickens, *Proc. Roy. Soc. (London)*, **A143,** 517 (1934).
3. A. Eucken, *Physik. Z.,* **12,** 1101 (1911), **14,** 324 (1913).
4. T. L. Ibbs and A. A. Hirst, *Proc. Roy. Soc. (London)*, **A123,** 134 (1929).
5. "International Critical Tables," McGraw-Hill, New York, 1929.
6. J. H. Keenan and F. G. Keyes, "Thermodynamic Properties of Steam," Wiley, New York, 1950 (22d impression).
7. F. G. Keyes, *Tech. Rept.* 37, Project Squid (Apr. 1, 1952).
8. F. G. Keyes, *Trans. ASME*, **74,** 1303 (1952).
9. W. B. Mann and B. G. Dickens, *Proc. Roy. Soc. (London)*, **A134,** 77 (1931).
10. Moser, Dissertation, Berlin, 1913.
11. L. S. Marks and T. Baumeister, "Mechanical Engineers' Handbook," 6th ed., McGraw-Hill, New York, 1958.

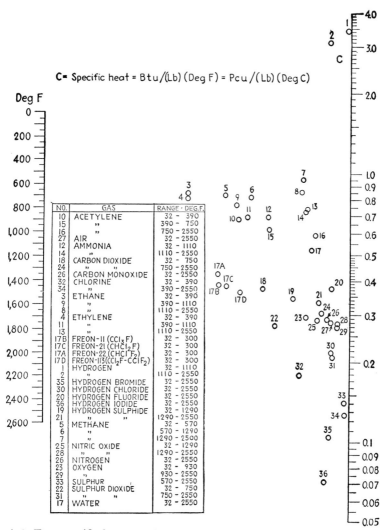

F⁢ɪɢ. A-1. True specific heats c_p of gases and vapors at 1 atm pressure. (*Chilton, Colburn, and Vernon, personal communication, based mainly on data from "International Critical Tables." From W. H. McAdams, "Heat Transmission," 3d ed., McGraw-Hill Book Company, Inc., New York, 1954.*)

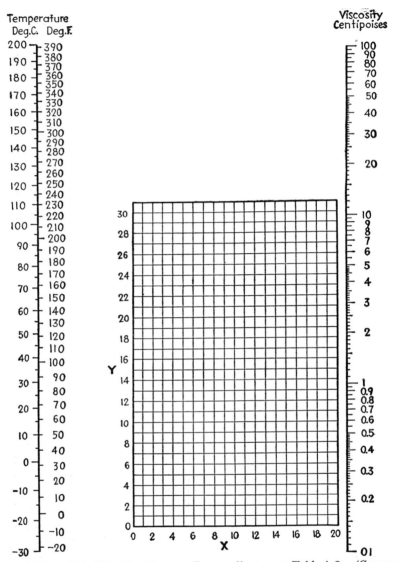

FIG. A-2. Viscosities of liquids at 1 atm. For coordinates, see Table A-3. (*Genereaux, personal communication. From W. H. McAdams, "Heat Transmission," 3d ed., McGraw-Hill Book Company, Inc., New York, 1954.*)

Table A-3. Viscosities of Liquids*
(Coordinates for Fig. A-2)

No.	Liquid	X	Y	No.	Liquid	X	Y
1	Acetaldehyde	15.2	4.8	56	Freon-22	17.2	4.7
2	Acetic acid, 100%	12.1	14.2	57	Freon-113	12.5	11.4
3	Acetic acid, 70%	9.5	17.0	58	Glycerol, 100%	2.0	30.0
4	Acetic anhydride	12.7	12.8	59	Glycerol, 50%	6.9	19.6
5	Acetone, 100%	14.5	7.2	60	Heptane	14.1	8.4
6	Acetone, 35%	7.9	15.0	61	Hexane	14.7	7.0
7	Allyl alcohol	10.2	14.3	62	Hydrochloric acid, 31.5%	13.0	16.6
8	Ammonia, 100%	12.6	2.0	63	Isobutyl alcohol	7.1	18.0
9	Ammonia, 26%	10.1	13.9	64	Isobutyric acid	12.2	14.4
10	Amyl acetate	11.8	12.5	65	Isopropyl alcohol	8.2	16.0
11	Amyl alcohol	7.5	18.4	66	Kerosene	10.2	16.9
12	Aniline	8.1	18.7	67	Linseed oil, raw	7.5	27.2
13	Anisole	12.3	13.5	68	Mercury	18.4	16.4
14	Arsenic trichloride	13.9	14.5	69	Methanol, 100%	12.4	10.5
15	Benzene	12.5	10.9	70	Methanol, 90%	12.3	11.8
16	Brine, CaCl₂, 25%	6.6	15.9	71	Methanol, 40%	7.8	15.5
17	Brine, NaCl, 25%	10.2	16.6	72	Methyl acetate	14.2	8.2
18	Bromine	14.2	13.2	73	Methyl chloride	15.0	3.8
19	Bromotoluene	20.0	15.9	74	Methyl ethyl ketone	13.9	8.6
20	Butyl acetate	12.3	11.0	75	Naphthalene	7.9	18.1
21	Butyl alcohol	8.6	17.2	76	Nitric acid, 95%	12.8	13.8
22	Butyric acid	12.1	15.3	77	Nitric acid, 60%	10.8	17.0
23	Carbon dioxide	11.6	0.3	78	Nitrobenzene	10.6	16.2
24	Carbon disulphide	16.1	7.5	79	Nitrotoluene	11.0	17.0
25	Carbon tetrachloride	12.7	13.1	80	Octane	13.7	10.0
26	Chlorobenzene	12.3	12.4	81	Octyl alcohol	6.6	21.1
27	Chloroform	14.4	10.2	82	Pentachloroethane	10.9	17.3
28	Chlorosulfonic acid	11.2	18.1	83	Pentane	14.9	5.2
29	Chlorotoluene, ortho	13.0	13.3	84	Phenol	6.9	20.8
30	Chlorotoluene, meta	13.3	12.5	85	Phosphorus tribromide	13.8	16.7
31	Chlorotoluene, para	13.3	12.5	86	Phosphorus trichloride	16.2	10.9
32	Cresol, meta	2.5	20.8	87	Propionic acid	12.8	13.8
33	Cyclohexanol	2.9	24.3	88	Propyl alcohol	9.1	16.5
34	Dibromoethane	12.7	15.8	89	Propyl bromide	14.5	9.6
35	Dichloroethane	13.2	12.2	90	Propyl chloride	14.4	7.5
36	Dichloromethane	14.6	8.9	91	Propyl iodide	14.1	11.6
37	Diethyl oxalate	11.0	16.4	92	Sodium	16.4	13.9
38	Dimethyl oxalate	12.3	15.8	93	Sodium hydroxide, 50%	3.2	25.8
39	Diphenyl	12.0	18.3	94	Stannic chloride	13.5	12.8
40	Dipropyl oxalate	10.3	17.7	95	Sulphur dioxide	15.2	7.1
41	Ethyl acetate	13.7	9.1	96	Sulphuric acid, 110%	7.2	27.4
42	Ethyl alcohol, 100%	10.5	13.8	97	Sulphuric acid, 98%	7.0	24.8
43	Ethyl alcohol, 95%	9.8	14.3	98	Sulphuric acid, 60%	10.2	21.3
44	Ethyl alcohol, 40%	6.5	16.6	99	Sulphuryl chloride	15.2	12.4
45	Ethyl benzene	13.2	11.5	100	Tetrachloroethane	11.9	15.7
46	Ethyl bromide	14.5	8.1	101	Tetrachloroethylene	14.2	12.7
47	Ethyl chloride	14.8	6.0	102	Titanium tetrachloride	14.4	12.3
48	Ethyl ether	14.5	5.3	103	Toluene	13.7	10.4
49	Ethyl formate	14.2	8.4	104	Trichloroethylene	14.8	10.5
50	Ethyl iodide	14.7	10.3	105	Turpentine	11.5	14.9
51	Ethylene glycol	6.0	23.6	106	Vinyl acetate	14.0	8.8
52	Formic acid	10.7	15.8	107	Water	10.2	13.0
53	Freon-11	14.4	9.0	108	Xylene, ortho	13.5	12.1
54	Freon-12	16.8	5.6	109	Xylene, meta	13.9	10.6
55	Freon-21	15.7	7.5	110	Xylene, para	13.9	10.9

* From J. H. Perry, "Chemical Engineers' Handbook," 3d ed., McGraw-Hill, New York, 1950.

No.	Gas	X	Y	No.	Gas	X	Y
1	Acetic acid	7.7	14.3	29	Freon-113	11.3	14.0
2	Acetone	8.9	13.0	30	Helium	10.9	20.5
3	Acetylene	9.8	14.9	31	Hexane	8.6	11.8
4	Air	11.0	20.0	32	Hydrogen	11.2	12.4
5	Ammonia	8.4	16.0	33	$3H_2 + 1N_2$	11.2	17.2
6	Argon	10.5	22.4	34	Hydrogen bromide	8.8	20.9
7	Benzene	8.5	13.2	35	Hydrogen chloride	8.8	18.7
8	Bromine	8.9	19.2	36	Hydrogen cyanide	9.8	14.9
9	Butene	9.2	13.7	37	Hydrogen iodide	9.0	21.3
10	Butylene	8.9	13.0	38	Hydrogen sulfide	8.6	18.0
11	Carbon dioxide	9.5	18.7	39	Iodine	9.0	18.4
12	Carbon disulfide	8.0	16.0	40	Mercury	5.3	22.9
13	Carbon monoxide	11.0	20.0	41	Methane	9.9	15.5
14	Chlorine	9.0	18.4	42	Methyl alcohol	8.5	15.6
15	Chloroform	8.9	15.7	43	Nitric oxide	10.9	20.5
16	Cyanogen	9.2	15.2	44	Nitrogen	10.6	20.0
17	Cyclohexane	9.2	12.0	45	Nitrosyl chloride	8.0	17.6
18	Ethane	9.1	14.5	46	Nitrous oxide	8.8	19.0
19	Ethyl acetate	8.5	13.2	47	Oxygen	11.0	21.3
20	Ethyl alcohol	9.2	14.2	48	Pentane	7.0	12.8
21	Ethyl chloride	8.5	15.6	49	Propane	9.7	12.9
22	Ethyl ether	8.9	13.0	50	Propyl alcohol	8.4	13.4
23	Ethylene	9.5	15.1	51	Propylene	9.0	13.8
24	Fluorine	7.3	23.8	52	Sulfur dioxide	9.6	17.0
25	Freon-11	10.6	15.1	53	Toluene	8.6	12.4
26	Freon-12	11.1	16.0	54	2,3,3-trimethylbutane	9.5	10.5
27	Freon-21	10.8	15.3	55	Water	8.0	16.0
28	Freon-22	10.1	17.0	56	Xenon	9.3	23.0

*From J. H. Perry, "Chemical Engineers' Handbook," 3d ed., McGraw-Hill, New York, 1950.

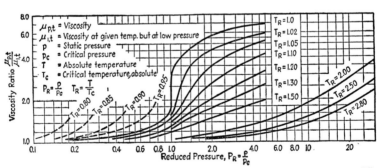

FIG. A-3. Effect of pressure on viscosities of gases at several temperatures. [*Comings and Egly, Ind. Eng. Chem.*, **32**, 714–718 (1940). *From W. H. McAdams, "Heat Transmission,"* 3d ed., *McGraw-Hill Book Company, Inc., New York, 1954.*]

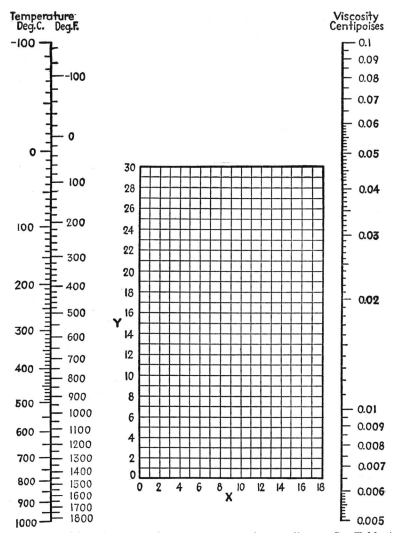

FIG. A-4. Viscosities of gases and vapors at 1 atm; for coordinates, See Table A-4. (*Genereaux, personal communication. From W. H. McAdams, "Heat Transmission," 3d ed., McGraw-Hill Book Company, Inc., New York, 1954.*)

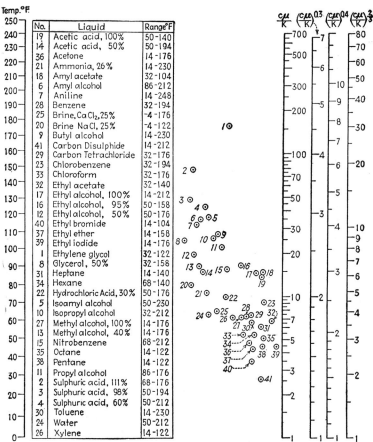

No.	Liquid	Range°F
19	Acetic acid, 100%	50-140
14	Acetic acid, 50%	50-194
36	Acetone	14-176
21	Ammonia, 26%	14-230
18	Amyl acetate	32-104
6	Amyl alcohol	86-212
7	Aniline	14-248
28	Benzene	32-194
25	Brine, CaCl$_2$, 25%	-4-176
20	Brine NaCl, 25%	-4-122
9	Butyl alcohol	14-230
41	Carbon Disulphide	14-212
29	Carbon Tetrachloride	32-176
23	Chlorobenzene	32-194
33	Chloroform	32-176
32	Ethyl acetate	32-140
17	Ethyl alcohol, 100%	14-212
16	Ethyl alcohol, 95%	50-158
12	Ethyl alcohol, 50%	50-176
40	Ethyl bromide	14-104
37	Ethyl ether	14-158
39	Ethyl iodide	14-176
1	Ethylene glycol	32-122
8	Glycerol, 50%	32-158
31	Heptane	14-140
34	Hexane	68-140
22	Hydrochloric Acid, 30%	50-176
5	Isoamyl alcohol	50-230
10	Isopropyl alcohol	32-212
27	Methyl alcohol, 100%	14-176
13	Methyl alcohol, 40%	14-176
15	Nitrobenzene	68-212
35	Octane	14-122
38	Pentane	14-122
11	Propyl alcohol	86-176
2	Sulphuric acid, 111%	68-176
3	Sulphuric acid, 98%	50-194
4	Sulphuric acid, 60%	50-212
30	Toluene	14-230
24	Water	50-212
26	Xylene	14-122

FIG. A-5. Prandtl numbers $c\mu/k$ for liquids. (*Chilton, Colburn, and Vernon, personal communication, based mainly on data from "International Critical Tables."*) NOTE: To obtain $c\mu/k$ at a specified temperature for a given liquid, as usual a straight line is drawn from the specified temperature through the numbered point for the liquid to the $c\mu/k$ scale; to obtain $c\mu/k$ raised to one of the three fractional powers shown, a *horizontal* alignment is made from the $c\mu/k$ scale. (*From W. H. McAdams, "Heat Transmission," 3d ed., McGraw-Hill Book Company, New York, 1954.*)

TABLE A-5. PRANDTL NUMBERS $c_F\mu/k$ AND OTHER PROPERTIES FOR GASES AND VAPORS AT 1 ATM*

Gas or vapor	$c_F\mu/k$	k, Btu/(hr)(sq ft)(°F)/(ft)	μ, centipoises	Temp, °F
Air.....................	0.69	......	......	212
Air.....................	0.71	......	0.0185	77
Ammonia................	0.86	......	......	212
Argon..................	0.66	......	......	212
Argon..................	0.67	0.0101	0.0223	77
Carbon dioxide..........	0.75	......	......	212
Helium.................	0.71	......	......	212
Methane................	0.75	......	......	212
Nitric oxide.............	0.72	......	......	212
Nitrogen, oxygen.........	0.70	......	......	212
Steam (low pressure)......	1.06	......	......	212
98% H_2 + 2% N_2.......	0.59	0.1021	0.0093	77
80% H_2 + 20% N_2.......	0.44	0.0691	0.0131	77
65% H_2 + 35% N_2.......	0.43	0.0520	0.0149	77
45% H_2 + 55% N_2.......	0.45	0.0370	0.0164	77
25% H_2 + 75% N_2.......	0.53	0.0254	0.0171	77

* Data from W. H. McAdams, "Heat Transmission," 3d ed., McGraw-Hill Book Company, Inc., and van Heerden et al., *Chem. Eng. Sci.*, **1**(2): 51–66 (1951).

Outside diameter, in.	Size number, BWG	Wt per ft, lb[b]	Thickness, in.	Inside diameter, in.	Surface, sq ft per ft of length		Inside sectional area, sq in.	Velocity, ft/sec for 1 U.S. gal/min	Capacity at 1 ft/sec velocity	
					Outside	Inside			U.S. gal/min	Lb water/hr
½	12	0.493	0.109	0.282	0.1309	0.0748	0.0624	5.142	0.1945	97.25
	14	0.403	0.083	0.334	0.1309	0.0874	0.0876	3.662	0.2730	136.5
	16	0.329	0.065	0.370	0.1309	0.0969	0.1076	2.981	0.3352	167.5
	18	0.258	0.049	0.402	0.1309	0.1052	0.1269	2.530	0.3952	197.6
	20	0.190	0.035	0.430	0.1309	0.1125	0.1452	2.209	0.4528	226.4
⅝	12	0.656	0.109	0.407	0.1636	0.1066	0.1301	2.468	0.4053	202.7
	14	0.526	0.083	0.459	0.1636	0.1202	0.1655	1.939	0.5157	258.9
	16	0.424	0.065	0.495	0.1636	0.1296	0.1925	1.667	0.5999	300.0
	18	0.329	0.049	0.527	0.1636	0.1380	0.2181	1.472	0.6793	339.7
	20	0.241	0.035	0.555	0.1636	0.1453	0.2420	1.326	0.7542	377.1
¾	10	0.962	0.134	0.482	0.1963	0.1262	0.1825	1.758	0.5688	284.4
	12	0.812	0.109	0.532	0.1963	0.1393	0.2223	1.442	0.6935	346.8
	14	0.644	0.083	0.584	0.1963	0.1528	0.2678	1.198	0.8347	417.4
	16	0.518	0.065	0.620	0.1963	0.1623	0.3019	1.063	0.9407	470.4
	18	0.400	0.049	0.652	0.1963	0.1706	0.3339	0.9611	1.041	520.5
⅞	10	1.16	0.134	0.607	0.2291	0.1589	0.2893	1.108	0.9025	451.3
	12	0.992	0.109	0.657	0.2291	0.1720	0.3390	0.9465	1.057	528.5
	14	0.769	0.083	0.709	0.2291	0.1856	0.3949	0.8126	1.230	615.0
	16	0.613	0.065	0.745	0.2291	0.1951	0.4360	0.7360	1.358	679.0
	18	0.472	0.049	0.777	0.2291	0.2034	0.4740	0.6770	1.477	738.5
1	10	1.35	0.134	0.732	0.2618	0.1916	0.4208	0.7626	1.311	655.5
	12	1.14	0.109	0.782	0.2618	0.2048	0.4803	0.6681	1.497	748.5
	14	0.887	0.083	0.834	0.2618	0.2183	0.5463	0.5874	1.702	851.0
	16	0.708	0.065	0.870	0.2618	0.2277	0.5945	0.5398	1.852	926.0
	18	0.535	0.049	0.902	0.2618	0.2361	0.6390	0.5022	1.991	995.5
1¼	10	1.74	0.134	0.982	0.3271	0.2572	0.7575	0.4236	2.362	1181
	12	1.45	0.109	1.032	0.3271	0.2701	0.8369	0.3834	2.608	1304
	14	1.13	0.083	1.084	0.3271	0.2839	0.9229	0.3477	2.877	1439
	16	0.898	0.065	1.120	0.3271	0.2932	0.9852	0.3257	3.070	1535
	18	0.675	0.049	1.152	0.3271	0.3015	1.043	0.3075	3.253	1627
1½	10	2.12	0.134	1.232	0.3925	0.3227	1.193	0.2688	3.720	1860
	12	1.76	0.109	1.282	0.3925	0.3355	1.292	0.2482	4.030	2015
	14	1.36	0.083	1.334	0.3925	0.3491	1.398	0.2292	4.362	2181
	16	1.09	0.065	1.370	0.3925	0.3585	1.473	0.2180	4.587	2294
2	10	2.94	0.134	1.732	0.5233	0.4534	2.355	0.1362	7.342	3671
	12	2.40	0.109	1.782	0.5233	0.4665	2.494	0.1287	7.770	3885
	14	1.85	0.083	1.834	0.5233	0.4803	2.643	0.1213	8.244	4122
	16	1.47	0.065	1.870	0.5233	0.4896	2.747	0.1168	8.562	4281

[a] Prepared by T. B. Drew.

[b] In brass, specific gravity = 8.56; specific gravity of steel = 7.8.

[*] From W. H. McAdams, "Heat Transmission," 3d ed., McGraw-Hill Book Company, Inc., New York, 1954.

TABLE A-7. STANDARD DIMENSIONS FOR STANDARD-WEIGHT WROUGHT-IRON PIPE (Crane Company)*

Nominal size, in.	Nominal size, mm	Actual diameters		Nominal thickness, in.	Circumference		Transverse areas			Length of pipe per sq ft		Length of pipe containing 1 cu ft, ft	Nominal weight, lb/ft		Number of threads per in. of screw
		External, in.	Approximate internal, in.		External, in.	Internal, in.	External, sq in.	Internal, sq in.	Metal	External surface, ft	Internal surface, ft		Plain ends	Threaded and coupled	
⅛	3	0.405	0.269	0.068	1.272	0.845	0.129	0.057	0.072	9.431	14.199	2533.775	0.244	0.245	27
¼	6	0.540	0.364	0.088	1.696	1.144	0.229	0.104	0.125	7.073	10.493	1383.789	0.424	0.425	18
⅜	10	0.675	0.493	0.091	2.121	1.549	0.358	0.191	0.167	5.658	7.747	754.360	0.567	0.568	18
½	13	0.840	0.622	0.109	2.639	1.954	0.554	0.304	0.250	4.547	6.141	473.906	0.850	0.852	14
¾	19	1.050	0.824	0.113	3.299	2.589	0.866	0.533	0.333	3.637	4.635	270.034	1.130	1.134	14
1	25	1.315	1.049	0.133	4.131	3.296	1.358	0.864	0.494	2.904	3.641	166.618	1.678	1.684	11½
1¼	32	1.660	1.380	0.140	5.215	4.335	2.164	1.495	0.669	2.301	2.767	96.275	2.272	2.281	11½
1½	38	1.900	1.610	0.145	5.969	5.058	2.835	2.036	0.799	2.010	2.372	70.733	2.717	2.731	11½
2	50	2.375	2.067	0.154	7.461	6.494	4.430	3.355	1.075	1.608	1.847	42.913	3.652	3.678	11½
2½	64	2.875	2.469	0.203	9.032	7.757	6.492	4.788	1.704	1.328	1.547	30.077	5.793	5.819	8
3	76	3.500	3.068	0.216	10.996	9.638	9.621	7.393	2.228	1.091	1.245	19.479	7.575	7.616	8
3½	90	4.000	3.548	0.226	12.566	11.146	12.566	9.886	2.680	0.954	1.076	14.565	9.109	9.202	8
4	100	4.500	4.026	0.237	14.137	12.648	15.904	12.730	3.174	0.848	0.948	11.312	10.790	10.889	8
4½	113	5.000	4.506	0.247	15.708	14.156	19.635	15.947	3.688	0.763	0.847	9.030	12.538	12.642	8
5	125	5.563	5.047	0.258	17.477	15.856	24.306	20.006	4.300	0.686	0.756	7.198	14.617	14.810	8
6	150	6.625	6.065	0.280	20.813	19.054	34.472	28.891	5.581	0.576	0.629	4.984	18.974	19.185	8
7	175	7.625	7.023	0.301	23.955	22.063	45.664	38.738	6.926	0.500	0.543	3.717	23.544	23.769	8
8	200	8.625	8.071	0.277	27.096	25.356	58.426	51.161	7.265	0.442	0.473	2.815	24.696	25.000	8
8	200	8.625	7.891	0.322	27.096	25.073	58.426	50.027	8.399	0.442	0.478	2.878	28.554	28.809	8
9	225	9.625	8.941	0.342	30.238	28.089	72.760	62.786	9.974	0.396	0.427	2.294	33.907	34.188	8
10	250	10.750	10.192	0.279	33.772	32.019	90.763	81.585	9.178	0.355	0.374	1.765	31.201	32.000	8
10	250	10.750	10.136	0.307	33.772	31.843	90.763	80.691	10.072	0.355	0.376	1.785	34.240	35.000	8
10	250	10.750	10.020	0.365	33.772	31.479	90.763	78.855	11.908	0.355	0.381	1.826	40.483	41.132	8
11	275	11.750	11.000	0.375	36.914	34.558	108.434	95.033	13.401	0.325	0.347	1.515	45.557	46.247	8
12	300	12.750	12.090	0.330	40.055	37.982	127.676	114.800	12.876	0.299	0.315	1.254	43.773	45.000	8
12	300	12.750	12.000	0.375	40.055	37.699	127.676	113.097	14.579	0.299	0.318	1.273	49.562	50.706	8

* From W. H. McAdams, "Heat Transmission," 3d ed., McGraw-Hill Book Company, Inc., New York, 1954.

Solids	Density, lb/cu ft	Specific heat, Btu/(lb)(°F)	Temp, °F
Alumina (fused), refractory.............	153–181	0.20	60–1200
Aluminum (Al).......................	166.7	0.225	61–579
Aluminum oxide (alumina)..............	243.5	0.183	32–212
Andalusite (Al₂SiO₅)...................	199.8	0.228	
Antimony (Sb).......................	422	0.052	392
Arsenic, gray........................	358	0.0822	32–212
Asbestos (insulation)..................	124–174	0.20	32–212
Ashes...............................	....	0.20	32–212
Asphalt:			
Bermudez.........................	67.4	0.55	
Gilsonite..........................	64.9	0.55	
Trinidad..........................	87.4	0.55	
Babbitt metal:			
Lead base.........................	....	0.039	60–462
Tin base..........................	465	0.071	60–464
Beeswax............................	59.9	0.82	60–144
Benzoic acid (C₇H₆O₂).................	81.2	0.287	60
Beryllium (Be).......................	113.6	0.52	
Bismuth (Bi)........................	612	0.0302	68–212
Boron (B)..........................	152	0.307	32–212
Borax (Na₂B₄O₇·10H₂O)...............	107	0.385	95
Brass:			
Muntz metal (60% Cu, 40% Zn)......	524	0.105	60–1630
Red (85% Cu, 15% Zn).............	546	0.104	60–1952
Yellow (67% Cu, 33% Zn)...........	528	0.105	60–1688
Brick, red..........................	118	0.22	32–212
Cadmium (Cd).......................	540	0.057	212
Calcium (Ca)........................	96.6	0.170	32–358
Calcium carbonate (CaCO₃).............	168–184	0.210	32–212
Calcium chloride (CaCl₂)..............	134	0.292	60
Camphor (C₁₀H₆O)...................	62.4	0.44	68–353
Carbon (C), graphite..................	138	0.160	52–1789
Cellulose............................	95	0.32	32–212
Chalk...............................	....	0.215	32–212
Charcoal............................	(18–38)	0.165–0.25	75
Chromite (chrome ore, FeCr₂O₄).........	281	0.22	
Chromium (Cr).......................	449	0.187	1112
Cinders.............................	....	0.18	32–212
Clay................................	112–162	0.224	68–208
Cobalt (Co).........................	556	0.204	1832
Coke................................	....	0.376	100–2200
Concrete............................	137	0.156–0.27	32–212
Constantan..........................	....	0.098	32–212

* Data from North American Mfg. Co.'s "Combustion Handbook."

Solids	Density, lb/cu ft	Specific heat, Btu/(lb)(°F)	Temp, °F
Copper (Cu).........................	559	0.1259	1652
Cork:			
Natural (insulation).................	15	0.419	77
Granulated.........................	(5.4–7.3)	0.43	77
Corundum (Al₂O₃)....................	250	0.198	42–208
Cupric oxide (CuO)...................	374–405	0.227	68–212
Cuprous oxide (Cu₂O).................	375	0.111	32–212
Diatomaceous earth...................	(12.5–25)	0.21	77
Dolomite............................	181	0.222	68–208
Earth (humus).......................	....	0.44	32–212
Ebonite.............................	....	0.33	32–212
Fiberglas board......................	2–6	0.236	111
Firebrick:			
Fire clay...........................	137–150	0.243	60–2195
Insulating (2600°F).................	38.4	0.22	60–1200
Silica..............................	144–162	0.258	60–2195
Fosterite, refractory..................	153	0.25	60–1200
Galena (PbS)........................	467	0.0466	32–212
Glass...............................	144–187	0.15–0.23	32–212
Gneiss..............................	....	0.196	63–210
Granite.............................	162–175	0.192	54–212
Graphite............................	138.3	0.20–0.38	32–2200
Gypsum.............................	145	0.259	50–212
Hematite (Fe₂O₃).....................	....	0.165	59–210
High-alumina refractory...............	128	0.23	60–1200
Hornblende..........................	....	0.195	32–212
Iron, wrought.......................	487–493	0.115	59–212
Kaolin..............................	131	0.22	60–1200
Lava................................	....	0.197	77–212
Lead (Pb)...........................	708	0.0319	61–493
Lead oxide (PbO)....................	574–593	0.049	69–212
Lead slag wool.......................	....	0.178–0.235	150–718
Limestone...........................	168–175	0.216	59–212
Lodestone (magnetite).................	322	0.156	32–212
Magnesia (85%), insulation............	11–13	0.276–0.283	150–279
Magnesite, refractory.................	171	0.27	60–1200
Magnesium oxide (MgO)..............	108.6	0.249	68–212
Marble..............................	162–175	0.210	32–212
Mercuric chloride (HgCl₂).............	339		
Mercurous chloride (Hg₂Cl₂)...........	446	0.05	68
Mica................................	....	0.10	68
Monel metal.........................	550	0.129	60–2415
Naphthalene (C₁₀H₈)..................	71.8	0.325	68–140
Nickel (Ni)..........................	556	0.109–0.161	64–1832
Oxalic acid (C₂H₂O₄·2H₂O)............	103.8	0.338–0.416	0–100
Paraffin.............................	54–57	0.622	95–104

Solids	Density, lb/cu ft	Specific heat, Btu/(lb)(°F)	Temp, °F
Phosphorus (P)	113.8	0.183	32–124
Pitch (coal tar)	62–81	0.45	60–212
Plaster	90	0.20	
Porcelain	143–156	0.26	59–1742
Potassium chlorate (KClO₃)	145	0.205	122
Potassium nitrate (KNO₃)	129.2	0.19	59–212
Pyrex	....	0.196	68–212
Pyrites, copper	....	0.129	59–210
Quartz	165	0.17–0.28	32–212
Quicklime	....	0.217	32–212
Rock wool	(7–12)	0.201–0.250	149–652
Rosin	68	0.525	68–450
Rubber	62–125	0.481	60–212
Salt, rock (NaCl)	135	0.219	55–113
Sand	162	0.195	59–212
Shellac (lac)	75–76	0.40	60–212
Silica (SiO₂)	180	0.191	32–212
Silica aerogel (Santocel)	(5.3)	0.205–0.274	147–630
Silicon (Si)	145	0.183–0.203	135–450
Silicon carbide:			
Refractory	136–159	0.20	60–1200
SiC	199	0.23	60–950
Slag, blast furnace (powdered)	(22.5)		
Slag wool	(9.4–18.7)	0.17	77
Soda, baking	137	0.231	32–212
Sodium carbonate (Na₂CO₃)	151.5	0.306	
Sodium nitrate (NaNO₃)	140.5	0.231	
Sugar, cane, crystalline	102	0.301	68
Sulfur (S)	119–130	0.190	59–130
Tartaric acid (C₄H₆O₆)	104	0.287	97
Uranium	1167	0.028	32–208
Wood, oak	48	0.57	32–212
Wood, pine	30	0.67	32–212
Zinc oxide (ZnO)	350	0.125	32–212

U.S. No.	Sieve opening		Tyler screen scale, equiv mesh
	Mm	In. (approx equiv)	
3½	5.66	0.223	3½
4	4.76	0.187	4
5	4.00	0.157	5
6	3.36	0.132	6
7	2.83	0.111	7
8	2.38	0.0937	8
10	2.00	0.0787	9
12	1.68	0.0661	10
14	1.41	0.0555	12
16	1.19	0.0469	14
18	1.00	0.0394	16
20	0.84	0.0331	20
25	0.71	0.0280	24
30	0.59	0.0232	28
35	0.50	0.0197	32
40	0.42	0.0165	35
45	0.35	0.0138	42
50	0.297	0.0117	48
60	0.250	0.0098	60
70	0.210	0.0083	65
80	0.177	0.0070	80
100	0.149	0.0059	100
120	0.125	0.0049	115
140	0.105	0.0041	150
170	0.088	0.0035	170
200	0.074	0.0029	200
230	0.062	0.0024	250
270	0.053	0.0021	270
325	0.044	0.0017	325
400	0.037	0.0015	400

TABLE A-10. COMPARISON TABLE OF U.S., BRITISH, AND GERMAN SIEVE SERIES WITH TYLER EQUIVALENTS*

Tyler[1] Equiv mesh	U.S.[2] No.	U.S.[2] Opening, mm	British Standard[3] No.	British Standard[3] Opening, mm	IMM[4] No.	IMM[4] Opening, mm	German DIN[5] DIN No.	German DIN[5] Mesh/sq cm	German DIN[5] Opening, mm
3½	3½	5.66	...	.....	...	.....	1	1	6.000
4	4	4.76							
5	5	4.00							
6	6	3.36	5	3.353	...	.....	2	4	3.000
7	7	2.83	6	2.812					
					5	2.540			
8	8	2.38	7	2.411	...	.....	2½	6.25	2.400
9	10	2.00	8	2.057	...	.....	3	9	2.000
10	12	1.68	10	1.676	...	.....	4	16	1.500
					8	1.600			
12	14	1.41	12	1.405					
					10	1.270			
14	16	1.19	14	1.204	...	.....	5	25	1.200
					12	1.509			
16	18	1.00	16	1.003	...	.....	6	36	1.020
20	20	0.84	18	0.853					
					16	0.795	8	64	0.750
24	25	0.71	22	0.699					
					20	0.635			
28	30	0.59	25	0.599	...	.....	10	100	0.600
							11	121	0.540
32	35	0.50	30	0.500	...	.....	12	144	0.490
35	40	0.42	36	0.422	30	0.424	14	196	0.430
42	45	0.35	44	0.353	...	.....	16	256	0.385
					40	0.317			
48	50	0.297	52	0.295	...	.....	20	400	0.300
60	60	0.250	60	0.251	50	0.254	24	576	0.250
65	70	0.210	72	0.211	60	0.211	30	900	0.200
80	80	0.177	85	0.178	70	0.180			
100	100	0.149	100	0.152	80	0.160	40	1,600	0.150
					90	0.139			
115	120	0.125	120	0.124	100	0.127	50	2,500	0.120
150	140	0.105	150	0.104	120	0.104	60	3,600	0.102
170	170	0.088	170	0.089	...	.....	70	4,900	0.088
					150	0.084			
200	200	0.074	200	0.076	...	.....	80	6,400	0.075
250	230	0.062	240	0.066	200	0.063	100	10,000	0.060
270	270	0.053	300	0.053					
325	325	0.044							
400	400	0.037							

* Courtesy of W. S. Tyler Company.
[1] For complete specifications of Tyler standard scale sieves see Table A-9.
[2] National Bureau of Standards LC-584 and ASTM E-11.
[3] British Standards Institution, London BS-410: 1943.
[4] Institution of Mining and Metallurgy, London. This sieve series has been largely replaced by the BSI series.
[5] German Standard Specification DIN 1171.

314

TABLE A-11. MILLIVOLT-TEMPERATURE CONVERSIONS FOR THERMOCOUPLES*

To convert an observed millivolt (mv) reading to a temperature, first find the cold-junction correction from the upper part of the table. Add this to the observed millivolt reading. Opposite this corrected millivolt reading in the lower part of the table, read the temperature in °F. *Example:* An iron-constantan thermocouple, with its cold junction at 70°F, generates 40 mv. The correction is 2.02 mv, and, by interpolation, 42.02 mv corresponds to 1346.6°F.

Cold-junction Correction, mv

Cold-junction temp, °F	Iron-constantan	Chromel-alumel	Platinum–platinum, 10% rhodium	Platinum–platinum, 13% rhodium	Copper-constantan (1938 calib.)	Copper-constantan (1921 calib.)
32	0.879	0.684	0.092	0.089	0.67	0.71
50	1.44	1.08	0.148	0.145	1.06	1.11
60	1.73	1.30	0.180	0.176	1.28	1.33
70	2.02	1.52	0.212	0.208	1.50	1.56
80	2.30	1.74	0.245	0.241	1.73	1.78
90	2.59	1.97	0.279	0.275	1.96	2.01
100	2.88	2.20	0.313	0.309	2.19	2.23

Temperature, °F

Total mv	Iron-constantan	Chromel-alumel	Platinum–platinum, 10% rhodium	Platinum–platinum, 13% rhodium	Copper-constantan (1938 calib.)	Copper-constantan (1921 calib.)
0	0	0	0	0	0	0
1	34.7	46.4	275.2	273.6	47.2	45.2
2	69.3	91.4	490.4	480.8	92.0	89.6
3	104.0	135.4	687.1	665.9	134.4	135.2
4	137.9	178.3	874.8	840.2	174.8	175.4
5	171.7	221.8	1056.3	1007.3	214.0	213.6
6	205.3	265.8	1231.7	1167.0	252.0	252.8
7	238.3	310.5	1401.7	1320.9	288.7	291.2
8	271.3	355.5	1566.7	1469.7	324.3	328.4
9	304.3	400.5	1727.8	1614.4	359.3	364.7
10	336.9	445.4	1884.7	1755.0	393.6	400.3
11	369.4	489.5	2038.2	1892.0	427.0	436.3
12	402.0	533.2	2189.6	2025.2	460.0	470.8
13	434.7	577.1	2340.1	2156.7	492.3	504.3
14	467.0	620.4	2490.9	2287.2	524.0	536.9

* Data from North American Mfg. Co.'s "Combustion Handbook."

Total mv	Iron-constantan	Chromel-alumel	Platinum–platinum, 10% ruodium	Platinum–platinum, 13% rhodium	Copper-constantan (1938 calib.)	Copper-constantan (1921 calib.)
15	499.7	663.3	2642.4	2417.5	555.7	568.3
16	532.3	706.3	2794.6	2548.2	586.6	599.0
17	565.0	748.8	2947.9	2678.7	617.1	629.1
18	597.3	791.4	3102.4	2810.3	647.4	658.3
19	630.0	834.2	......	2942.6	677.4	686.6
20	662.7	876.3	......	3075.8		
25	825.0	1087.0				
30	985.3	1299.6				
35	1140.6	1516.4				
40	1288.8	1740.5				
45	1431.8	1972.6				
50	1573.9	2215.5				
55	1715.9	2472.0				
60	1857.9					
65	2000.0					
70	2142.1					

AUTHOR INDEX

Page numbers refer to text in which works are mentioned.   Bibliographies are given at ends of chapters.

SUBJECT INDEX

321